Logistic
Support
Analysis
Handbook

Dedicated to
my wife, Kim,
my daughter, Catherine,
and my son, Christopher,
whose love, encouragement, and understanding
made this book possible.

Logistic Support Analysis Handbook

James V. Jones

McGraw-Hill, Inc.

New York   St. Louis   San Francisco   Auckland   Bogotá   Caracas
Lisbon   London   Madrid   Mexico City   Milan   Montreal   New Delhi
Paris   San Juan   São Paulo   Singapore   Sydney   Tokyo   Toronto

FIRST EDITION
THIRD PRINTING

© 1989 by **McGraw-Hill, Inc.**

Library of Congress Cataloging-in-Publication Data

Jones, James V.
   Logistic support analysis handbook / by James V. Jones.
     p. cm.
   Includes index.
   ISBN 0-8306-3351-0
   1. Logistics—Handbooks, manuals, etc. 2. United States—Armed
Forces—Procurement—Handbooks, manuals, etc. I. Title.
U168.J66 1989
355.6′212′0973—dc20   89-34647
                                       CIP

For information about other McGraw-Hill materials, call 1-800-2-MCGRAW in the U.S. In other countries call your nearest McGraw-Hill office.

Acquisitions Editor: Larry Hager
Technical Editor: Deborah D. Daly
Director of Production: Katherine G. Brown
Series Design: Jaclyn J. Boone

Printed in Mexico

Contents

12 LSA Program Management

Foreword

We in the Logistics Departments of colleges and universities have been looking for an introductory textbook on Logistics Support Analysis (LSA). James V. (Jim) Jones has provided that text as a followup to his other two successful texts: *Integrated Logistics Support Handbook and Design Engineering: Reliability, Maintainability, and Testability*. It provides the beginning logistics baccalaureate student with an excellent overview of the LSA process, which resides in a lengthy and highly technical military standard, MIL-STD 1388.

His objective, which he achieves throughout the text, is to provide a guide for both practicing logistics engineers and young logistics students who are learning the basic principles and concepts of logistics. The text also lends itself to the nonlogistics engineer who wants some basic knowledge on how integrated logistics support (ILS) and LSA fit into their programs. The text provides a detailed discussion of each facet of the LSA process, describing in detail each LSA task and subtask, along with how each task or task group relates to the overall LSA process.

A very important factor of logistics that the text emphasizes is the total systems engineering approach, along with the concept of concurrent engineering, necessary to complete a successful LSA program. The relationship of the ILS disciplines to the LSA process is described in detail. Other engineering discipline contributions and involvement in the LSA program are discussed. The analyses and studies performed by non-ILS organizations, that are an integral part of the LSA process, are also described.

This is a very comprehensive book on LSA. One chapter is dedicated to taking the results of the LSA process and folding it into life cycle costing (LCC), and then using the LCC output to refine the LSA. The text contains a detailed description of the LSA record. Additionally, a description and example of each LSA summary report are provided. LSA program management is discussed, starting in the proposal stage and continuing through proposal preparation and costing, program startup, program control, and finally, program completion.

Jim Jones is an outstanding logistician. He lectures and conducts training seminars on ILS and LSA both nationally and internationally. As a logistics consultant, he advises and assists both government and contractor organizations in ILS and LSA programs. Additionally, Jim is a logistics adjunct faculty member at National University in Southern California. He is also a valuable member and supporter of the Society of Logistics Engineers (SOLE).

We at Colorado Tech in Colorado Springs, CO, have adopted this text for our LSA course, which is part of our Bachelor of Science Degrees in Defense Systems Management and Logistics Systems Management.

Robert G. Stein, Ph. D.
Dean, School of Arts, Sciences and Management
Colorado Tech

Introduction

Logistics Support Analysis is a key to national security. Weapon systems must be capable of continually performing assigned missions, whether strategic or tactical. The application of logistics support analysis concepts and techniques during the development of weapon systems, or any other system or equipment, is the most viable method available to produce systems that can be efficiently and economically supported. After all, if a system cannot be supported so that it can be depended upon to perform its intended mission when and where necessary, the system is ineffective and, therefore, national security is in jeopardy.

Each system represents a link in the overall national security chain, and this chain is only as strong as its weakest link. Through the use of logistics support analysis, systems are continually analyzed as they are designed and developed in order to identify and correct supportability deficiencies. Additionally, logistics support analysis provides a single source for the identification of all the resources that will be required to support operation and maintenance of the system when it becomes operational. The combination of a supportable design and a detailed logistics support package results in a system that has the ability to continually perform its assigned mission.

The purpose of this text is to provide an indepth study of the logistics support analysis process and how it can best be applied to development programs. Chapters 1 and 2 discuss the general areas of integrated logistics support and logistics support analysis as a foundation for subsequent chapters. The detailed tasks of the logistics support analysis process are presented in chapters 3 through 7. Chapter 8 deals with analyses performed by engineering disciplines that form a significant portion of the inputs required to develop a complete logistics support analysis. The process for recording and reporting the results of the logistics support analysis, the logistics support analysis record, is presented in chapter 9.

The concept of life cycle cost, with emphasis on long-term system support costs, is provided in chapter 10. Chapter 11 addresses the organizational inter-relationships necessary for the logistics support analysis process to be success-ful. Finally, chapter 12 presents issues relevant to acquiring and managing logistics support analysis programs. Additionally, a compendium of reports pro-duced through the logistics support analysis record system, including report descriptions and examples, is provided in Appendix A to demonstrate the extent and potential of the support resource identification process.

The logistics support analysis process is essentially logistics systems engi-neering. The successful completion of a logistics support analysis program will result in a system that is as supportable as possible and in complete identifica-tion of all resources that will be needed to sustain system operation throughout its life cycle.

Acknowledgments

A special thanks to Mr. Jerome F. Kern of LSW, Inc., Landover, Maryland, for his assistance in preparing the LSA Summary Reports that appear in Appendix A. These reports were generated using LEADS™, LSW's proprietary LSA package.

1

Introduction to ILS

Logistics is the science of planning and implementing the acquisition and use of resources necessary to sustain the operation of military forces. These resources include spare parts, operation and maintenance manuals, tools and test equipment, facilities, and trained personnel. Without logistics, military forces could not operate. Logistics planning does not just happen, nor do resources appear through some mystic process. The science of logistics is dedicated to participating, as an equal partner to design engineering, in the process that produces military systems. The goal of logistics is military systems that optimize resource use while minimizing costs. This is not a goal that is easily attained; however, the process of logistics support analysis provides the vehicle for reaching this goal.

INTEGRATED LOGISTICS SUPPORT

Integrated Logistics Support (ILS) is the organization charged with the responsibility of managing the technical disciplines that plan and develop logistics support for military forces. In general, this means that ILS is the management organization that plans, coordinates, and directs the activities of many technical disciplines associated with the identification and development of logistics support requirements and resources for military systems. These technical disciplines, commonly referred to as the *principal logistics elements*, are dedicated to a specific aspect of the overall logistics support program. The efforts of each element must be orchestrated by a single entity to ensure that the resources needed to sustain operations are available when needed.

The ILS organization is an integral part of the engineering effort that designs military systems. Logistics engineers work hand in hand with other

Introduction to ILS

engineers to ensure that support is considered in the design process. Logistics analyses are conducted to identify ways in which the design can be changed to improve support or supportability. Additional analyses are performed to identify the resources that will be required to support the system when it is used. Logistics support resources are the biggest expense associated with a military system over its useful life, so it is imperative that ILS plan for the most economical use of these resources as possible.

Goals of ILS

The ILS organization has four goals in meeting its responsibilities. These goals, shown in FIG. 1-1, are to cause logistics support considerations to influence the design of a system, to identify and develop support requirements related to and supportive of readiness objectives of the system, to acquire the necessary support, and to provide the required support for the minimum cost.

Logistics Support Analysis

One of the biggest problems that ILS has faced is how to coordinate the activities of these disciplines to achieve the best logistics support package possible. There are endless stories about how the ILS disciplines failed to coordinate information during the design of a weapon system, which resulted in technical manuals that did not match the equipment, spare parts that were not interchangeable with the original equipment, training courses that did not address the actual equipment design, and useless or unnecessary support equipment. In fact, there was no established method for the disciplines to formally communicate, so it is easy to understand why such errors occurred.

Another problem for ILS disciplines was that it was next to impossible to have any input into the design process because of the disjointed methods of collecting and analyzing support information. As a result, the process known as *logistics support analysis* (LSA) was developed.

Generally speaking, any analysis method or technique that addresses logistics support or that is used to identify logistics support resources is a logistics support analysis. However, the term LSA now has a more specific meaning. The LSA process was developed with four goals in mind (FIG. 1-2). The first goal is to use the results of the LSA process to influence the equipment design process to consider supportability requirements; that is, to use LSA to identify ways of making the weapon system easier to support. The second goal is to identify

---

- Support Influence Design
- Identify and Develop Resource Requirements
- Acquire Necessary Support
- Provide Required Support for Minimum Cost

Fig. 1-1. ILS goals.

---

1. Cause *logistics support* considerations to influence *design*.
2. Identify support *problems* and cost *drivers early*.
3. Develop logistic support *resource requirements* for system *life*.
4. Develop a *single* logistics support *database*.

Fig. 1-2. LSA goals.

the support problems and items that drive the cost of support early enough in the design process to change the design to fix or eliminate support problems. The third goal is to develop a complete set of projections of the total support resources that will be required to support the weapons system or equipment over its complete life cycle. The final goal of LSA is to develop and use a single database for all analyses.

These goals should not be surprising because they are a continuation of the goals that have traditionally been pursued by the ILS organization. Prior to LSA, each ILS discipline collected, analyzed, and stored data for its own use. The result was a mismatch of information or lack of continuity, which caused some of the problems just noted. By using a single database, each discipline can be assured that the information being used is the same that others are also using, and the results that one discipline generates is readily available to others.

The LSA process can be successful only if applied to a program where these goals can be achieved. There are two methods of planning logistics support: sequential and integrated. The difference between these two methods occurs when the support system is designed in relationship to the design of the equipment. LSA cannot be effective if applied using the sequential method because the first two goals—support influencing design and identification of problems and cost drivers early—are not possible because the system design is complete before the support planning begins. Therefore, the integrated method must be used to realize the full benefit of the LSA process.

There are two distinct areas in LSA: doing the analyses, and recording the results. Too often, logisticians get caught up in the documentation part of LSA and forget that the real purpose of LSA is to perform the analyses. The LSA program is structured in a manner that allows detailed identification of specific requirements for each program. This structure enables tailoring of requirements to match the specific complexity of weapon system or equipment being designed, and it encourages emphasis on analyses, rather than merely filling in the boxes on data sheets. LSA has proven to be a significant step forward in ILS planning and the development support resource requirements.

PRINCIPAL LOGISTICS ELEMENTS

The ILS organization contains technical disciplines that specifically address the support aspects of maintenance planning; manpower and personnel; supply

Maintenance Planning
Manpower and Personnel
Supply Support
Support and Test Equipment
Training and Training Devices
Technical Documentation
Computer Resources
Packaging, Handling, Storage,
and Transportability
Facilities
Reliability and Maintainability

Fig. 1-3. Principal ILS elements.

support; support and test equipment; training and training devices; technical documentation; computer resources; packaging, handling, storage, and transportability; facilities; and reliability and maintainability. These areas, as illustrated in FIG. 1-3, are commonly referred to as the principal elements of ILS. Each of these elements is the responsibility of an ILS discipline that is staffed with logistics engineers trained in that specialty.

Maintenance Planning

Much of the support of military systems is centered around maintenance of equipment. A primary function of ILS is to develop a concept for the maintenance program to support a military system and then to plan the detailed maintenance actions that must occur to support the system. The way maintenance is performed on equipment does not just happen. It is the result of extensive planning and preparation that starts during the preconcept phase and continues through full-scale development.

The maintenance planning process begins with the *maintenance concept*, which is a statement of general guidelines to be used in developing the maintenance plan for an item of equipment. The guidelines established by the maintenance concept are the foundation for maintenance planning. Areas addressed by the maintenance concept include: a strategy for allocation of maintenance tasks to the different levels of maintenance, the repair policy with regard to similar

Maintenance tasks at the organizational level will be limited to unscheduled removal and replacement of failed modules or components and scheduled maintenance that can be accomplished without the aid of special tools or support equipment. Intermediate-level maintenance will have the capability of repairing electronic, electromechanical, and hydraulic assemblies, including the replacement of failed components. Overhaul, refurbishment, and fabrication of structural parts will be accomplished at the depot level. Maximum use will be made of existing tools, support equipment, test equipment, and associated support resources.

Fig. 1-4. Typical maintenance concept.

types of items contained in the equipment, the criteria for scheduling maintenance tasks, and the anticipated availability of resources, in gross terms, to support maintenance. An example of a typical maintenance concept statement is shown in FIG. 1-4.

The requirements for maintenance then drive the decisions for resources necessary to support maintenance actions. Logistics engineers are responsible for maintenance planning and analysis throughout the maintenance engineering process.

Maintenance Concept The maintenance concept is initially developed by the government during the concept phase. The initial concept is the result of an analysis of pertinent information concerning maintenance of equipment. The maintenance concept provides a description of the anticipated environment, both operationally and logistically, where the equipment will operate. This description might include the organizational structure of both the using and supporting units that will perform maintenance.

An assessment of existing and emerging maintenance technologies is used to determine existing opportunities that could significantly impact the maintenance program for the new equipment. These technological opportunities could include new ways of performing maintenance tasks, improved methods for testing and identification of faults, design configurations that enhance maintenance, and changes in materials that reduce failures.

Historical logistics and maintenance data of similar equipment provides an invaluable source of information that is used in developing the maintenance concept. The historical data forms a measurement base against which the logistics and maintenance support of the new equipment can be gauged. This data provides lessons learned on previous equipment that can be applied to the new equipment.

Refinement The proposed maintenance concept is refined by comparing the concept with the projected resources and constraints that will exist when the equipment is fielded. The intent of this refinement is to cause as few changes as possible to the existing maintenance system when the new equipment becomes operational.

The proposed operational and maintenance operations are compared with the existing operations to determine the optimum maintenance concept. The resulting maintenance concept considers the complexity of the new equipment, its mobility requirements, permissible time to be spent in maintenance, critical maintenance skills that must be considered by maintenance planning, and the minimum maintenance procedures that must be accomplished to ensure the capability of the equipment to perform its assigned mission.

Levels of Maintenance

The term *levels of maintenance* is commonly used to describe the different capabilities for performing maintenance that are inherent with the organizational structure of the military services. There are basically three levels of maintenance common to all services: organizational, intermediate, and depot. The type of maintenance that each level is capable of performing is dependent on the tools, test equipment, and training of personnel available. The goal of maintenance planning is to do maintenance on equipment at the lowest level possible, or closest to the user of the equipment. This limits the amount of time that equipment is waiting for maintenance when it fails. And, it limits the amount of resources required to be available to support maintenance.

Organizational Maintenance Maintenance performed by the owner, or user, of the equipment is categorized as organizational (''O'' level) maintenance. The capabilities of ''O'' level are normally limited to periodic servicing of equipment, troubleshooting to identify failures, and removing/replacing major components. Again, the limiting factors as to what maintenance can be done at ''O'' level are the tools, test equipment, and training of personnel. Using a piece of electronic equipment as an example, ''O'' level might be limited to daily testing of the equipment to determine its capability to perform its mission, removing the failed item when it fails, and replacing the entire failed item with one that works. Remember, at ''O'' level, the equipment user's mission is to fulfill a requirement using the equipment; therefore, maintenance planning must consider every possibility of short-term actions to keep the equipment working. It is not uncommon for ''O'' level maintenance actions to be limited to a mean time to repair (MTTR) of less than 1 hour.

Intermediate Maintenance Maintenance actions that are not within the capabilities of ''O'' level are passed to the next higher level which is intermediate (''I'' level) maintenance. ''I'' level has greater capabilities to perform maintenance because that is its primary mission: providing maintenance support to subordinate units. Because the complexity of maintenance tasks increases at ''I'' level, it has a greater range of tools and test equipment available and personnel are trained in performing the required maintenance tasks. ''I'' level maintenance on the example electronic equipment might consist of testing items, removed by ''O'' level for repair, and replacing failed modules.

In some instances, ''I'' level also repairs circuit card assemblies by replacing failed components. This can only be done if the required test equipment is available to fault isolate to the failed component and to test repaired units to verify that the repair action corrected that problem. It is important that personnel are trained to accomplish this task.

Depot Maintenance Maintenance actions that cannot be accomplished at ''O'' or ''I'' level are passed to Depot (''D'' level) Maintenance, which has the capability to do anything necessary to repair failed equipment. Normally, ''D'' level maintenance facilities have the widest range of tools, test equipment, and knowledgable maintenance personnel. Fabrication of structural parts, major overhauls and refurbishment, and complete rebuilding of equipment can be done at ''D'' level. Again, referring to the example electronic equipment, ''D'' level would be capable of relocating all components on circuit card assemblies, fabricating replacements for damaged chassis parts, or rebuilding the entire equipment.

Manpower and Personnel

Systems cannot operate and maintain themselves. Regardless of the weapon system being designed, personnel will be required to operate and maintain the equipment when it is delivered to the government. Therefore, it is important that the logistician planning for operation and maintenance of the system has a basic understanding of how the military services classify personnel, how personnel requirements are determined, and how a weapon system acquisition program may impact personnel resources. ILS is charged with the responsibility of identifying the quantity and skills of military and civilian personnel needed to support operations and maintenance. This is accomplished by maintenance engineers and personnel specialists who participate in the design and analysis process as the system is being developed.

Planning for personnel requirements must be accomplished as early as possible in the acquisition process to ensure that sufficient personnel with the proper skills are available to support the equipment when it is fielded. Personnel resources are limited and may be one of the key factors that determines the level and quality of support provided to a weapon system. ILS disciplines have the ability to provide a positive impact on personnel resources availability through accurate documentation of detailed justifiable personnel requirements.

Supply Support

Operation and maintenance actions require material in the form of spare and repair parts. Identification and acquisition of the materials necessary to support operation and maintenance of military systems is another key responsibility of the ILS organization. The disciplines of provisioning and supply support fulfill this requirement. Provisioning is the process for identifying and obtaining the initial stock of spare parts required to support fielded equipment. Supply support takes over from provisioning and addresses physical distribution, stocking locations, and allocations of stocking levels. Spare parts are required to support both scheduled and unscheduled maintenance, so they must be available in adequate quantities. It is logical that if spare parts are not available, very little maintenance can be accomplished and the result would be an inoperative inventory of military equipment.

The objective of supply support is to have the parts available when and where required in the quantities necessary to support maintenance. On the other hand, it is the responsibility of provisioning and supply support to minimize the number and types of spares and repair parts that are procured in order to limit the cost of supporting the system. Either too much or too little is unacceptable when addressing spare and repair parts.

Support and Test Equipment

Most military systems require additional items of equipment to support operations or maintenance. Any item of equipment that is required to support operation or maintenance is categorized as support equipment (SE). The support equipment can be a special item designed for only one specific use or it can be items that have multiple uses. There are several different ways to classify SE: by its use for performing testing or actual maintenance, or by its availability, application, complexity, or cost. The most frequent method used to classify SE is to refer to the items as either common or special support equipment. Each of these categories has a broad coverage that is open to interpretation depending on the specific application.

Normally common support equipment consists of items that are already in use by the military and have application to more than one specific support role. Special support equipment is normally limited in use to a single application. Whenever possible, common support equipment should be used to perform operation or maintenance tasks in order to limit costs of support resources. Support equipment specialists and test engineers conduct analyses to identify and develop these requirements as a portion of the overall maintenance planning process.

Training and Training Devices

Trained and qualified operator and maintenance personnel are required to support military systems if the equipment is to be capable of continually performing its mission. The training and training device logistics element is charged with development of the system training program. The purpose of the training program is to ensure that the training provided to military personnel is coordinated with the other ILS disciplines and is developed in a manner that is comprehensive and contains all the pertinent information required to operate and maintain the equipment when it is in actual operation.

Training can be divided into four categories: 1) operator training; 2) maintenance training; 3) supervisor training; and 4) instructor training. These categories of training can be subdivided into two phases: initial and sustainment. The development of a training program and identification of equipment required to support training is accomplished by training analysts as a part of the total ILS effort. These training specialists participate in the logistics support and maintenance planning process to identify training requirements and develop appropriate training courses for operation and maintenance personnel. Training devices and equipment required to support training are also developed by this group.

Technical Documentation

The equipment user needs instructions to operate and maintain the system. These instructions are provided in the form of technical documentation normally referred to as a technical manual (TM). The technical manual is the only documentation that is received by the ultimate equipment user that provides operation or maintenance instructions. Therefore, it is one of the most important documents that a contractor prepares. The generic term technical manual, or technical order (TO), actually refers to a series of documents. Included in this series can be an operator's manual, maintenance manual for each level of maintenance, lubrication orders (LO), depot maintenance work requirements (DMWR), repair parts and special tools list (RPSTL) and illustrated parts breakdown (IPB).

The purpose of a TM is to provide the user or maintenance personnel with, in a single reference, all the information and instructions required to operate and maintain the equipment. TMs contain detailed narrative and pictorial descriptions of operation and maintenance procedures, necessary support and test equipment, reference information, and identification of spare and repair parts. The lack of proper technical manuals will significantly degrade the user's ability to operate and maintain the equipment, which, in turn, renders the equipment ineffective in performing assigned missions.

Computer Resources

Computers are used to operate and maintain many military systems. The facilities, hardware, software, documentation, and personnel needed to operate and maintain these computers are identified through the analysis of operation and maintenance of the system by logistics engineers. The resources to support computers become an integral part of the support package for the system.

Packaging, Handling, Storage, and Transportability

The physical movement of a system must be accomplished in a manner that does not reduce its effectiveness. No matter how well an item of equipment performs, it must be provided to the user in a usable condition. The purpose of packaging, handling, storage, and transportability (PHS&T) is to plan, develop, and manage the activities necessary to ensure that equipment is serviceable when it reaches the ultimate user. PHS&T planning starts in the concept phase and continues throughout the acquisition cycle. This effort is often overlooked because it does not relate directly to the development of the equipment; however, it plays a key role in achieving supportability goals. The serviceability and timely availability of equipment and spare parts reduce overall life-cycle costs.

The PHS&T program consists of all activities required to provide, plan, develop, and manage the successful delivery of items to the user. This can only be achieved through a coordinated effort. PHS&T must be involved with all aspects of the acquisition cycle. Specific areas that the PHS&T program must address include program control, distribution and delivery concepts, special packaging, handling, and storage requirements, and development of specific

PHS&T design requirements. Requirements for special packaging, handling, and storage should be avoided if at all possible. The identification of such requirements should be made as early as possible in order to conduct tradeoff studies to determine if the need(s) can be fulfilled using standard procedures. Special requirements have a negative impact on life-cycle cost and should be avoided unless absolutely necessary. Logistics engineers plan and implement the procedures and measures necessary for packaging, handling, storage, and transporting military systems.

Facilities

Operation and maintenance of most military systems and other logistics support operations require some type of facilities. The general military definition of a facility is any real property, which includes parcels of land and buildings, structures, or utilities built on or in the land. When resource requirements for support of operation and maintenance of equipment, training, and storage are being determined, the availability of adequate facilities must be considered as an important portion of overall planning. Most operation and maintenance tasks, especially above crew level, require a suitable location for accomplishment. Facilities can be either fixed or mobile. They can also be categorized by their intended use (e.g., maintenance, supply, training, etc.).

One point to be remembered when considering facilities required to support an item of equipment is that normally there is not a one-to-one relationship between an item of equipment and its supporting facilities. Most facilities support numerous types of equipment, therefore, facility planning must also consider factors related to the support of a general population of equipments or similar tasks being accomplished in support of several different programs. ILS is responsible for identifying the needs for facilities, planning facility utilization, and developing the justification for acquisition.

Reliability and Maintainability

The areas of reliability and maintainability address how long a system will operate without failing and how long it takes to fix an item when it fails, respectively. These disciplines are sometimes within the scope of the ILS organization and sometimes they are not, depending on a company's organization. In either case, reliability and maintainability play an important role in determining the support that will be needed when a system is used. Logistics engineers use a significant amount of input information from the analyses performed by reliability and maintainability engineers to develop system support requirements. In most cases, the reliability of the system drives the amount of resources that will be required to sustain operations. And, equally important, the ease of maintenance dictates how quickly a failed item can be returned to an operational status.

PRODUCT LIFE CYCLE

ILS activities begin with the early planning for an item of equipment and continue throughout its useful life. This process is the same for all items, whether a small piece of equipment or a major weapon system. The product life cycle is divided into seven distinctly different phases, and ILS is involved in each phase. These phases are: 1) Preconcept, 2) Concept, 3) Demonstration/Validation, 4) Full-Scale Development, 5) Production, 6) Deployment/Operation, and 7) Disposal. Each phase has a definite start and end, although the phases may overlap. Figure 1-5 illustrates the phases of the product life cycle.

Preconcept Phase

The product life cycle begins with the preconcept phase where the need for a new equipment is identified. This need may be based on an evaluation of an existing equipment that can no longer perform its mission or it can be based on a new type of mission for which an item of equipment does not exist. The purpose of the preconcept phase is to fully define the new need, develop a complete mission profile for the new equipment, identify in gross terms the resources that exist or must be developed to fulfill the need, and establish priorities for continuing the development process. The preconcept phase can last

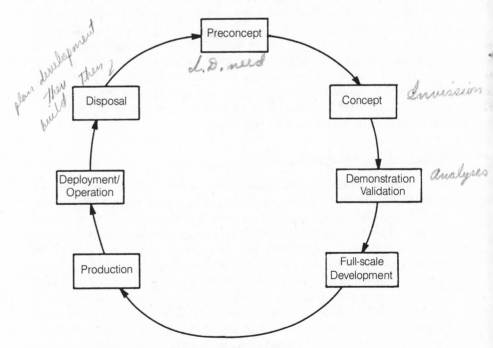

Fig. 1-5. Product life cycle.

from a few months to many years, depending on the urgency of need for the new equipment and the feasibility of the concepts being considered.

Concept Phase

When the need has been fully defined, along with resource identification and establishment of priorities, the next step is to develop alternative approaches for fulfilling the need. The concept phase is where this occurs. The positive attributes and risks involved with each alternative are evaluated to ensure that the alternatives selected are capable of fulfilling the need.

The result of the concept phase is selection of the most feasible alternative, or alternatives, for further study. If an alternative cannot be identified, then the cycle reverts back to the preconcept phase for redefinition of the need. As with the preconcept phase, the duration of the concept phase for a particular program is dictated by many variables in need, feasibility, and resource availability.

Demonstration/Validation Phase

The alternative, or alternatives developed during the concept phase must now be completely explored to determine if the alternative will actually fulfill the need. Up to this point, the alternative has been a general approach to solving the need. The purpose of demonstration and validation (DEMVAL) is two-fold: 1) to take the concept and transform it into an actual functioning item and demonstrate that it actually works, and 2) to validate that the item will fulfill the need defined during the preconcept phase. Failure of all alternatives to pass DEMVAL returns the process to the concept phase for identification of more alternatives. The demonstration and validation phase normally lasts only long enough to prove the concepts under consideration. This could be as little as 12 to 18 months.

Full-scale Development Phase

The alternative, or alternatives that pass DEMVAL proceed to full-scale development (FSD), also called full-scale engineering development (FSED). During FSD, the proposed equipment undergoes a complete engineering process to develop an equipment design that meets all the requirements of the need and that will perform in the field. The purpose of FSD is to produce an equipment design that is reliable, maintainable, producible, and supportable. As will be shown in later chapters, a large percentage of ILS activity occurs during FSD. The FSD phase timing is based on the time required to take the design from demonstration and validation to production readiness.

Production Phase

Actual manufacturing of the new equipment occurs during the production phase. This is the first appearance of the complete, operationally ready equipment. The design of the equipment is frozen at the start of production and cannot be changed without formal approval of the government. Production of a system is normally as accelerated as possible in order to get a needed item into the hands of the user. The length of the phase is determined by the amount of time required to procure or manufacture parts, assemble and test the system, and install it when required.

Deployment/Operation Phase

After the equipment is manufactured, the government assumes ownership and the deployment and operation phase begins. The equipment is fielded and starts fulfilling the need identified during the preconcept phase. The operation phase length is determined by the amount of time that the system fulfills a need. Some systems have a relatively short operational life, while others may remain in service for 25 years or more. As the equipment functions in its intended environment, its capability to fulfill the need is continually evaluated. The equipment's performance is also evaluated as new needs arise. This can be the beginning of the life cycle for another system or improvements and modifications to the current system.

Disposal Phase

When a new item of equipment is fielded, the item being replaced is phased out and the disposal phase begins for the old item. This phase continues until all of the old equipment is purged from the government inventory or redistributed to fulfill other needs. Disposal may be accomplished in a relatively short time or may require a significant effort to complete. Some items that contain hazardous or dangerous materials or components may require an extended amount of time and resources for disposal. This phase ends the life cycle of the product.

2

LSA Program

The integrated logistics support disciplines described in chapter 1 have evolved over many years of participating in design and development programs. Each discipline has a definite purpose and goal in developing the logistics support package for a military system. The problem that has plagued the ILS disciplines for years is that the majority of their tasks have been done after the design of the system is complete, so they had no input to the design process to make the system easier or more cost-effective to support when it is fielded.

Design engineers are concerned with creating a system design that meets performance requirements. In most cases, design engineers don't consider support requirements as a system is being designed. This situation, represented at FIG. 2-1, is the sequential method of support development. Design engineers design the system, and then, logistics engineers develop the support package based on the final design. The combination of the system design and the support package become the final overall system delivered to the military. The problem with this method is that if logistics engineers find ways of improving the design so that it is easier or more cost-effective to support, it is too late to do anything to the design before it goes into production. That is the reason that the logistics support analysis program concept was developed. The real purpose of a formal logistics support analysis program is to provide a method of interjecting logistics support concerns into the design process so that the final system design is as easy and cost-effective to support as possible. Figure 2-2 shows how the LSA process is supposed to work. As the design is created, logistics engineers work with design engineers to identify and improve key support related design features. This is a simple concept, but it can be difficult to implement for two very basic reasons. First, logistics engineers must be able to quantify and communicate support related design features to design engineers

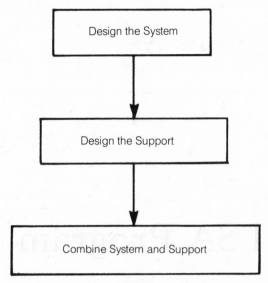

Fig. 2-1. Sequential support development.

so that they can be implemented. Second, design engineers must use this information as the design is developed.

The role of logistics engineers as upfront participants in the design process is relatively new and most have limited experience or expertise in developing design parameters. Logisticians have traditionally tended to deal in facts, figures, and other finite information rather than in theory or broad concepts. This

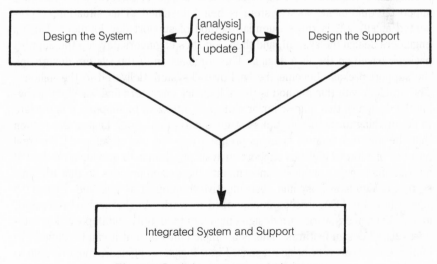

Fig. 2-2. Logistics support analysis process.

- Cause logistics support considerations to influence design
- Identify support problems and cost drivers early
- Develop logistics support resource requirements for system life
- Develop a single logistics support database

Fig. 2-3. Logistics support analysis program goals.

new role requires both a new mind set and the ability to deal with the big picture. Design engineers, on the other hand, must also expand their thinking to include support issues as an integral part of the design. It is not good enough for a design to meet performance requirements; the design must also be supportable for a reasonable cost. The concept that a compromise or degradation in performance may be permissible if it significantly increases supportability must be recognized as an acceptable guideline for the overall system design. This situation is why the government has mandated that logistics support analysis will be an integral part of all military development programs. The logistics support analysis program provides a formal method for integrating support with design.

PROGRAM GOALS

There are four explicit goals of any LSA program. These four goals, shown in FIG. 2-3, are to cause support consideration to influence the design, identify support cost drivers early in the design program, identify the resources necessary to support the system when it becomes operational, and to combine all support related information into a single database. Each of these goals represents a significant effort on the part of the logistics organization.

Influencing the Design

This is the most difficult task for logistics engineers. There is only one way that support considerations can influence the design, and that is for logistics engineers to be totally involved in the early stages of a program in a capacity where they have the opportunity to make a contribution to the upfront design process. In order to understand how these contributions can be made, it is necessary to first understand how the upfront design process works. Figure 2-4 shows the major events that occur in the upfront design process.

System Requirements Definition ⎞
System Requirements Review   ⎬ concept phase
System Specification Review   ⎠
Initial Design Review
Preliminary Design Review
Critical Design Review

Fig. 2-4. Upfront design process major events.

The system requirements definition establishes the top level requirements that the design must meet. At this point, supportability criteria for the design should be included as a requirement that has the same priority for attainment as performance. The overall concepts of how maintenance of the system will be accomplished will drive specification requirements for maintainability and testability of the system. The purpose of the system requirements review is to determine if the alternatives for system design fulfill the requirements that were established at the system requirements definition. Again, this is a point where supportability considerations for the system should be thoroughly reviewed to see if the goals are being met.

After it is determined that all the system requirements can be met by a design alternative, a system specification is prepared that describes in detail all the criteria for the system design. All of these events occur in the concept and demonstration and validation phases of the system life cycle. At this point, no hardware has been designed or built, and everything is still very fluid and much easier to change than in future iterations of the design process that occur at the initial, preliminary, and critical design reviews. These design reviews occur dur-

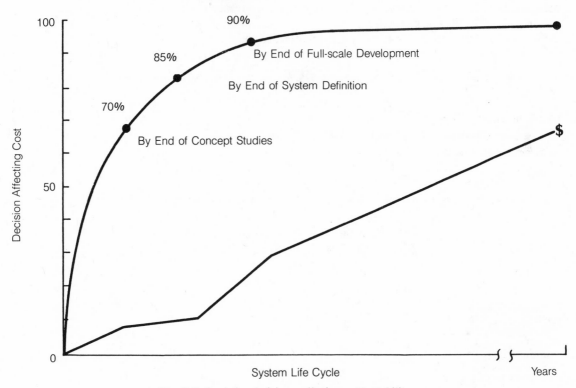

Fig. 2-5. Logistics decisions affecting supportability.

ing full-scale development and address detailed hardware design and how supportability concerns have been implemented or addressed.

As an illustration of the importance of addressing supportability issues during this early point in the life cycle, FIG. 2-5 shows that, based on recent studies, approximately 85 percent of the decisions that affect supportability and related support costs occur before the start of full-scale development. Historically, logisticians have not been involved in the design process at all until after the start of full-scale development. This means that in the past the most impact that logistics engineering could provide were on only 15 percent of the design decisions relating to supportability. This is the overwhelming driver for having logistics engineers participate in the upfront process to influence design.

Cost Drivers

Support for military systems generate the largest single cost during the life cycle of a system. As will be shown in chapter 10, the costs for operation and support for typical military systems far outweigh the costs that are incurred when the military initially purchases a system. Therefore, it is extremely important that system design characteristics that significantly affect the cost of operation or support be identified as early as possible in the design process to determine if less expensive alternatives, which do not significantly degrade performance or other specification requirements, are available and can be selected. This is the area where logistics engineers can best influence the design, by providing inputs that make the design easy and cost-effective to operate and support. Determining which system characteristics cost drivers is the key; it is not easy but can be done if approached in a logical manner and if the data necessary to feed the identification process is available.

The best starting point for identifying cost drivers is past experience. If the new system being designed is to replace an existing system, then the logical place to look for new system cost drivers is to find out the cost drivers for the existing system. Through a detailed analysis process, cost drivers for the existing system can be determined from historical data such as those shown in FIG. 2-6. The next step is to see what design characteristics of the existing system contributed to these cost drivers. With the cost driving characteristics of the existing system identified, the new design can be analyzed to determine if the

---

Field Reliability Data
Failure Analysis Data
Maintenance Records
Spares Usage Data
Field Evaluations
Field Surveys
Mission Availability Data

Fig. 2-6. Cost driver input data.

---

same characteristics are to be incorporated or if new, more cost-effective features can be selected. This is how logisticians now get a chance to influence the 85 percent of decisions that they previously couldn't. This process is a very good example of an upfront logistics support analysis.

Support Resource Identification

The traditional role of logistics disciplines has been to identify the resources that will be required to support a system when it is fielded. These resources include spares and repair parts, support and test equipment, trained personnel, facilities, and technical documentation. This goal of the logistics support analysis program is included as a program goal to give added emphasis to the fact that support requirements must be identified in a formally coordinated and documented process. All too often in the past, support resource needs were identified using "rule of thumb or best guess" methods rather than analysis techniques that coordinated requirements into a single support package. The logistics support analysis program provides a methodology, through the use of the maintenance task analysis process and logistics support analysis records, to identify and justify all support resource requirements, thereby achieving this goal.

Database

The last goal of the logistics support analysis program is to collect and maintain all logistics-related information in a single database. The reason for this goal, which appears to be a common sense approach to retaining and using data, is that in the past few years, computers and computerized databases have become standard methods by which logistics disciplines increase efficiency and productivity. The problem that has occurred is that as computer use became an accepted way of doing business, specific computer applications were developed for each discipline with little sharing or interchange of data. The first applications for computers in the logistics arena was in the generation of provisioning documentation for spares requirements.

Other applications were developed for reliability, maintainability, and technical manual preparation. The problem that developed were independent databases that required duplication of effort to generate and maintain, provided there was no correlation of information between databases. This is why the logistics support analysis record system was developed, to provide an efficient method for creating a single database for all logistics-related data.

PROGRAM REQUIREMENTS

The establishment and implementation of a logistics support analysis program is a requirement of all government contracts for design and development of weapon systems and other equipment. The government documents that contain the requirements for the LSA program are MIL-STD 1388-1A, Logistics Support Analysis, and MIL-STD 1388-2A, DoD Requirements for a Logistics Support Analysis Record. The purpose of MIL-STD 1388-1A is to provide a formalized process for performing LSA. MIL-STD 1388-2A provides the requirements for creation and use of a single logistics database to record the results of the logistics support analysis process.

PROGRAM TASKS

MIL-STD 1388-1A contains detailed descriptions of the requirements of an LSA program and the individual tasks that must be performed. The LSA program consists of a series of 15 interrelated tasks that are divided into five sections: Program Planning and Control; Mission and Support Systems Definition; Preparation and Evaluation of Alternatives; Determination of Logistics Support Resource Requirements; and Supportability Assessment as shown in FIG. 2-7. Each program section has a definite purpose and contribution to meeting the overall LSA program goals. Additionally, due to the many aspects of ILS that the LSA program addresses, most tasks are divided into subtasks that can be tailored to fit a specific application of LSA. MIL-STD 1388-1A is also unique in that it provides not only a description of each task, but it also identifies the

---

MIL-STD 1388-1A
Task section 100—Program planning and control
    Task 101—Early LSA strategy
    Task 102—LSA Plan
    Task 103—Program and design reviews

Task Section 200—Mission and support systems definition
    Task 201—Use study
    Task 202—Mission hardware, software, and support system standardization
    Task 203—Comparative analysis
    Task 204—Technological opportunities
    Task 205—Supportability and supportability-related design factors

Task Section 300—Preparation and evaluation of alternatives
    Task 301—Functional requirements identification
    Task 302—Support system alternatives
    Task 303—Evaluation of alternatives and tradeoff analysis

Task Section 400—Determination of logistics support sequence requirements
    Task 401—Task analysis
    Task 402—Early fielding analysis
    Task 403—Post-production support analysis

Task Section 500—Supportability assessment
    Task 501
    Supportability test, evaluation, and verification

Fig. 2-7. LSA program tasks.

Task Inputs	Subtasks	Task Outputs
Input #1	Subtask #1	Output #1
Input #2	Subtask #2	
Input #3	Subtask #3	
	Subtask #4	
	Subtask #5	Output #2

Fig. 2-8. Standard LSA task format and organization.

inputs required to perform a task and the outputs that performing a task are expected to generate. As each task is discussed in following chapters, the task inputs and outputs will be illustrated, as shown in FIG. 2-8, to depict how the LSA process addresses each aspect of both the design and supportability in order to achieve the goals of the program.

Another interesting aspect of MIL-STD 1388-1A is that in many cases the information required to complete a task must be supplied by the government. This is an important point since prior to LSA there was little definition as to what information a contractor could expect to be supplied by the government. Each task that requires information from the government is identified, to include the types of information, so that the availability of the information can be coordinated.

For years, ILS has accomplished many logistics-related tasks as a matter of course with little or no detailed guidance. Many of these tasks have significant impact on the overall logistics resources required to support a weapon system, but detailed directions did not exist that forced the analyst to consider them each time. This led to a haphazard approach to logistics analyses. If a contractor will follow the guidance of MIL-STD 1388-1A to the letter, the resulting equipment design and logistics support package will be the best possible balance between system performance, supportability, and life-cycle cost.

DATABASE

The methods and procedures for preparation and use of an LSA database are described in MIL-STD 1388-2A. (See Appendix D for a brief description of MIL-STD 1388-2B.) The basis for the LSA database is the logistics support analysis record (LSAR) for each item contained in the design. The LSAR for an item contains all the analysis results output by the LSA process in a series of 15 individual data records shown in FIG. 2-9. A set of individual records is prepared for each maintenance or support significant item in the system and forms the basis for identification and documentation of resource requirements. Chapter 9 is an indepth discussion of the LSAR system, how databases are created and maintained, and the reports and other information that are generated for use in the analysis process to achieve program goals of influencing the design, identifying cost drivers, and identification of the resources that will be required to support the system.

LSA Data Record A	Operation and Maintenance Requirements
LSA Data Record B	Item Reliability (R) and Maintainability (M) Characteristics
LSA Data Record B1	Failure Modes and Effects Analysis
LSA Data Record B2	Criticality and Maintainability Analyses
LSA Data Record C	Operation and Maintenance Task Summary
LSA Data Record D	Operation and Maintenance Task Analysis
LSA Data Record D1	Personnel and Support Requirements
LSA Data Record E	Support Equipment and Training Material Description and Justification
LSA Data Record E1	Support Equipment and Training Material Description and Justification (Cont.)
LSA Data Record E2	Unit Under Test Description and Justification
LSA Data Record F	Facility Description and Justification
LSA Data Record G	Skill Evaluation and Justification
LSA Data Record H	Support Items Identification
LSA Data Record H1	Support Items Identification (Application Related)
LSA Data Record J	Transportability Engineering Characteristics

Fig. 2-9. LSAR data records.

PROGRAM TAILORING

One of the innovative features of MIL-STD 1388-1A is that it contains information and guidance on tailoring an LSA program to fit a specific application. Tailoring of an LSA program is necessary to get the most benefit for the program expense. Not all tasks are applicable to all programs or contracts. The major factors that guide program tailoring (FIG. 2-10), are program phase, system size, design status, and desired program outputs. Each of these factors must be considered when determining which tasks are applicable to a specific program.

Program Phase

Most LSA tasks are best suited for a specific phase of the system life cycle where the results of the task have the greatest potential for meeting a program goal. Tasks that are performed in inappropriate phases usually result in wasted effort and useless information. For example, as shown in chapter 6, the purpose of the 400 series tasks is to identify the detailed support resources for the system. These tasks can only be performed when detailed design information is available, normally in the full-scale development phase. Performance of these tasks during the concept phase, where no detailed design information is avail-

Program Phase
System Size
Design Status
Desired Program Outputs

Fig. 2-10. Program tailoring factors.

able, would be totally inappropriate. Subsequent chapters that address individual tasks will identify the most appropriate phase for task completion.

System Size

An LSA program should be tailored based on the size of the system being designed. The program required by MIL-STD 1388-1A is targeted for a major system such as a tank, aircraft, or other major system. LSA programs for smaller systems, such as a power generation unit or communications radio, do not normally require that all tasks be implemented. The reason for this differentiation is that major systems require support systems and organizations to sustain operations where smaller systems fit into a category of items that have established support systems. Because these smaller systems do not require that a new or revised support system be developed, several of the LSA tasks would provide no real return for the expense of task performance. The tailoring of tasks due to system size is identified in subsequent chapters where appropriate.

Design Status

The status of the system design might be a deciding factor in tailoring of LSA requirements. The full benefit of an LSA program can be achieved only when applied to all phases of a development program where the design goes through each previously described event and milestone. If the system is completely designed before the LSA program is implemented, there is little expectation that the program can influence the design for supportability, so there is no reason to perform tasks that are supposed to influence the design. The best example of this situation is the recent trend to acquisition of off-the-shelf systems. When the design is already complete, the only benefit from the LSA program is identification of support resource requirements. Therefore, selection of tasks for a specific program must consider the status of the design as a parameter for inclusion of specific tasks.

Desired Program Outputs

The bottom line for tailoring an LSA program is to determine what program outputs are most appropriate and useful in achieving a supportable system design and development of the required logistics support package. The decision as to what tasks are most appropriate, in consideration of the tailoring factors described previously, must be based on the desired program outputs. If the purpose of the LSA program is to influence the design, then those tasks that provide the analysis outputs for inputs to the design process should be selected. If, on the other hand, the only purpose of the program is to identify support resources, tasks that provide this output should be chosen. One point to remember when selecting specific tasks is that, because of the interrelationship between certain tasks, required inputs to tasks selected must be reviewed to determine if other tasks should also be selected so inputs are available for tasks that provide the desired program outputs.

3

Program Planning and Control
Task Section 100

The key to successful completion of a logistics support analysis program is detailed planning before the program starts and adequate program controls to continually monitor progress and direction for the duration of the program. The purpose of the program planning and control section, Task Section 100 of MIL-STD 1388-1A, is to provide a standard method for initiation, control, and management of the logistics support analysis program. Task Section 100 contains three tasks, shown in FIG. 3-1, which define the strategy, planning, and review actions necessary to ensure that the program starts with the proper direction and attentions to achieve the program goals. Each of the tasks in Task Section 100 require input and agreement from both the government and the contractor. This joint effort in planning and controlling the LSA program provides the responsibility and visibility for attaining program goals. These tasks are applicable to any phase of an LSA program, but are critical in the early phases of product development. Without the upfront planning and controls established by Task Section 100, an LSA program will not be effective in influencing the design for supportability or in developing a coordinated and cost-effective logistics support resource package for the system. Therefore, these tasks are the cornerstone of a successful LSA program.

EARLY LSA STRATEGY — TASK 101

The first task of the LSA program is unique in that there is no other task contained in any document previously mentioned that required someone to stop and think about how a program should best be accomplished. The purpose of Task 101 is to require both the government and the contractor to make conscious decisions, based on available facts and historical data, as to what should

Task	Title
101	Early LSA Strategy
102	LSA Plan
103	Program and Design Reviews

Fig. 3-1. Task Section 100.

be done with regard to LSA before any other tasks of the program are started. This task should be done by the government before the request for proposal (RFP) is written. It surely should be done before any contract is awarded; otherwise, the LSA program may not provide the best return on the investment possible. Likewise, the contractor should develop a strategy for the LSA program as part of the proposal preparation process to recommend the most appropriate goals for the LSA program and the best alternatives for meeting these goals.

When a system is designed and developed through a series of consecutive or follow-on contracts rather than a single start to finish contract, this task should be readdressed by both the government and the contractor prior to the start of each contract. Figure 3-2 shows the inputs, subtasks, and outputs of Task 101.

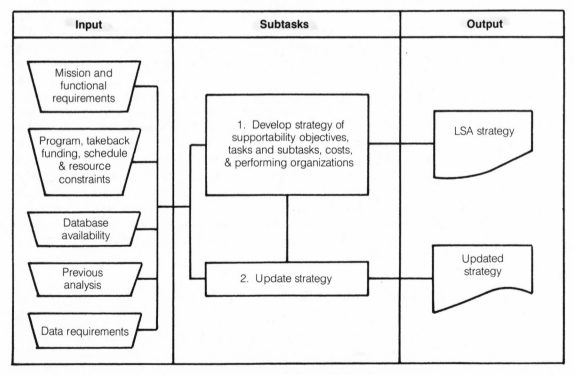

Fig. 3-2. Task 101—Early LSA strategy.

Task Inputs

A significant amount of information is needed to support accomplishment of development of the early LSA program strategy. This information includes many items that are contributors to causing requirements for logistics resources, but are not immediately applicable to conducting the LSA program. The expected mission and functional requirements for the new system are needed to determine, in gross terms, if there are any immediately apparent causes for a drastic increase or change in support requirements for the new system in comparison with existing systems and their support structures. This information is also needed to quantify the types of logistics support resources that will be of major concern during the LSA program.

The anticipated program schedule and funding constraints are used to determine where the most return on investment for logistics analyses can be realized and to develop a strategy for determining which tasks of the LSA program will be implemented based on program phase. Available databases or existing information that can be used to support analyses will reduce costs and provide historical information as inputs to tasks. By using available reliable data and historical information rather than estimates, the confidence level in tasks outputs can be raised. Identification of data items and reports that will be required contract deliverables provides guidance for tailoring the logistics support analysis record portion of the LSA program to extract any reports possible from the logistics database. Any other available information that is pertinent to the logistics support analysis process or in developing an implementation strategy for the program should be identified and used whenever possible. As indicated in MIL-STD 1388-1A, the government is the primary source for all of the inputs to this task.

Subtasks

There are two subtasks contained in Task 101, initial development of the LSA program strategy and subsequent updates as the program progresses through each phase of the life cycle. The subtasks are necessary to ensure that the overall program strategy continues to reflect the needs of the government or contractor in producing a system that is logistically supportable.

Subtask 1. Develop a Strategy The strategy developed for the LSA program must be consistent with the proposed design, maintenance concept, and operational scenario for the new system. The key to developing the strategy is to identify the tasks that are required to achieve the specific goals of the acquisition program and to determine which tasks will provide the best return on investment. Another significant decision that must be made in developing the strategy is to identify who will accomplish the LSA tasks and when the tasks should be done. The completed strategy should address each point of the design and operation of the system and how the LSA program should be conducted in order to receive maximum benefit. A major consideration for the detailed strategy is determining, based on the program schedule and the funding available, which tasks provide the most cost-effective benefits in terms of impacting the design, if possible, and development of the final logistics support package for the system when it becomes operational.

The basic question that must be answered by the strategy is, "How can the LSA program be most effectively implemented in consideration of the program schedule and funding and the status of the system design"? If the system design is still in the conceptual stages and sensitive to changes to improve supportability, then the LSA tasks that provide inputs to the design process that can improve system supportability should be implemented. If the system design is mature and past the point of sensitivity to all but the most overwhelming change requirements, tasks that address changing the design may not be cost-effective unless there are overriding reasons for expending the time and funds to complete those tasks. These are the types of decisions that must be reached to develop an effective and cost-efficient LSA program strategy.

Subtask 2. Update   The second part of this task is to update the strategy as the program proceeds. All too often, a strategy is never reviewed to determine if changes are required based on better information or changes in program direction. Most system development programs require several years to complete. From the start of a program to its end, many changes in program direction, system mission, and functional requirements that drive new or different logistics support requirements can occur. The LSA strategy should be updated, at a minimum, each time the program changes due to schedule modifications, major design changes, changes in funding, or as indicated by the results of analyses.

Task Outputs

The output of Task 101 should be a definitive statement of the major goals of the LSA program, identification of the tasks to be implemented to meet the program goals, schedule and funding requirements and commitments to support the LSA program, and general guidance for conducting the LSA program. For the government, the early LSA strategy becomes the basis for preparation of future funding requirements and generation of logistics statements of work that later become contractual requirements that are levied on contractor-developed military systems. Contractors developing an early LSA strategy do so to optimize company profitability while providing effective and cost-efficient support for completing the requirements for the LSA program. A contractor's initial LSA strategy is normally found in the response to the government's request for proposal to develop a system and conduct an LSA program.

LSA PLAN — TASK 102

An LSA plan (LSAP) describes how the LSA program will implement the strategy developed in Task 101. The purpose of the LSA plan is to document the processes and procedures that will be used to manage and control the LSA program. Figure 3-3 shows the inputs and outputs of Task 102 and the subtasks necessary to produce and update the LSA plan. The plan must address each facet of the program to include identification of detailed responsibilities for accomplishing each program task, interrelationship between the LSA program and other design and development programs, management and control of the LSA program, and other coordinating efforts required. The LSAP must be completed early in the program to be in place to guide the LSA effort. It is not unusual for a contractor to be required to submit a draft or preliminary LSAP to the government as a part of the overall response to an RFP. Therefore, the contractor must understand the LSA process and be able to apply this understanding to the specific requirements of an RFP before any contract is awarded.

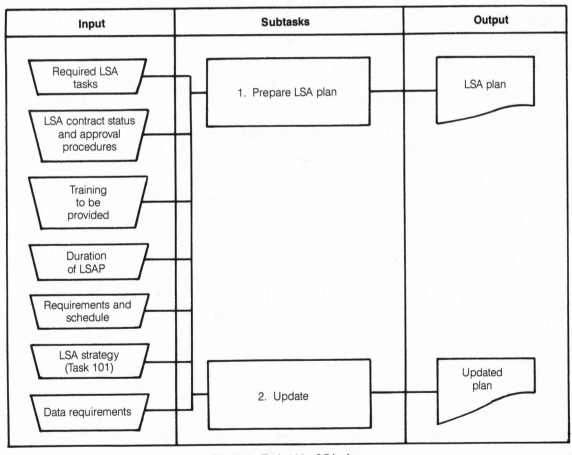

Fig. 3-3. Task 102—LSA plan.

Task Inputs

The primary inputs to preparation of the LSAP are the outputs from Task 101, the contractual and schedule requirements being stipulated by the government, and the data requirements that must be met by the LSA program. These inputs are integrated with the contractor's methodology for performance of all LSA requirements and the management and coordination processes to be used. All information available that impacts or enhances the performance of LSA tasks or aids in development of the management and control processes for the program should be included in the plan.

Subtask 1. Prepare LSA Plan   An LSAP provides a detailed description of the complete LSA program. A key requirement for an acceptable plan is that it must address each task, explaining how the task will be accomplished, the schedule for accomplishment, information required to complete the task, and how the output will be used to meet the LSA program goals. The plan must integrate the activities of all ILS disciplines in a manner that streamlines the ILS process while receiving the maximum benefit from each discipline. Additionally, the plan must identify how the LSA program will interface with and coordinate activities of all other engineering and supporting disciplines. The point must be made that without clear coordination of this overall participation by all activities involved with the design and development of the system, the LSA program will not be capable of achieving the primary program goals.

Figure 3-4 provides a basic outline for an LSAP. Note that the outline covers the complete spectrum of activities that are related to implementation and conduct of the LSA program. The management portion of the plan is essential to integration of the efforts of each ILS and engineering discipline. The detail of the plan should be such that anyone who wanted to understand the intent of the LSA program could learn each point by simply reading the LSA plan. A comprehensive LSAP repeatedly proves its value throughout a program by assuring continuity and coordination of all LSA activities.

Subtask 2. Update   The LSAP should be updated as changes occur to the program. The dynamic nature of the LSA program causes changes to occur in the procedures and processes that are identified in the LSA plan; therefore, the LSAP must be continually updated to account for the changes. Most contracts require that the LSAP be updated quarterly throughout the LSA program. Remember that the LSA plan is the single controlling document for the detailed mechanics of how the LSA program is conducted.

Task Outputs

The obvious output of this task is a dynamic document that is the foundation for the LSA program. However, there are also some not so obvious outputs of this task that can have a significant impact on the final results. One of the keys to a successful LSA program is detailed and continual coordination between the LSA organization and engineering disciplines. The LSA plan should

LSA PLAN

1.0 INTRODUCTION
    1.1   Purpose of Plan
    1.2   Scope of Plan
    1.3   Reference Documents
    1.4   Summary of Plan
    1.5   Plan Updating Process
2.0 SYSTEM DESCRIPTION
    2.1   Hardware & Software Description
    2.2   Support Equipment Description
        2.2.1 Common Support Equipment (CSE)
        2.2.2 Peculiar Support Equipment (PSE)
    2.3   Maintenance Concept
        2.3.1 Crew Level Maintenance
        2.3.2 Organizational Level Maintenance
        2.3.3 Direct Support Level Maintenance
        2.3.4 General Support Level Maintenance
        2.3.5 Depot Level Maintenance
        2.3.6 Military Occupational Specialty
        2.3.7 Support Equipment Maintenance
3.0 LSA/LSAR PROCESS
    3.1   Purpose and Scope
    3.2   LSA Application
        3.2.1 System Level LSA
        3.2.2 ILS Element Level LSA
        3.2.3 Supportability Assessment and Verification
    3.3   LSA Process
        3.3.1 LSA Input
        3.3.2 LSA Tasks
        3.3.3 LSA Modeling Techniques
    3.4   Logistic Support Analysis Record (LSAR)
        3.4.1 Input Data Sheets
        3.4.2 Sample Input Sheets
    3.5   LSA Control Numbers
        3.5.1 LCN Structure
    3.6   Selection of LSA Candidates
    3.7   Automated Data Processing (ADP)
    3.8   LSAR Summaries
    3.9   LSAR Updating
    3.10 LSA Data Delivery
4.0 LSA PROGRAM
    4.1   Responsibilities for LSA
        4.1.1 Data Sheet Responsibility
        4.1.2 Input Data Responsibility
    4.2   Government Interfaces
        4.2.1 Organization
        4.2.2 ILS Organization
        4.2.3 LSA Communication
        4.2.4 Utilization of Data
    4.3   Subcontractor/Vendor Interface
        4.3.1 Subcontractor Control
        4.3.2 Government Review of Subcontractor Data
    4.4   Government Interface
        4.4.1 Government Reviews
    4.5   LSA Program Schedule

Fig. 3-4. LSA plan outline.

provide the vehicle for establishing this interface. Another benefit is the use of the LSAP as a training document for employees. The plan should also provide detailed information for control and coordination between the contractor and the government of all LSA matters. A properly prepared and maintained LSA plan is an invaluable tool in achieving the goals of the LSA program.

PROGRAM AND DESIGN REVIEWS — TASK 103

The LSA program and its progress toward meeting the program goals should be a topic of discussion at every meeting between the government and the contractor. The impact of the LSA program should be felt in every other activity concerned with the overall design effort because each of these activities has an impact on the LSA program. The purpose of Task 103 is to formally require that LSA be addressed at each program and design review held by the government or the contractor. This gives LSA a system support ability and visibility equal to that given design throughout the program. Figure 3-5 shows the inputs, subtasks, and outputs of Task 103.

Task Inputs

The requirements for conducting reviews and meetings are normally contained in the contract statement of work. The statement will, at a minimum,

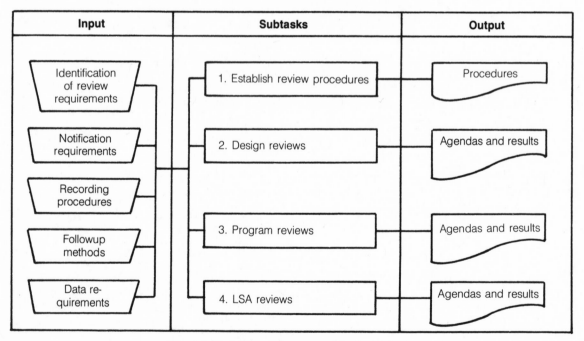

Input	Subtasks	Output
Identification of review requirements	1. Establish review procedures	Procedures
Notification requirements	2. Design reviews	Agendas and results
Recording procedures		
Followup methods	3. Program reviews	Agendas and results
Data requirements	4. LSA reviews	Agendas and results

Fig. 3-5. Task 103—Program and design reviews.

identify each review or meeting that must be held during the course of the contract and may also identify the general topics to be discussed at specific reviews. The other contractual inputs are data reporting requirements for submittal of recommended agendas prior to each review or meeting and the preparation and submittal of minutes afterwards. The LSA plan prepared by Task 102 would also provide inputs to this task through identification of review requirements and the schedule for reviews and meetings. Several other LSA tasks, as shown later, also provide inputs for discussion topics at design and program reviews. Other inputs to this task would come from such documents as the program management plan and the master program schedule that give more detailed information for reviews and meetings.

Subtask 1. Establish Review Procedures Prior to conducting any formal reviews, it is necessary to establish accepted and agreed upon procedures for how the meetings will be conducted, how the agendas will be determined, and who is responsible for recording the events that occur during the meetings. Many contracts require formal delivery of proposed meeting agendas and subsequent meeting minutes are part of the contract data requirements list. The significant thing that must occur relative to the LSA program is to identify exactly how the results of the analysis process will be introduced and addressed at reviews. It is important that sufficient emphasis be placed on reviewing and using the results of the LSA process to improve overall supportability rather than trying to micromanage the LSA program. The topics that should be addressed, as appropriate, at reviews are listed in FIG. 3-6.

Subtask 2. Design Reviews A series of design reviews are conducted throughout the development of a system. The LSA program should be a topic of discussion at each of these reviews, especially during the system requirements review (SRR), the preliminary design review (PDR) and the critical design review (CDR). These reviews are where the government approves the contractor's proposed equipment design. Each of these meetings provides a forum where the LSA program input to the design process should be discussed with supportability and support-related topics having equal merit as design perform-

---

1. Status of LSA program by task and WBS element
2. Supportability assessment of proposed design
3. Support alternatives under consideration
4. System alternatives under consideration
5. Evaluation and tradeoff analysis results
6. Comparative analysis results
7. Design or redesign actions proposed or taken
8. Review of supportability-related design requirements
9. Progress toward achieving supportability goals
10. Design problems affecting supportability
11. Schedule or analysis problems affecting supportability

Fig. 3-6. LSA topics for program and design reviews.

ance capabilities. Figure 3-7 lists the typical design reviews for a developmental and production program. All design reviews should address the progress toward meeting LSA program goals. Any problems that require redesign or where the design is not meeting supportability requirements must be emphasized as critical issues. All too often system performance is the only issue that is addressed at design reviews. Supportability and support-related issues must receive equal attention in order to achieve a balance between performance, support, and cost.

Subtask 3. Program Reviews Program reviews are normally held monthly during the early stages of a program and may later be held quarterly when the design becomes more firm. These reviews tend to address management and contract issues and highlight design issues with regard to schedule. Logistics may be overlooked if not stressed as a management concern for both the contractor and the government. LSA should always be a subject for discussion at these reviews. Additionally, the contractor should hold program reviews with subcontractors to integrate the total program effort. Each subcontractor having responsibility for conducting an LSA program should be required to include the program results in any program review. The areas of interest should be the same as those for design reviews.

Subtask 4. LSA Reviews Specific reviews are normally held for the purpose of reviewing the progress of the LSA program. These LSA reviews are normally held quarterly at the contractor's facility since both the product and the data required to support the reviews are at that location. The topics of discussion are the same as mentioned above, but the level of detail of the discussions should be greater than occur at a program or design review. It is important to remember that the purpose of these reviews is to determine how the LSA process is being used to verify or improve the supportability of the equipment being designed. Often the LSA review becomes a session of arguing about how a specific LSA document or data record should be completed, rather than addressing and pursuing the goals of the LSA program. Such occurrences are counterproductive and produce less than desirable results.

The purpose of the LSA review is to present the current status of the program with regard to schedule and completion of program tasks and to discuss support-related issues. The most important issue for every LSA review is the adequacy of the program to impact the design for support-related issues and to develop a support package for the system being designed that is cost-effective and within program constraints.

System Requirements Review
Preliminary Design Review
Critical Design Review
Functional Configuration Audit
Physical Configuration Audit
Production Readiness Review

Fig. 3-7. Typical design reviews.

Task Outputs

The results of Task 103 should be an initial understanding between the contractor and the government as to how logistics-related issues will be addressed at each design, program, and LSA review. Subsequently, the results of each review should be documented in a manner that allows a clear understanding of the issues that were presented, discussed, and resolved. The minimum acceptable output for this task is an open line of communications between the contractor and the government to allow an unencumbered flow of supportability and support-related information that is necessary for successful program completion.

4

Mission and Support Systems Definition
Task Section 200

The tasks contained in Task Section 200 are designed to identify the mission or missions that the new system or equipment will be required to perform, quantify the supportability goals of the design program, and provide inputs to the tradeoff analyses that are used to determine the optimum supportability design and support resources utilization for the new system. As stated in chapter 2, two of the goals of the LSA program are to influence the design and to identify the cost drivers and problem areas early so that they can be fixed or eliminated whenever possible. The five tasks in Task Section 200 provide a systematic process that leads to the accomplishment of these goals. These tasks consider the support structure and requirements of any previous similar systems, the support infrastructure in place for the new system, existing support available for the new system, and new technologies available to increase supportability or reduce support resource requirements.

USE STUDY — TASK 201

The use study provides the basis for all logistics planning and readiness analyses of the new system. In general terms, the use study identifies how, when, and where the new system will be used and identifies all the qualitative supportability factors required for other analyses. This task should be accomplished for every LSA program. A tremendous amount of objective and subjective data and information is required to perform analyses or computations to determine the logistic resources that are required to support a system.

One of the problems that continually plagues the logistics disciplines is the lack of creditable information early in the program for use in making these analyses. When the information is not available, the only solution is to make assumptions based on whatever information is available. This is no easy task, and the results will vary considerably between disciplines when assumptions must be made about the same points. This causes even more confusion because the changes in assumptions or available data will invalidate any consolidated results of analyses.

The purpose of the use study is to conduct a single analysis to identify all the information that will be needed by any ILS discipline to complete required analyses. With only one document serving as the source for all quantitative information, the task of creating a support system for an equipment is much simpler and effective. Figure 4-1 shows the inputs, subtasks, and outputs of Task 201.

Task Inputs

The inputs to Task 201 are basically any available information or data that describes who, what, when, where, why, and how the system will be used. Potential sources of information include the product specification, related contractual documents, decision and briefing papers, data from previous similar systems or programs, contractor prepared proposals, and visits and other information gathering processes. The key to preparing an accurate and usable use

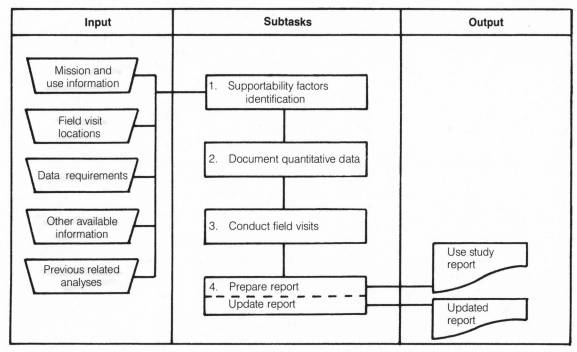

Fig. 4-1. Task 201—Use study.

study document is to assimilate and correlate all the information available from all possible sources. There can never be too much information for this task.

Subtasks

There are four subtasks in Task 201, sequenced to develop and produce a use study that documents all the data and information that is relevant to the use and support of the new system. Systematic completion of the subtasks will produce a document that describes everything there is to know about the intended use of the new system.

Subtask 1. Supportability Factors Identification   The first step in conducting a use study is to identify and document the pertinent supportability factors that are related to the intended use of the new system. The factors that should be considered include mission and deployment scenarios, mission or sortie frequency and duration, mobility requirements, basing concepts, projected service life, operation and storage environments, human interaction and limitations, and operations in conjunction with other systems or equipments. Each of these factors can have a significant impact on the support of the new system. This portion of the use study may consist of a collection of statements that address the areas mentioned above. The point is that each item of consideration must be adequately defined so that supportability requirements can be determined.

An aspect of the use study that should not be overlooked is the application of this information to determining the impact of changes in system mission. Because many systems are assigned new or modified missions due to changing tactical or strategic requirements, it is imperative that the impacts of these changes are viewed in light of support requirements. For example, suppose that the U.S. Air Force plans and builds an aircraft that has the mission of air-to-air combat. Subsequently, the U.S. Navy chooses to use the same aircraft in a carrier-based mode for similar roles. The change in support requirements for the new mission are significant due to differing support structures even though there may be little change in the basic aircraft design. The use study prepared for the U.S. Air Force program should be used as a basis for identification of changes in supportability and support resources for the new aircraft mission.

Subtask 2. Document Quantitative Data   The next step in preparing a use study is to develop and document discrete quantitative supportability data on the new system, that will be used for analyses and calculation purposes by the ILS disciplines. Much of the information (i.e., required mean time between failure and mean time to repair) is available from the procurement specification or other sources that give detailed facts and figures that can be used for determining detailed support resource requirements. Later in the program, the actual figures that are achieved can be compared with the specified requirements to identify shortfalls that cause increases in resources or necessitate changes to meet specification parameters. Figure 4-2 shows typical quantitative

1. New system mission
2. Mobility requirements
3. Deployment scenario
4. Expected usage (hours, miles, sorties, etc.)
5. Expected useful life
6. Basing concepts
7. Interfaces and supporting systems
8. Operational and storage environments
9. Number of systems
10. Special mission or environmental requirements
11. Maintenance concept
12. Existing system being replaced
13. Existing maintenance and support system
14. Resources required to support existing system

Fig. 4-2. Use study quantitative information.

information prepared in the use study process. As can be seen in this figure, the quantitative data is used by virtually every analysis that determines requirements for logistics support resources. When detailed information is not available, appropriate assumptions can be developed that are used as a starting point until the actual information is available. This allows changes in supportability parameters to be identified and the program to continue rather than waiting for information and losing the ability to impact the design.

Subtask 3. Conduct Field Visits In some cases, it may be advantageous to conduct field visits to operational units or sites to gather information for the use study. The government may conduct these visits as part of the decision-making process during the early stages for formulating system requirements. When a contractor is required to conduct such fact-finding visits, the government is responsible for access requirements to the necessary information sources. In actuality, this subtask is normally performed by the government, rather than placing the requirement on a contractor. The reason for this is that the filed visit information is necessary for determining upfront system requirements before generation of basic system and program documents. If the government conducts site visits or similar events to gather information, the contractor who is performing the LSA program must be provided the results for preparation of the use study.

There are several informal and indirect methods by which contractors gain information from operational sites. Many contractors, especially larger companies, provide field service engineering at various operational sites. Field engineers can perform informal visits while at these sites to gather information to be used at a later date, or they may be able to provide historical information from previous assignments. Company employees having prior military experience can also be a source of information about specific sites or existing systems. The consolidation of the results from all these sources can provide a wealth of information for the final use study report.

Subtask 4. Prepare/Update Report The final step in conducting the use study is to prepare a report of the results of the task that should document the findings of the previous subtasks for use by all ILS disciplines. The publication and dissemination of the report is extremely important in order to ensure that everyone uses the same source information for studies, analyses, and calculations.

As the information in the use study changes, the impact of the changes will be readily identifiable across all disciplines if the use study report was the source for data used in the original effort. Tradeoff analyses can be effective when the baseline information has been documented so that all changes can be studied and evaluated in context of the overall system, rather than on a chance basis. The use study should be continuously updated to reflect the most accurate and timely information available.

Task Output

The single output of Task 201 is the use study report. Figure 4-3 is the basic outline for a typical report, which contains all the available information about the use of the new system, any or all systems being replaced, and the support structure that is in place where the new system will be used. Updated reports

---

1.0 General
    1.1 Scope and purpose
    1.2 System description
    1.3 System mission profile
2.0 Quantitative Supportability Factors
    2.1 Operating requirements
    2.2 Number of systems supported and fielding plan
    2.3 Transportation factors
    2.4 Maintenance factors
    2.5 Environmental factors
3.0 Summary of System Being Replaced
    3.1 Operating requirements
    3.2 Number of systems supported and locations
    3.3 Transportation factors
    3.4 Maintenance factors
    3.5 Environmental factors
4.0 Existing Support Available for New System
    4.1 Maintenance capabilities
    4.2 Supply support
    4.3 Personnel
    4.4 Facilities
    4.5 Support equipment
    4.6 Test equipment
    4.7 Technical data
5.0 Other Available Supportability Information

Fig. 4-3. Use study report (outline).

should be issued whenever required to maintain a single source of accurate information about the new system use.

MISSION HARDWARE, SOFTWARE, AND SUPPORT SYSTEM STANDARDIZATION — TASK 202

The purpose of Task 202 is to develop criteria for the new system design that will make maximum use of the existing or planned logistic support resources. The thrust of this task is to make the most of resources that are already available, rather than having to develop a whole new set of resources specifically for the new equipment. Standardization has proven to be extremely cost-effective because it allows the new system to be supported with currently available resources that are already used by other systems. A contractor may be required to develop a detailed standardization program in accordance with MIL-STD 680A, Contractor Standardization Program Requirements, which should

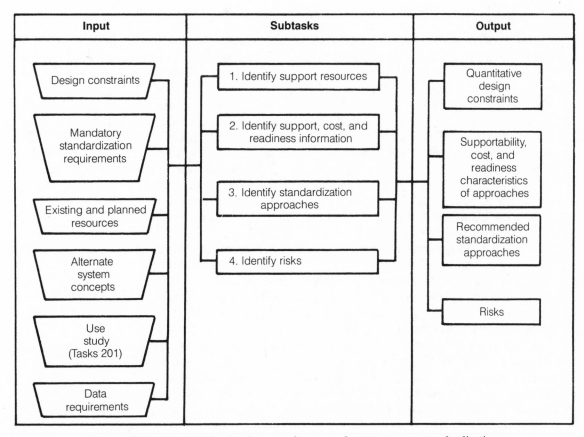

Fig. 4-4. Task 202—Mission hardware, software, and support system standardization.

be integrated into the performance of this task. Figure 4-4 shows the inputs, subtasks, and outputs of Task 202.

Task Inputs

Inputs for Task 202 come from several sources. The product specification normally contains basic guidance for standardization. Any design constraints imposed by the government are also contained in the product specification. The use study prepared in Task 201 should be the guide for information about currently available resources for use on the new system.

Subtasks

Task 202 consists of four subtasks. These subtasks go through logical steps in developing a standardization plan for the system design process. They first identify the resources that are available and the problems that must be addressed by standardization, and then develop an approach for application of standardization requirements to the design. The last subtask deals with the attendant risks to adopting the resulting standardization approach.

Subtask 1. Identify Support Resources The use of existing and planned resources that will be available to support the new system has a significant impact on the life-cycle of the system. The purpose of this first subtask is to document the parameters of the system design that must meet established standardization criteria. The use study report, an output of Task 201, should be the starting point for this process. Standardization requirements can affect all aspects of the design. Typical areas of interest include part selection, target support and test equipment, basic physical system characteristics, and interfaces with existing systems. Product specifications normally contain requirements for standardization, although the requirements may not be readily and specifically identified as such. Examples of these requirements are stipulations as to the parts and materials that can or cannot be used in the system, equipment that must be used for support or testing, electrical and mechanical interfaces that must be met, maximum physical dimensions and weight, and human operating and maintenance constraints. Each of these aspects constitute standardization of the new system with existing support resources.

A set of candidate design criteria for standardization should be prepared for each alternative system design being considered. The purpose of the criteria is to identify design features and characteristics that should be tailored to fit the support systems and resources that are already available, thereby eliminating the need to develop new resources. For example, a design criterion could be that the new design should be capable of being tested using an existing item of test equipment. In this example, the designers would have to make whatever design considerations are necessary to use the existing test equipment.

Subtask 2. Identify Support, Cost, and Readiness Information Identification of resources for standardization criteria development leads to the next step of using other related information to develop the final design criteria. Information on support, cost, and readiness must be used as inputs to the final criteria preparation in order to develop alternative standardization approaches that meet the requirements of the product specification. All this information is necessary for standardization planning. In some cases, existing technology may be inadequate to support new systems and any attempt to standardize that aspect would be counterproductive.

The key to this subtask is to quantify each standardization approach under consideration using all available information about each design alternative. The thrust of this subtask is to analyze each aspect of standardization to evaluate impact on support, cost, or readiness and determine the best balance for all three. For example, the product specification may require an existing test station to be used for intermediate level maintenance fault detection. If the technologies of the new system exceed the performance characteristics of the stipulated test station, extreme costs may be incurred in adapting the system for testing the equipment. An alternative test station may prove to be more cost-effective and result in a lower life-cycle cost for system support. This is when a tradeoff analysis must be performed to identify when standardization is not appropriate. On the other hand, standardization aspects of selecting alternative testing methods such as built-in test may negate the requirement for extensive test equipment. Another common standardization requirement is use of existing parts and materials whenever possible. The cost for development, acquisition, stocking, and inventory management of new items can be extensive. By using existing items in the military supply system, these costs can be avoided. These are the types of tradeoff analyses that determine the best balance between support and cost.

Subtask 3. Identify Standardization Approaches The purpose of this subtask is to choose the best standardization approach for each aspect of the system design based on the information generated in preceding subtasks. Life-cycle cost estimating should be used whenever possible in completing this requirement because the long-term worth of each alternative must be identified in order to make a creditable decision. There may be other requirements that must be met that cannot be evaluated based on lowest cost. For example, there may be minimum performance or support requirements that must be met regardless of cost. In these cases, additional information should be used when making a final decision. Historically, maximum use of standardization normally provides the most efficient and economical system by reducing requirements for new or changed support.

Subtask 4. Identify Risks The last step in completing Task 202 is to identify the risks associated with the standardization approach chosen for the design. These risks may include limited resource availability, technology related problems, overloading existing facilities, etc. Virtually every resource has some limiting factor that must be considered when planning for its use or availability. The purpose of this subtask is to force the analyst to make a conscious decision as to what risks are being taken when choosing a standardization approach for each aspect of the design. This allows the decision to be rethought if the situation changes or better information becomes available that affects the availability of resources.

Task Outputs

The results of this task should be a definitization of the detailed areas where standardization will be applied to the system design, and clear highlighting of any exceptions that are being taken to specification requirements. It is critical that this information be provided to design engineers in the form of specific statements of criteria that must be met by the final design. These criteria should be topics of discussion and concern that are addressed at each design and program review conducted per Task 103.

COMPARATIVE ANALYSIS — TASK 203

The purpose of Task 203 is to use experience and information gained from previous or existing systems to systematically identify the areas of the design that should be targeted for improvement in the new system. Additionally, analyses of previous systems should be used to identify drivers in the areas of supportability, cost, and readiness that could be improved in the design of the new system. Basically, this task stresses learning from past history rather than making the same mistakes again. The inputs, subtasks, and outputs of Task 203 are shown in FIG. 4-5.

Task Inputs

Accomplishment of Task 203 requires detailed input information on previous or existing systems that closely resemble or contain portions that closely resemble the system being designed. This input information is used as a basis for developing comparisons with the new system to identify performance, support, and cost drivers and considerations. Also required are the data requirements for the new system, system design alternatives being considered, the use study report produced by Task 201, and the results of any other available relevant analyses that have already been performed.

Subtasks

There are eight subtasks contained in Task 203. Each subtask deals with a specific portion of developing and using the baseline comparison technique for identifying existing or potential support or cost problems with the new system design based on historical experience of previous similar systems.

Subtask 1. Identify Existing Systems for Comparison The first step in making a comparative analysis is to identify existing or similar systems that have merit for comparative analysis purposes. Several different comparative systems may be considered, each having differing applicability based on design, mission, support systems, etc. If the proposed design of the new equipment has several alternatives, a comparative system will probably be required for each alternative. The more similar the comparison system to the new system, the more creditable the results of the analysis. Anytime there is a one-for-one replacement with little or no change in mission or support infrastructure, the system being replaced should be used for comparison. For example, if the U.S. Army was developing a new tank to replace the current M-1 main battle tank, the obvious comparison system for the new design would be the M-1 tank. The only exception to this rule is when the system being replaced is so obsolete that it in no way resembles the technologies used in the new system. In this case, other composite systems may be more appropriate; however, much

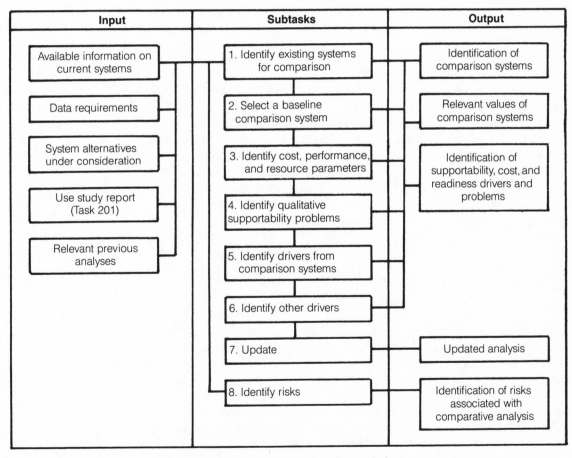

Input	Subtasks	Output
Available information on current systems	1. Identify existing systems for comparison	Identification of comparison systems
Data requirements	2. Select a baseline comparison system	Relevant values of comparison systems
System alternatives under consideration	3. Identify cost, performance, and resource parameters	Identification of supportability, cost, and readiness drivers and problems
Use study report (Task 201)	4. Identify qualitative supportability problems	
Relevant previous analyses	5. Identify drivers from comparison systems	
	6. Identify other drivers	
	7. Update	Updated analysis
	8. Identify risks	Identification of risks associated with comparative analysis

Fig. 4-5. Task 203—Comparative analysis.

of the usage data that is mission-related may still be valid and should be used for comparison purposes.

Subtask 2. Select a Baseline Comparison System In some cases, due to technological advances or other circumstances, there may not be an existing system that can be used for a comparative analysis. It may be possible to develop a composite model using subsystems or sections of several systems that results in a baseline comparison system (BCS) having the overall traits and characteristics of the new system. The BCS can then be used to make a comparative analysis for the new system. If the U.S. Air Force was developing a new aircraft that was dissimilar to all existing aircraft, but contained subsystems that closely resembled the subsystems in the new aircraft, a composite system could be created. For example, if the propulsion system of the F-14, the avionics of the F-16, the weapon systems of the F-18, the airframe of the F-15, and the landing system of the F-4 closely resembled the corresponding subsystems in the new aircraft, the data on each of these subsystems could be used to develop a composite of the expected performance, support requirements, and costs of the new system. These parameters when combined into a system level package become the basis for comparison to the new system. This is the theory behind developing a baseline comparison system.

Subtask 3. Identify Cost, Performance, and Resource Parameters After the comparison system or BCS have been identified, the next step in the comparative analysis process is to identify the cost, performance, and resource parameters of these systems. This process identifies every possible piece of information available relative to the operation and support costs, requirements for logistics support resources, reliability and maintainability values, and performance parameters of the comparative systems. Information compiled might include mean time between failure, mean time to repair, repair turnaround time, number of spares required, cost for spares, number of repair actions per assembly per year, critical failure items, cost for support per year, manpower requirements, support equipment requirements, training requirements, performance of the system in speed, accuracy, availability, and projected life-cycle cost parameters.

The source for this data may be previous LSA programs, maintenance information databases, product specifications, or any other repository of real or statistical data. The objectivity and accuracy of this information is critical to performing a comparative analysis. The government may prove to be the best source for this information if the contractor was not involved with the design or production of the comparative system or composite baseline subsystems.

Subtask 4. Identify Qualitative Supportability Problems In addition to the quantitative information collected in subtask 3, pertinent qualitative information about the supportability of the comparative system should be documented. This information may come from field visits during preparation of the use study or from other analyses. In either case, all other information about the comparison system should be taken into account in identifying supportability problems that have occurred in the past on similar systems that should be prevented on the new system. In other words, undesirables in performance, support, or cost of a qualitative nature should be of concern during the design process for the new system. Sometimes the raw numbers do not tell the whole story and require further interpretation to determine the real cause for concern in performance, support, or cost.

Subtask 5. Identify Drivers from Comparison Systems Using the results of each previous subtask, an analysis should be performed to identify the cost, support, and readiness drivers of the comparative systems. Each aspect of the system should be reviewed to determine exactly what design feature contributed to the limitations of the system. Drivers should be identified in every conceivable area where possible. At a minimum, the design features or segments that experienced the highest failure rates, elements in the life-cycle cost that were higher than projected, requirements for support resources, and continual or unplanned maintenance problems should be identified, and then analyzed to determine which are applicable to the new system. Those applicable to the new system must be categorized as potential drivers and should receive top priority for resolution. Addressing these areas should give the highest return when applying limited resources to improving the supportability of the new system. In other words, if these potential drivers are improved, all other things remaining equal, the new system should be a better system overall than the comparison system.

Subtask 6. Identify Other Drivers In some cases, there may not be a comparable system nor anything that can be used to model a BCS. Or, the comparison between previous systems and the new system does not provide visibility to some of the drivers of performance, support, or cost. When this occurs, an attempt should still be made to quantitatively and qualitatively identify the potential drivers of the new system.

Drivers may take the form of changes in the costs for acquiring support resources such as escalation in parts and materials or consumable resources used during operation or maintenance. Other drivers may include shortages of critical resources that were previously in plentiful supply when the existing system was developed. Sometimes, due to lack of information, the analysis may be more qualitative than quantitative; however, a conscious decision must be made as to what the perceived drivers may be in order to focus the analysis process in a direction that has the potential to increase the overall system effectiveness.

Subtask 7. Update As better information becomes available concerning either the new system or the comparative systems, the comparative analysis should be updated to determine if the results of previous analyses are still valid. The updating of this task is critical to keep the efforts of design and logistics activities focused on those design areas that provide the greatest potential for improvement. When the preliminary predictions for the new system, such as mean time between failure and mean time to repair, are developed, the comparison can be updated to determine if the changes in these and other performance, support, or cost parameters resolve drivers or create new ones. The iterative LSA process provides capability to refine this information to optimize the final system design.

Subtask 8. Identify Risks It is necessary to quantify the risks that are involved with each comparative analysis in order to understand the limitations that should be placed on using the results of the comparative analysis process. Although a comparative system may closely resemble the new system, it is not the new system and the differences, even subtle, may be sufficient to make any analysis result questionable. Therefore, the risks inherent with the process and the specific analysis must be identified. Knowing early in the comparison process those areas that are most susceptible to creating erroneous results goes a long way toward reducing the risks attendant to the baseline comparison process.

Task Outputs

Task 203 provides significant information to the design process. This information is basically an identification of the physical and functional characteristics that are anticipated to drive performance, support, and cost of the new system being designed. This information on drivers highlights to design engineers the critical aspects that must be addressed to optimize the final design. Design criteria addressing each driving factor may be developed to provide minimum or maximum parameters or characteristics that would result in the best balance between performance, support and cost. Each factor should be addressed during design reviews to determine if the system design process is considering ways of eliminating or controlling drivers or taking measures to ensure that a reasonable balance is being achieved.

TECHNOLOGICAL OPPORTUNITIES — TASK 204

The purpose of Task 204 is to identify technologies that can be applied to the new design to improve supportability, reduce costs, or achieve a better balance between the two without reducing performance. Examples of new technologies currently being used are advanced electronics, composite materials, extensive built-in test capabilities, automated processes, and miniaturization. By using state-of-the-art technology in the design of the new system, the results should be an improvement in overall performance, supportability, and life-cycle cost. Figure 4-6 shows the inputs, subtasks, and outputs of this task.

Task Inputs

There are many sources for inputs to Task 204, depending on the type of system being designed and the range of new technologies that are available for consideration for incorporation. The output of Task 203 that identifies the drivers for support or cost should be a key input because these are the areas where a change could provide the most benefit. Research and development efforts normally provide inputs for new technologies that are available. This task relies to a large degree on the ability of engineers to search for new ideas to solve existing problems.

Subtasks

There are three subtasks contained in Task 204. The purpose of the first two subtasks is to identify opportunities for using new technologies to solve problems that have occurred on previous similar systems and to update the identification process as new technologies are identified. The third subtask identifies the risks that are involved with using the new technologies identified by the first two subtasks.

Subtask 1. Identify Design Approaches The use of new technology

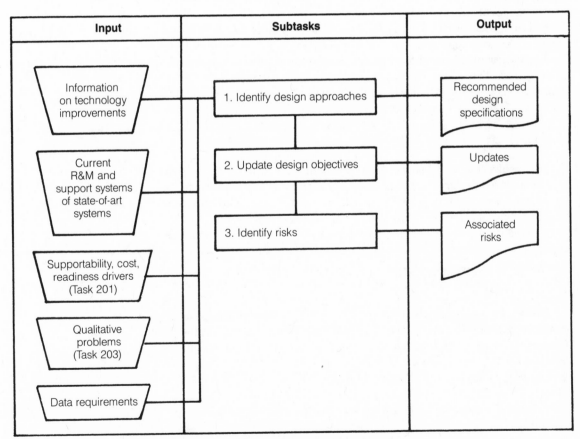

Fig. 4-6. Task 204—Technological opportunities.

to improve supportability starts with identification, first, of the areas that need improvements, and, second, applicable technologies. Basically, this task looks for ways of increasing the supportability of a new system by using new technology in the design. The best place to start is to use the drivers identified in Task 203 as the first targets for improvement. Once the targets for improvement are identified, the available technologies can be analyzed to determine which, if any, are applicable to the new system. In some cases, the use of a new technology may not be cost-effective or cost-efficient, so each possible alternative should be studied to see if eliminating the driver warrants use of the new technology. The result of this subtask should be identification of the technologies that do provide a better, more cost-effective method of achieving the supportability goals of the new system.

Subtask 2. Update The results of this task should be continually updated. The technological advances that occur during a system development provide a constant source of potential applications to new systems. As the detailed design evolves, new requirements for applying new ideas occur that require this task to be repeated.

Subtask 3. Identify Risks It is important to identify and document the risks involved with applying any new technologies to the new system design. The use of new or unproven features in a new system can create risks either with the production of the new system or with the supportability when fielded. Identification of these risks allows development of alternatives or workarounds should the risks prove unacceptable.

Task Outputs

The results of Task 204 should be documented in the form of design criteria or recommended design specifications that can be used to guide design engineers in the incorporation of the identified new technologies into the system design. Additionally, the risks associated with using each technology should be documented so that the impact of each can be reviewed as the design matures.

SUPPORTABILITY AND SUPPORTABILITY- RELATED DESIGN FACTORS — TASK 205

The purpose of this task is to use the results of the previous tasks to develop a complete set of support and supportability characteristics for the new system. These characteristics should be used as guidelines for design engineers during the design process for producing a system that has the desired supportability characteristics. Outputs from this task can also be used in future contracts or other documents related to system design or supportability. The inputs, subtasks, and outputs of Task 205 are illustrated in FIG. 4-7.

Task Inputs

The outputs from Tasks 202, 203, and 204 are the primary inputs to Task 205. Each of the previous tasks dealt with a specific issue with regard to developing supportability characteristics for the system. Task 205 now combines these individual desired design attributes into a single requirements listing. Other inputs are the alternative system design concepts being considered and the reporting requirements imposed by the government.

Subtasks

There are five subtasks in Task 205. The subtasks progress through a systematic review and consolidation of design requirements to produce the final required characteristics that will be provided to design engineers.

Subtask 1. Identify Supportability Characteristics The first step in this task is to quantitatively identify the supportability characteristics in terms of support concepts, reliability and maintainability parameters, operation and support costs, and logistics support resources required for the new system.

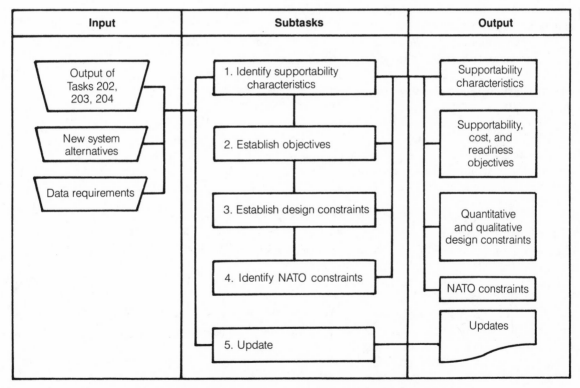

Fig. 4-7. Task 205—Supportability and supportability-related design factors.

The characteristics addressed in the identification process include standardization requirements from Task 202, drivers for support and costs resulting from Task 203, and technological opportunities to resolve these drivers from Task 204. This is accomplished using the results of previous LSA tasks and forms the initial data to be used by all ILS disciplines for analyzing the new system.

Subtask 2. Establish Objectives After the supportability characteristics have been identified, the quantitative supportability objectives for the new system can be established. These objectives are expressed in terms of the support, cost, and readiness levels the new system design should achieve. Some of the characteristics may be a restatement or refinement of the information extracted from the product specification, while others may be developed from additional sources of data collected while performing Tasks 201, 202, 203, or 204. Objectives can include repair turnaround time, mean time to repair, support equipment utilization rates, manpower requirements per maintenance action, etc. In other words, the results of this subtask define supportability goals and objectives for the new system.

Subtask 3. Establish Design Constraints In addition to the design goals previously established, the design constraints for the new system, within which the goals must be met, must be established. These constraints, again, should be the summation of all the constraints developed in Tasks 202, 203, and 204. The government can also impose constraints on the design through contractual requirements stated in the product specification or statement of work, which can address part and materials selection, physical dimensions and weight, human interface factors, testing requirements, and any other aspect of the design that impacts supportability or requirements for support resources.

Subtask 4. Identify NATO Constraints As a member of the North Atlantic Treaty Organization (NATO), the United States is obligated to plan for interoperability of new equipment with that of other NATO members. The LSA process should consider that applicability of NATO standard items for fulfilling requirements as needed and should include it in the identification of design constraints.

Subtask 5. Update The results of Task 205 should be continuously updated as the design process and logistics support analysis process evolve. This task uses the results of other tasks and should be kept current with the results of other interrelated tasks because the design objectives and constraints established by this task form the basis for all subsequent analyses and tradeoff decisions. The purpose of the tasks contained in Task Section 200 is to define the missions and support systems of the new system. This process is iterative in that the tasks are continually updated throughout the design process to ensure that the logistics support package developed for the new system meets the actual needs that will be encountered when the system becomes operational.

Task Outputs

The outputs of Task 205 are a culmination of the results of all the tasks contained in Task Section 200. The supportability characteristics identified by these tasks are used as inputs to Task Sections 300, 400, and 500 because they are the basis for meeting supportability requirements for the system. These characteristics are also recorded in the logistics support analysis record and on the LSA Data Records A and B, as will be discussed in detail in chapter 9. The dissemination of design constraints for supportability and prudent use of support resources should be accomplished by preparation of specific statements of design criteria for design engineers. The outputs of this task should also be inputs to Task 102 when developing or updating the LSAP and as inputs to Task 103 for subjects of discussion at all design and program reviews to highlight the need and show progress toward meeting each required characteristic and constraint.

5

Preparation
and Evaluation
of Alternatives
Task Section 300

The purposes of the tasks contained in Task Section 300 are to identify, develop, and evaluate the alternatives available for supporting the new system. There are three tasks in this section. The first task defines the functions of the new system and the operation and maintenance tasks that are required to support these functions. The second task develops alternative concepts for providing the necessary support. The final task consists of a series of interrelated evaluation techniques necessary to determine the best overall support alternative. Normally, all three tasks are accomplished sequentially to fully develop each proposed support alternative and provide the best opportunity for proper selection. These tasks are iterative in nature and start the process of generating detailed information that is recorded in the logistics support analysis record (LSAR).

FUNCTIONAL REQUIREMENTS IDENTIFICATION — TASK 301

The purposes of Task 301, a two-part task, are to first identify the functions that the new system must perform and, second, identify all the operation and maintenance tasks that must be performed to support the system in its intended environment. This is significant in the development of the overall logistics support package for the new system and in identification of ways of improving the detailed design to be more supportable. Figure 5-1 illustrates the inputs, subtasks, and outputs of this task.

Task Inputs

For identification of the functions that the new system will perform, inputs for Task 301 are required from the product specification and from design engineering that identify the alternative design concepts being considered for the new system. The outputs of Tasks 201 and 203, in conjunction with the failure modes, effects, and criticality analysis and the reliability centered maintenance analysis, are used to identify operation and maintenance tasks that will be required to support the system. Support requirements from the product specification are also used to determine the system maintenance concept.

Subtask 1. Identify System Functions The first step in the functional identification process is to identify exactly what the new system must do in order to accomplish intended missions or tasks, which should result in a rather lengthy list of functions. For example, an aircraft would have to take off, fly, land, carry ordnance, provide life support to the crew, communicate with other aircraft or the ground, navigate, take pictures, use radar, etc. The list of possibilities, is rather large. However, this process is important for understanding what functions must be supported. This may seem like a task that has little bearing on logistics and the LSA process, but without knowing what a system is supposed to do and the intended environment, it is much more difficult to plan for its support, or recommend design changes that do not degrade its ability to perform critical functions.

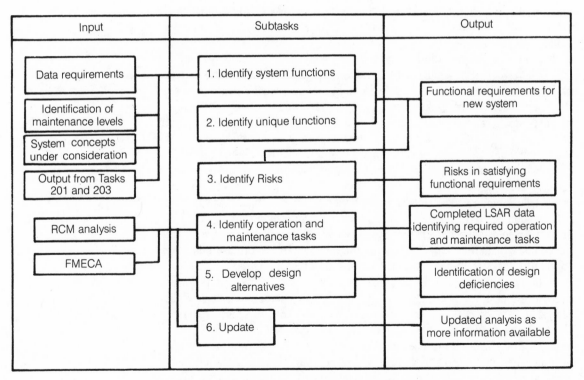

Fig. 5-1. Task 301—Functional requirements identification.

Subtask 2. Identify Unique Functions   The next step in accomplishing this task is to identify those functions in subtask 1 the new system must perform that are unique. The reason for this is that new functions often create new support problems or require new methods of support or new types of support resources. A function may be unique due to new technology in the design or new operational concepts. These unique functions should receive special attention when planning support for the new system. By recognizing early in the system design that there are unique functions that the system must perform, the planning for alternatives to support these functions can be initiated to resolve supportability problems.

Subtask 3. Identify Risks   The identification of functions, especially unique functions, focuses attention on the ability of the current, or planned, support system to provide the necessary support to the new system. This allows the early identification of risks involved with the supportability of the system due to functional requirements. Early identification of supportability risks allows time for design changes or modifications to the functional requirements to eliminate or reduce the risks before the design is completed.

Subtask 4. Identify Operation and Maintenance Tasks   The second part of Task 301 is to identify all the operation and maintenance tasks that must be performed in order for the new system to be able to accomplish the functions identified in subtask 1. Subtask 4 is one of the keys to developing a detailed logistics support package for the new system and requires detailed analysis of every facet of the new system. In essence, the result of this subtask should be a list of everything that has to be done to keep the system operating or fix it when it breaks. For a large system, this list could consist of several thousand maintenance tasks. The place to start this analysis is the failure modes, effects, and criticality analysis (FMECA). The FMECA, described in chapter 8, is an indepth analysis of the total system that identifies all the ways that it can fail. Common sense says that a maintenance task should be required for every failure mode. This is not a one-for-one relationship because one maintenance task may be able to correct more than one failure mode; however, every failure mode should be addressed by a maintenance task.

In addition to the FMECA, the reliability-centered maintenance (RCM) analysis, also discussed in chapter 8, is used to identify the preventive maintenance tasks that are required to support the new system. Another method used to identify tasks is to analyze the functions identified in subtask 1 to identify operation and other support tasks that must be performed that were not covered in either the FMECA or the RCM analysis. Remember, this subtask should identify every operation and maintenance task that is required to support the new system. The results of this subtask are recorded in the LSAR.

Subtask 5. Develop Design Alternatives   The identification process accomplished in subtasks 1 through 4 normally identifies design deficiencies that cause supportability problems. The purpose of subtask 5 is to formally require that the ILS disciplines actively participate in the design process to develop alternative design approaches to solve these problems. As stated previously, one of the goals of the LSA program is to impact the design and make changes that improve supportability; this is one of the critical places where it is done.

Subtask 6. Update Task 301 must be continually updated throughout the design process. Each design change must be analyzed to identify new functions and operation and maintenance tasks, which will in turn drive other analyses that will be discussed later in this chapter. This is the iterative part of LSA because as more information becomes available on the detailed design, more functions and tasks can be identified and each new level of definition provides more information for analysis until the design is complete.

Task Outputs

Task 301 produces data that is recorded in the logistics support analysis record database. Functional requirements and any recommended redesign or supportability problems are also recorded on the LSA Data Record B. Reliability-centered maintenance data is also recorded on the LSA Data Record B and FMECA data is recorded on the LSA Data Records B1 and B2. All operation and maintenance tasks are recorded on the LSA Data Record C. A detailed discussion of these data records is provided in chapter 9.

SUPPORT SYSTEM ALTERNATIVES — TASK 302

Task 302 is the next step in developing the support system for the new system. In Task 301, the functional requirements of the new system were identified, along with all the operation and maintenance tasks required for support. The purpose of this task is to develop alternative methods for providing the necessary support, at the system level, to accomplish the functions and tasks that were identified in Task 301. Figure 5-2 shows the inputs, subtasks, and outputs of Task 302.

Task Inputs

The outputs of Task 205, supportability and supportability-related system characteristics, and Task 301, system function and operation and maintenance task requirements, are the major inputs to Task 302. Additionally, system design concepts and government specified requirements are used to develop support concepts and plans for the new system.

Subtasks

There are five separate subtasks in Task 302, but they can be grouped into three different activities. The first two subtasks deal with development and updating of concepts to support the new system. Subtasks 3 and 4 address preparation and updating of plans to implement the concepts developed in subtasks 1 and 2. Subtask 5 identifies the risks associated with each concept.

Subtask 1. Develop System Level Support Concepts   The concepts for system level support of the new system must address how the overall support will be provided. This is where every possible alternative must be considered. Not all alternatives considered progress further than the initial discussion stage, but concepts that have merit and appear to provide the basic support required should be given further consideration. For a concept to be considered feasible, it must meet the supportability requirements developed in Task 205, and it must be capable of accomplishing all operation and maintenance tasks identified in Task 301. The concepts may include number of levels of maintenance to be used, the possibility of having contractor support, a combination of military and contractor maintenance support, different sparing techniques, different testing or support equipment, or combinations or all of these. The purpose is to investigate any feasible alternative for providing the necessary support to keep the new system operational.

Subtask 2. Update Concepts   The evolution of the design and the availability of more detailed information as the program progresses allows the concepts to be updated and refined throughout the program. The update process should better define the advantages and disadvantages of each alternative concept and provide more usable information to the decision of which alterna-

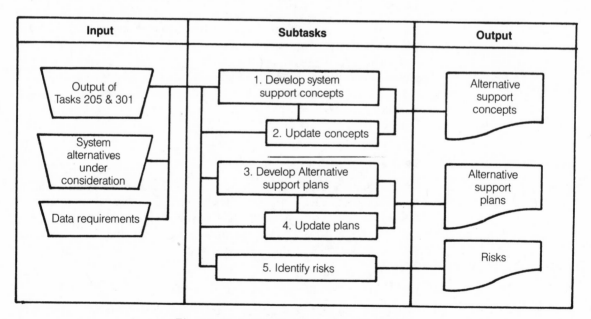

Fig. 5-2. Task 302—Support system alternatives.

58

tive is most desirable. This update is essential since the original concepts are normally based on previous history rather than detailed information about the new system. Failure to update the concepts could result in the wrong concept being selected, due to deficient or insufficient information.

Subtask 3. Develop Alternative Support Plans The support concepts developed in subtask 1 should be refined into support plans as detailed information becomes available. Subtask 3 requires that a support plan be developed for each support alternative, which should tell how the concept will be implemented and the ways that each support requirement will be fulfilled. Initially, the plan will be little more than an elaboration on the concept, but as the design matures, the plan becomes a detailed information document that addresses each aspect of support for the new system covering all levels of maintenance and all operation and maintenance tasks for both hardware and software.

Subtask 4. Update Plans As the alternative support concepts are updated as required by subtask 2, the corresponding support plan must also be updated. However, only those plans that are still under consideration are updated. The results of tradeoff analyses can be used as inputs to update these plans. The final support plan for the system is generated through this update process.

Subtask 5. Identify Risks An additional requirement of this task is to identify any risks involved with the alternative support concepts. These risks can be either qualitative or quantitative, but should be of a nature that is usable in the decision-making process in evaluating the alternatives. Things such as shortages of certain resources critical to the success of a support concept, or new and unproven methods, can develop into concerns that will end in the rejection of a concept. The identification of risks, or "what ifs", should be a significant contribution to the decision of what concept is chosen.

Task Outputs

Completion of Task 302 produces definitization of all the acceptable support concepts for the new system. Portions of these concepts are recorded on the LSA Data Record B where applicable for maintenance significant items. Formal documentation of the support plans is done in the form of an integrated logistics support plan or integrated support plan depending on contract data requirements. The outputs of this task become the basis for accomplishing tradeoff analyses to select the most appropriate support concept for the new system.

EVALUATION OF ALTERNATIVES AND TRADEOFF ANALYSIS — TASK 303

Task 303 is one of the most complex tasks of the LSA process. This task covers the complete spectrum of ILS disciplines and their impact on the total system being designed. The purpose of Task 303 is to evaluate each alternative support concept developed in Task 302 to determine the preferred method to be used to support the new system. The evaluation process requires the use of tradeoff analyses to determine the best alternative that meets the support, design, and operation requirements, while also having the best balance between cost, schedule, performance, readiness, and supportability. Figure 5-3 shows the inputs, subtasks, and outputs of Task 303.

Task Inputs

To continue the process for selection of the most appropriate support concept for the new system, Task 303 uses inputs from Tasks 205 and 302. These inputs, plus identification of system concept alternatives, specific tradeoff analyses required by the government, and system limits or constraints from the product specification, form the basis for detailed tradeoff analyses to identify the most acceptable support concept.

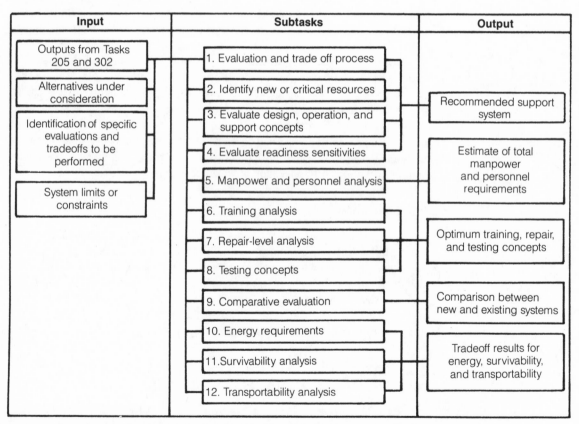

Fig. 5-3. Task 303—Evaluation of alternatives and tradeoff analysis.

Subtasks

Task 303 consists of twelve subtasks. The subtasks can be divided into three categories: development of the process that will be used to conduct the evaluation and tradeoff analyses, evaluations and tradeoff analyses that address segments of system support, and final evaluation of the composite of all segment evaluations and tradeoff analyses to select the most appropriate support concept.

Subtask 1. Evaluation and Tradoff Process The purpose of subtask 1 is to establish the criteria for each evaluation or tradeoff conducted in Task 303. It is extremely important that the process for conducting evaluations and tradeoffs is strictly controlled in order to provide reliable and usable results. The baseline information should be standard throughout the process. This allows a complete analysis of proposed changes as they occur. Figure 5-4 indicates requirements for conducting evaluations and tradeoff analyses. These requirements apply specifically to all evaluations conducted in this task; however, the requirements are applicable to any analysis that a logistician performs and should be used as a standard guideline when conducting evaluations and tradeoff analyses. This subtask should be completed and documented before any of the other subtasks in Task 303 are started.

Subtask 2. Identify New or Critical Resources A key consideration in the selection of a support alternative is the requirement for new or critical resources generated by the selection of that alternative. As has been discussed, the availability of scarce or limited resources required to support a new system is a driving factor in the selection of the most viable support alternative. One of the areas that should always be considered when looking at critical resources is personnel. There is not an unlimited supply of personnel, and within the personnel structure there are established limited job classifications that can be used to support new systems. Other new or critical resources may include spare and repair parts, test equipment, support equipment, precious metals, additional facilities requirements, and funds for procurement of resources.

Subtask 3. Evaluate Design, Operation, and Support Concepts The purpose of this subtask is to evaluate the new system support alternatives with regard to the proposed design, operation, and support concepts. The con-

---

1. Identify the quantitative and qualitative criteria to be used to select best alternative.
2. Choose or construct the appropriate model or relationship for conducting the evaluation or tradeoff analysis.
3. Conduct the initial evaluation or tradeoff analysis of each alternative under consideration (using the model or relationship developed in Step 2) and select the most appropriate alternative (based on the criteria identified in Step 1).
4. Conduct the sensitivity analysis to determine the risks or cost drivers of each alternative.
5. Document the results of the evaluation or tradeoff analysis.
6. Update the evaluations and tradeoffs as more detailed and accurate information becomes available.

Fig. 5-4. Conducting evaluations and tradeoff analyses.

tractor accomplishes this by conducting tradeoff analyses between each alternative and identifying which alternative provides the best balance for cost, schedule, performance, readiness, and supportability. The results of subtasks 4 through 12, which address specific aspects of system support, are inputs to this subtask. These subtasks look at readiness sensitivities, manpower and personnel requirements, training, repair levels, testing concepts, energy requirements, system survivability under combat situations, transportability requirements, and the comparative impact of decisions made on previous similar programs.

The reason for this overall evaluation requirement is that each of the individual evaluations and tradeoffs provide the best solution for a specific area, but the best solution for one area may contradict the solutions for other areas. This is where the balance between all requirements must be determined. For example, there may be two maintenance concepts, three levels of maintenance or two levels of maintenance, being considered for a system. The three levels of maintenance concept would remove and replace major subsystems at organizational level, repair subsystems at intermediate level, and repair assemblies at depot. The two levels of maintenance would repair subsystems at organizational level by removing and replacing assemblies and repair assemblies at depot level. These two concepts would have significantly different requirements for manpower and personnel, training, and testing concepts. The system design to allow easy testing and replacement of assemblies may also be different. The process for making the overall evaluation of these two concepts would be to conduct the appropriate evaluations and tradeoffs for each individual area using subtasks selected from subtasks 4 through 12 and then combining the results into an overall system level evaluation.

The requirement for manpower and personnel might show that fewer numbers of maintenance personnel would be required to support maintenance tasks for the two levels of maintenance concept, but these personnel would have to be more technically proficient. The two levels concept would require a comprehensive testing capability at organizational level, which might require a significant investment in the quantities of test equipment needed to support maintenance. The two levels of maintenance concept would probably result in an increase in the mean time to repair at organizational level since repair tasks normally require more time to accomplish than remove and replace tasks. These are examples of the types of issues that must be evaluated when selecting the best overall support concept. Life cycle cost analysis may also be used to predict which alternative provides support for the least system life cycle costs.

Subtask 4. Evaluate Readiness Sensitivities System readiness is the ultimate goal of the LSA process. It is important to know and understand the readiness parameters that are sensitive to variations in design and support parameters and it is also important to know those parameters that are not sensitive to changes in design or support. The purpose of this subtask is to identify those readiness parameters that can be influenced by variations in either design or support parameters. Basically, this identifies those areas where changes in design or support parameters can increase readiness. Knowing the things that can be improved allows emphasis to be placed where effort will have the most effect.

Reliability factors, such as mean time between failure or mean time between critical failure, and maintainability factors, such as mean time to repair or mean maintenance man hours per operation hour, and availability factors, such as inherent, achieved or operational availability, are examples of design and support parameters to which readiness has a high sensitivity level. In the discussion of subtask 3, it was shown that the maintenance concept for a system might increase or decrease the predicted mean time to repair at organizational level. This tradeoff would result in two different inherent availability predictions for the system. (Chapter 8 contains a detailed explanation of inherent availability.) While the life-cycle cost prediction for one maintenance concept might be significantly less than another under consideration, that concept may not meet the minimum requirements for system inherent availability and therefore would be unacceptable.

Subtask 5. Manpower and Personnel Analysis An analysis of the manpower and personnel requirements of each alternative is conducted to determine the total numbers of personnel, skill specialties, skill levels, and experience that will be required to support operation and maintenance of the system. A tradeoff analysis can then be conducted using the results of this analysis to determine the alternative that optimizes use of personnel.

Detailed information necessary for conducting an indepth analysis is generated by the maintenance task analysis process, LSA Task 401, which will be described in chapter 6. This process identifies the manpower and personnel qualifications required to perform each operation and maintenance task. The results of the task analysis can be extracted from the LSAR using selected LSA summary reports that are described in appendix A. If the development program is in its early stages and detailed design information is not available, data on similar systems prepared in LSA Task 203, baseline comparisons, can be used as the starting point for this analysis. Using the new or critical functions identified in the first part of Task 301 as the guide to focus on the primary changes in the new system allows deltas to the previous or similar systems to be developed. Because manpower is normally considered a critical logistics support resource, the number of persons required to support each concept can be a significant factor in selecting the concept that provides the best support while requiring a minimum amount of manpower and personnel resources.

Subtask 6. Training Analysis This subtask analyzes each proposed design and support concept to identify the optimum training methods required to implement each alternative. The training can consist of a combination of formal, informal, and on-the-job training. Additionally, tradeoff analyses can be performed to determine the feasibility and desirability of creating new skill specialties or shifting tasks between existing skill specialties to support the new system. As was discussed in subtask 5, the maintenance task analysis provides detailed information on the tasks that require special or unique training, and the LSA summary report system can produce detailed listings identifying each training task required for a support concept. Any formal training program represents a significant set of direct and indirect program costs because of the training support network that is required to develop and maintain the program. Use of informal or on-the-job training methods can reduce the direct costs for training, but these training methods do not ensure that the quality of training presented is in concert with achieving and maintaining the skills and proficiency that personnel need to accomplish operation or maintenance of the system.

Subtask 7. Repair Level Analysis A repair level analysis is conducted for each alternative design and support concept under consideration to determine the concept that makes optimum use of maintenance support resources. The repair level analysis process, described in detail in chapter 8, analyzes each maintenance significant item in the system to determine the most appropriate level of maintenance for repair of the item. Some decisions are based on the unique technologies or requirements needed to complete repair actions, while others are based on the most economical use of resources to complete the repair.

The results of the repair level analysis process are a significant input to the decision as to which overall maintenance concept is most applicable for a system. Within the analysis itself there may be conflicting results for different subsystems or maintenance significant items. The analysis for some items may recommend that repair actions be performed at a given level, but the overall results may indicate that to have the basic capability to perform maintenance at that level may not be cost-effective. These types of situations must be resolved through the tradeoff process to determine the most acceptable overall maintenance and support concept for the system.

Subtask 8. Testing Concepts Each alternative is evaluated to determine the optimum testing concept to be used. The concept may be composed of combinations of BIT, off-line testing, manual testing, and automatic testing. The key to this evaluation is to determine which alternative makes the best use of resources to accomplish testing. One of the major factors in determining the most acceptable testing concept is the inherent testability of the system design. (Inherent testability is discussed in chapter 8.) If the design has the testability characteristics that provide easy fault detection and fault isolation, maintenance time can be reduced significantly. A lack of inherent testability can drive testing costs out of sight. Once the basic testability of the design has been established, a decision must be made as to which methods of testing are most appropriate to support maintenance actions. The testing concept must support the maintenance concept. There is always a tradeoff between the cost and accuracy of manual testing, built-in test capabilities, and the use of sophisticated test equipment. The testing concept selected can be a driver with regard to manpower and personnel qualification requirements and training program requirements.

Manual testing is manpower intensive and requires more technical capabilities than automatic testing. This requires more training of personnel. Automatic testing, on the other hand, requires additional design capabilities and test equipment at each location where maintenance is performed. Built-in test capabilities are normally the least manpower intensive, but can be extremely expensive in terms of software and additional design capabilities. Each option must be considered in light of these factors. Additionally, the mean time to repair prediction for each level of maintenance includes the time required for fault detection and fault isolation, so the testing concept selection will have either a positive or negative impact maintainability and availability predictions for the system.

Subtask 9. Comparative Evaluation A comparative evaluation should be made between the exhibited capability of an existing system to achieve its supportability objectives and the projected ability of the new system to do likewise. The purpose of this subtask is to ascertain the feasibility of each alternative achieving the goals established for the new system. The BCS developed for Task 203 can be used in this subtask when no previous similar system exists. The difference between this subtask and Task 203 is that the purpose of Task 203 is to identify supportability characteristics for the new system, while the purpose of this subtask is to evaluate how each alternative design and support concept can best support the new system based on the support that was or is being provided for the previous or baseline comparison system.

The thrust of this evaluation should be to determine the supportability problems that occurred with the existing or baseline system and then analyze the application of the proposed support concepts to see if these problems are or can be solved by using one or more of the proposed concepts. Much of this evaluation is understandably subjective and qualitative, but it does provide a way of war-gaming each alternative concept against historical data and past support system performance to determine shortfalls or highlight critical issues that must be corrected before the new system becomes operational.

Subtask 10. Energy Requirements An analysis of the projected energy costs for each alternative is conducted to identify any problem areas that might arise due to fluctuations in the cost or availability of energy sources. Specific attention should be paid to petroleum and petroleum products that are required to support the new system. Sensitivity analyses may be required when the costs of petroleum are considered significant drivers for supportability. Because energy consumption may represent a significant cost for the operation of some systems, a life-cycle cost analysis that focuses on the energy uses of different design concepts may be beneficial in providing inputs to the design selection process. If the energy requirements for a new system are different in quantity or type of fuel from the existing system, an additional analysis may be required to determine the impact of this new requirement on the military fuels supply system and the capability of using organizations to provide the fuel within current fuel storage, handling, and distribution equipment assets and limitations.

Subtask 11. Survivability Analysis A survivability analysis is performed to determine which alternative provides the best characteristics for battle damage repair and other considerations of survivability in a combat environment. While this may seem like a requirement that is out of the normal realm of logistics concerns, remember that all systems are developed for wartime use when survivability is the primary consideration. Battle damage repair should always be a prime consideration in any system developed for use in a combat environment.

System design characteristics with regard to survivability include redundant mission critical subsystems, shielding, and dispersion or segmenting of functions within the system to limit the severity that a single battle damage event could have on the system's ability to perform its mission. Repair of battle damage is another aspect of survivability in that, when damage occurs, it is imperative that the system is repaired immediately so that it can resume its mission. Areas of system design that are of concern for battle damage repair include modularization of subsystems, assemblies, and subassemblies so that damaged items can be removed and replaced quickly, use of connectors or fasteners that allow expedient replacement actions, and a design that allows easy access to all portions of the system. These design attributes also increase the inherent maintainability of the system and should be routinely considered in the design process.

Subtask 12. Transportability Analysis Ease of transportability, the inherent capability of an item to be moved by towing, self-propulsion, or common carrier via highway, railway, waterway, airway, or sea, is always a consideration for design of a new system. A transportability analysis is conducted to determine which alternative optimizes the use of transportation resources. The efficient capability of a system to be moved by all required modes of transportation will achieve a higher operational availability and lower life cycle cost. Designs that require special or unique methods for packaging, handling, storage, or transportation should be avoided if at all possible. Incorporation of handling, tiedown, and sling points into designs is necessary to optimize transportability and complement storage, maintenance, and other handling requirements.

A system must be designed so that it can be handled and transported safely. Sectionalization and disassembly capability for transport purposes, with ease of reassembly for operational use or maintenance, should be a design consideration. The identification of transportability requirements should be made as early as possible in order to conduct tradeoff studies to determine if the need can be fulfilled using standard procedures. Special requirements have a negative impact on life cycle cost and should be avoided unless absolutely necessary. System transportation requirements are recorded in the LSAR on the LSA Data Record J.

Task Outputs

The major output of Task 303 is the recommended support concept for the new system. This output is recorded in the LSAR and forms the basis for detailed support and maintenance planning. In addition to the recommended concept, Task 303 produces outputs that are used to guide planning for resources. These outputs include: an estimate of the total manpower and personnel requiements for the system; the optimum training, repair levels, and testing concepts that are required to implement the recommended support concept; identification of support problems that are solved or must be solved by the concept for the new system; and any resulting design considerations for energy requirements, survivability, and transportability.

6

Determination of
Logistics Support
Resource Requirements
Task Section 400

The tasks discussed in Task Sections 200 and 300 developed the system supportability characteristics and determined the best support concepts for the system. The next step in the LSA process is to apply the results of these previous tasks to the system design to identify the detailed logistics support resources that will be required to support the system when it becomes operational and to identify other support issues relative to long-term support. Task Section 400 addresses three areas: identification of detailed logistics support resource requirements for support alternatives; assessment of the impact the new system will have on other existing systems; and planning for support after the end of the production phase of the acquisition process for the system. These tasks, especially Task 401, can be very costly to accomplish due to the quantity manpower required to perform the tasks and, also, the tasks result in the generation of a tremendous amount of documentation in the LSAR. Because each of these tasks require design information down to the lowest assembly and part levels, Task Section 400 is initiated during full-scale development of the system.

TASK ANALYSIS — TASK 401

Performance of a complete maintenance task analysis will result in the identification of all the logistic resources required to support the new system. The task analysis process is the most manpower intensive, and therefore, typically, the most expensive, requirement contained in the LSA program. However, if done correctly, it is the single most accurate method of identifying logistics support resource requirements, and it eliminates guesswork and rule of thumb estimates of resource requirements. The extra upfront expense of performing a complete task analysis pays for itself many times over throughout the life of the system, by eliminating waste and misuse of resources. Figure 6-1 shows the inputs, subtasks, and outputs of Task 401.

Task Inputs

The maintenance task analysis process requires input from virtually every previous LSA program task either directly or indirectly. The use study that is output from Task 201 identifies the operation and maintenance support resources that are available or planned for the new system, and it provides an explanation of the support system that is to be used and the operation and support concepts. Output from Task 205 is used to identify the supportability characteristics that were to be considered for incorporation into the design. The operation and maintenance tasks that were identified by Task 301 and recorded in the LSAR are the basis for starting the detailed maintenance task analysis.

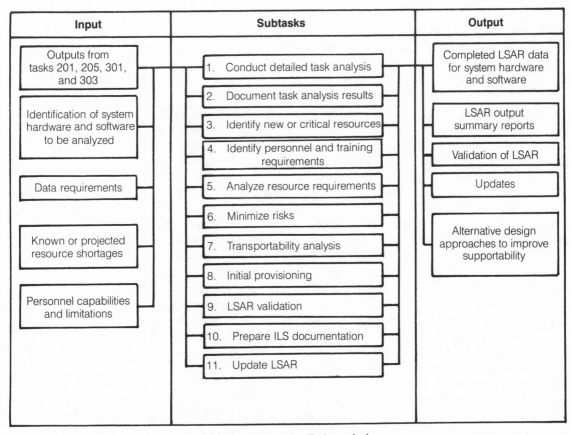

Input	Subtasks	Output
Outputs from tasks 201, 205, 301, and 303	1. Conduct detailed task analysis	Completed LSAR data for system hardware and software
Identification of system hardware and software to be analyzed	2. Document task analysis results 3. Identify new or critical resources 4. Identify personnel and training requirements	LSAR output summary reports Validation of LSAR
Data requirements	5. Analyze resource requirements	Updates
Known or projected resource shortages	6. Minimize risks 7. Transportability analysis 8. Initial provisioning	Alternative design approaches to improve supportability
Personnel capabilities and limitations	9. LSAR validation 10. Prepare ILS documentation 11. Update LSAR	

Fig. 6-1. Task 401—Task analysis.

Determination of Logistics Support Resource Requirements

The support concept that was chosen as a result of the evaluations and tradeoffs of Task 303 is applied to the analysis process of this task.

Complete engineering documentation of the system, down to the lowest assembly and part levels, is required so that all support resources can be identified. Contractually required data items must be identified to ensure that the results of the task analysis recorded in the LSAR will be capable of fulfilling these requirements. Any known or projected shortage of support resources must be identified so that the analysis can develop alternatives to solve or alleviate problems that would be caused by the shortages. Additionally, since the maintenance program is dependent on performance of personnel, the capabilities and limitations of maintenance personnel must be known so that maintenance tasks can be prepared that make maximum use of personnel resources while not exceeding acceptable performance limits.

Subtasks

There are eleven subtasks contained in Task 401. Subtask 1, conducting a detailed task analysis, is the cornerstone subtask and it produces the information necessary for each of the subsequent subtasks. The remaining ten tasks address the documentation of individual subtask results, specific support resource requirements for the system, or support risks identified during the analysis process. In most instances, subtasks 2 through 11 should not and cannot be implemented until sufficient data is generated by subtask 1.

Subtask 1. Conduct Detailed Task Analysis   A detailed maintenance task analysis is conducted to identify all the resources that are required to support the system. The task analysis process actually starts with the identification of required operation and maintenance tasks by LSA Task 301. These tasks are then analyzed to identify required support resources. Figure 6-2 illustrates the task analysis process. This process addresses each maintenance or operation task in minute detail to identify everything that happens when the task is performed, all the resources required to perform the task, and the conditions under which it is performed. As an example, suppose the FMECA results indicated that a specific unit would fail. Task 301 then identified the requirement for a maintenance task to repair the unit by removing a module within the failed unit and replacing it with a functional unit. The detailed maintenance task analysis would address every aspect of this maintenance action. Using the maintenance task code as a guide, the analyst would go through a process of listing each step in the maintenance task (i.e., performance of the testing required to identify the failed module, gaining access to the module by disassembling the unit, disconnecting and removing the failed module, replacing and reconnecting the functional module, reassembly of the unit, and testing of the unit to determine that the replacement of the module corrected the failure).

For each step in the maintenance task, the analysis would record the logistic support resources needed to perform the step (i.e., the number of personnel by skill level that would perform the step, the actual and elapsed time required to perform each step, any support or test equipment, tools, spare and repair parts used, facility requirements where the task is performed, special training necessary for personnel to be capable of performing the task, and any safety hazards that might occur or be present when the task is performed). By repeating this analysis process for every operation and maintenance task required to support the new system, the types and quantities of resources that will be needed to support the system can be identified. This process provides the most reliable identification of required support resources because it is based solely on the performance of operation and maintenance tasks.

Subtask 2. Document Task Analysis Results The purpose of subtask 2 is to formally require that the results of subtask 1, be recorded in the logistic support analysis record. This is an extremely important requirement because the LSAR is to be used as the single repository and source for all logistic support data and information. The results of the maintenance task analysis process are recorded in narrative form on the LSA Data Record D. A companion LSA Data Record D1 is also prepared for each maintenance task that con-

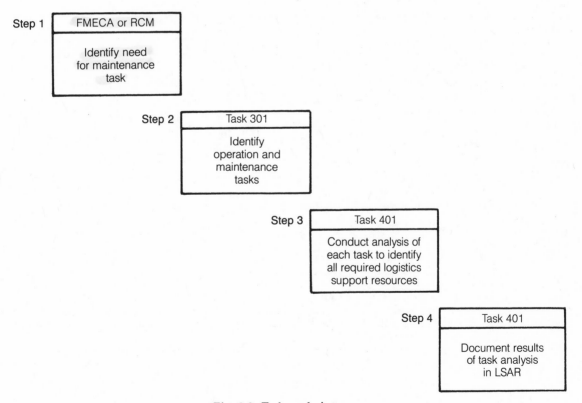

Fig. 6-2. Task analysis process.

tains a tabular listing of all the support and test equipment, tools, and spare and repair parts required to perform the task. The consolidation of all LSA Data Records D1 prepared for a system will provide identification of all the logistic support resources required to support operation and maintenance. Figure 6-3 lists the resources that should be identified as the result of the maintenance task analysis process. This logistics support resource database provides inputs to the LSA summary report generation process that produces information reports on specific system support requirements. Chapter 9 contains a complete discussion of the LSAR, LSA Data Records, and the LSA summary report process. A description and example of each LSA summary report is provided in appendix A.

Subtask 3. Identify New or Critical Resources   Identification of new or critical resources is a continuing concern of the LSA process. Previously, Task 303, subtask 2, required a similar identification; however, that task deals with the overall system requirements. This subtask can now address the detailed requirements for new or critical resources because the maintenance task analysis process identifies all the resources that are necessary to support the system down to the lowest levels. The results of this subtask should be a quantitative analysis, whereas the results of Task 303, subtask 2, tend to be qualitative. There are two ways of accomplishing this subtask, both of which are necessary to assure that all new or critical resources are adequately addressed. The first way is that as the analyst is performing a maintenance task analysis, the need for a new or critical resource is identified based on the information contained in the use study or other task inputs. This initial identification should be documented in a manner prescribed in the LSA plan. The second way that resources are identified and quantified is by generation of LSA summary reports that address overall system level resource requirements. Both of these methods are beneficial in completing this subtask. By early identification during the maintenance task analysis process, the need for new or critical resources can be highlighted as a significant issue to be addressed by further analyses and by management. Summarization of overall requirements then identifies the range and quantities of these resources that are needed based on the system analysis.

There are several actions that must take place after either method identifies the need for a new or critical resource. When the analyst first identifies a

---

Provisioning • Maintenance Manhours • Personnel and Skills • Human Factors Engineering • Allocation of Maintenance Tasks • Repair Parts Identification • Support Equipment • Operator and Maintenance Publications • Facility Requirements • Reliability, Availability, and Maintainability • Transportation, Transportability, and Handling

---

Fig. 6-3. Resources identified by task analysis.

need, the need must be verified as the only solution to the requirement. The verification process enables either the design to be changed to eliminate the need or advance planning to begin for fulfilling the need.

When the summarization process produces detailed results that resources are new or critical, the design characteristics that created the need should be reexamined to determine if the supportability characteristics developed by Task 205 have been incorporated into the final system design. The results of this sub-task should be changes to the design whenever possible to limit the range and quantities of new or critical resources required to support the system or a detailed identification of the magnitude of the requirements.

Subtask 4. Identify Personnel and Training Requirements The maintenance task analysis results in identification of the total personnel requirements to support the new system. Additionally, the training requirements for operator and maintenance personnel are also identified. Personnel requirements are based on the number and type of personnel required to accomplish all maintenance tasks. The method for determining personnel requirements is dependent on documentation of the results of maintenance task analyses in the LSAR. The LSA summary report generation process is designed to extract the personnel skill levels, maintenance levels where tasks are performed, and the elapsed and actual task performance times from the LSA Data Records D and D1, and to produce summary reports that provide identification of the personnel requirements for performance of maintenance at each maintenance level and by skill level. This information can be displayed in a number of options to identify total personnel requirement to support maintenance of the system.

Training requirements are based on knowing the exact tasks that personnel must be trained to accomplish. The LSA summary report generation process, again, provides the data necessary to fulfill this requirement. LSA summary reports can be generated that identify all the training requirements necessary for personnel to be able to perform necessary maintenance tasks. This process of identifying personnel and training requirements, based on the data contained in the LSAR, results in extremely accurate information for use in acquiring necessary personnel resources and development of viable training programs.

Subtask 5. Analyze Resource Requirements The maintenance task analysis process normally identifies many areas where the supportability of a new system can be optimized or where a design change is necessary to meet minimum supportability goals. Subtask 5 established the formal requirement for logisticians performing LSA to provide information to design engineers that will improve supportability. This is one of the major goals of the overall LSA program, influencing the design to achieve optimum supportability. One of the methods for performing this analysis is to analyze the result of each maintenance task analysis that indicates the planned maintenance action does not meet established criteria either for time required or resource use.

The LSA summary report system will produce reports that identify tasks that exceed time limitations for each maintenance level. Reports can also be generated that identify where each type of resource is required to support a maintenance task. Using these types of reports is extremely helpful in focusing analysis efforts on those maintenance tasks that are candidates for design or supportability improvement. Another analysis method is to analyze where each type of resource is being used to determine if there is a duplication of resource requirements (i.e., two different types of test equipment being required when a single type may be capable of performing all required testing functions). This also applies to tool usage, where, for example, several different sizes of fasteners used in the system require a range of tools for removal when only one tool would be required if all fasteners were standardized.

Subtask 6. Minimize Risks   Several previous tasks contained subtasks that required the identification of risks associated with alternatives or courses of action. The purpose of subtask 6 is to determine if the results of the maintenance task analysis supports the risks or if the detailed information resulting from the task analysis reduces or eliminates the risk. If the risk still exists, the results of the task analysis should allow the risk to be quantified. This information can then be used by management to specifically address the critical risks of the program that are related to support resources and supportability of the new system.

Subtask 7. Transportability Analysis   An analysis is conducted to determine the transportability requirements of the new system. The purpose of the analysis is to identify transportability problems caused when the new system exceeds established transportation limits or requirements for safe handling. MIL-STD 1366, Definition of Transportation and Delivery Mode Dimensional Constraints, contains data on the standard dimension limits for military systems. Designs that exceed standard limits of 8 feet in height, 8 feet in width, 32 feet in length, and 11,200 pounds when prepared for transport should be avoided since they will require special handling and transportation. If the system, or a portion of the system, is to be transported inside cargo trucks or standard cargo shipping containers, the standard limits are reduced to 7 feet in height, 6.5 feet in width, 18.5 feet in length, and 10,000 pounds. These dimensions are used as guidelines when planning for transportation.

Dynamic and environmental limitations of the system or any of its components and hazardous materials contained in the system must also be considered. Sensitive or fragile items may require special handling or unique packaging due to the type of material used or the design. The dynamic limitations of the design must be identified and compensated for by proper transportability planning. Susceptibility to damage from acceleration or vibration during handling or shipment must be considered when selecting packaging and packing material. The addition of fixtures for securing the system during transit reduces the possibility of damage from induced stress. A system that is hazardous or dangerous to transport creates special problems due to safety considerations and should be at the top of the list for resolution. The protection of personnel involved with the physical movement aspects of a system is always a priority issue. Logistics engineers must coordinate efforts with system safety, maintainability, and human engineering to effectively eliminate hazards or devise methods to reduce them to acceptable levels. System safety not only maintains a Hazard Log that identifies all known system hazards, they are ultimately responsible for the solutions to eliminating hazards.

Maintainability and human engineering are also involved in identifying and solving hazards and hazardous actions. This is one area where every ILS discipline is involved in formulating answers to the problems caused by hazards. The results of the transportability analysis are recorded on an LSA Data Record J. A data record is prepared for each major segment of the system that is transportable. Detailed packaging requirements for each assembly or part used in the system may be recorded on the LSA Data Record H. Both of these data records are discussed in chapter 9.

Subtask 8. Initial Provisioning   This subtask requires that items that require initial provisioning be documented appropriately in the LSAR. Provisioning is the process for identifying and obtaining the initial stock of spare parts required to support fielded equipment. The method for accomplishing provisioning has been developed over the years through trial and error. Until 1974, each branch of the military had its own way of documenting requirements for spare parts due to the unique needs of that branch. This caused many problems. First, there was no uniform way of correlating the parts used by one service with those of another. Second, the databases that were developed by the services were incompatible. In 1974, MIL-STD 1552, Uniform Department of Defense Requirements for Provisioning Technical Documentation, and MIL-STD 1561, Uniform Department of Defense Provisioning Procedures, were issued. These documents established a standard method for accomplishing and documenting provisioning requirements. MIL-STD 1552 has been superseded by MIL-STD 1388-2A, thereby incorporating the provisioning process into the LSA process. No other method of documenting provisioning requirements should be used.

Provisioning is accomplished by generating data lists, called provisioning lists, that identify the parts of an equipment. Logically, this should not be done until the design is final. Therefore, provisioning activities occur as late in the full-scale development phase as possible, but early enough to allow procurement and delivery of spares required to support the first equipment fielded. The identification of items for initial provisioning is accomplished as an extension of the maintenance task analysis process. When a maintenance task requires that an item be removed and replaced, a spare is required. Repair of an item may require a repair part. The end result of this process is a fully justified provisioning list of only the items necessary to support maintenance. This information is recorded on the LSA Data Record D1.

The provisioning process uses the LSA Data Record D1 entries to initiate corresponding LSA Data Records H and H1. Additional data is then entered on these data records to complete the preparation of the provisioning data for the system. The LSA summary report system is then used to prepare provisioning technical documentation for the system. Provisioning technical documentation (PTD) is any data submitted to the government as part of the provisioning process. There are several different types of provisioning lists that a contractor may be required to prepare. The PTD prepared for a system may include a provisioning parts list, long lead time items list, interim support items list, tool and test equipment list, common bulk item list, and repairable items list. The data reflected on these lists is basically the same. The difference in these lists is the type of items they are prepared for and the intended use of the lists.

The provisioning parts list (PPL) is a complete listing of all the parts that make up an item of equipment. This list is prepared by the contractor and submitted to the government at, or before, the provisioning conference. A complete PPL not only identifies everything that is required to build the equipment, it also provides information about each part. This information is divided into cataloging data that describes the part and application data that tells how it is used and maintained. A long lead time items list identifies those spare and repair parts that require additional lead time for procurement that exceeds the standard procurement times to support production. The interim support items list identifies spare and repair parts that are required to support initial testing or operation of the system before it becomes fully operational. A tool and test equipment list (TTEL) contains information about unique tools and test equipment that is required to perform maintenance on the equipment. The format of the list is the same as for a PPL. Submittal of the TTEL is dependent on the contract delivery requirements and is normally submitted with the PPL.

It is easier to document the usage of bulk items such as wire, adhesives, solder, etc., using the common bulk items list (CBIL). The CBIL is a companion document to the PPL. In a large item of equipment, a common bulk item could possibly be used several hundred times, which might require an identical number of entries on the PPL. The item would require only one entry on the CBIL because it consolidates all usages into a single total quantity required for the equipment. The repairable items list (RIL) is an abbreviated version of a PPL. It contains provisioning data on the repairable items contained in the equipment. Submittal of the RIL normally precedes the PPL. In many cases, the RIL is used to cross-check the maintenance task list to ensure that all items identified by provisioning as repairable have been addressed by maintenance engineering. The provisioning process, when accomplished properly, provides information to the government about the type and quantity of spare and repair parts that are required to support maintenance. It also identifies the configuration of an item of equipment. When submitted to the government, the list becomes part of the Defense Logistics Service Center (DLSC) master data file that contains information on parts procured by the government. The LSA summary report system has the capability to produce any or all of the provisioning documentation required for a system.

Subtask 9. LSAR Validation The LSAR should be validated whenever possible to ensure that the database is consistent with the system design. The design process is actually a series of changes that occur to the system over a rather lengthy period of time when the design evolves from a concept to the final production configuration. When changes occur to the system that are not reflected in the LSAR, the logistic support resources requirements are inaccurate. In many cases, this is the biggest single problem of an LSA program, uncontrolled documentation.

There are two ways of conducting the validation, by checking the LSAR against engineering documentation or by checking the LSAR against the actual system. Both methods work and should be used. Often, the initial maintenance task analysis is accomplished using engineering documentation before the system is built. Once the system is built or a prototype constructed, the maintenance task should be tried on the system to see if it is correct. This practice validates the accuracy of the LSAR and also provides the ability to update the maintenance task times contained in the LSAR with actual measured times. The LSAR is normally reviewed and validated, at least partially, at each LSA review conducted jointly by the contractor and the government. Validation should also be accomplished as an integral portion of any review, audit, or demonstration. Examples of these validation opportunities include preliminary and critical design reviews, functional and physical configuration audits, and the maintainability demonstration.

Subtask 10. Prepare ILS Documentation   The LSAR serves as the single source of logistics data for documentation purposes. Therefore, ILS documentation must be prepared using the LSAR database whenever possible. Many contractually deliverable data items can be prepared by generation of LSA summary reports. MIL-STD 1388-2A contains a matrix that identifies the standard government data items that can be satisfied by certain summary reports. Figure 6-4, while not all-inclusive, identifies typical data requirements that can be extracted from the LSAR. Other ILS documents should be initiated using the data contained in the LSAR. The most significant of these other documents are the system operation and maintenance technical manuals. The narrative description of each maintenance task that is recorded on the LSA Data Record D should be used as the basis for preparation of the system technical manuals. This ensures that the maintenance procedures delivered to the actual system operator and maintenance personnel matches the system support concept. Detailed training course materials should also be prepared based on this same source information so that all aspects of system support are in concert.

Subtask 11. Update LSAR   LSA is an iterative process where the analyses, especially maintenance task analysis, are conducted repeatedly until the design is finalized and all the resources required to support the system have been identified. Subtask 11 requires that the LSAR be updated throughout the life of the new system in order to maintain an adequate and accurate record of the required support resources. Updates continue as new and more detailed information becomes available. Additionally, the interface between the LSA program and other engineering programs such as reliability, maintainability, testability, safety, and human engineering provides data for the LSAR, which also must be updated as more detailed information becomes available. The LSA plan must identify how this exchange of information and updating process will be managed and controlled so that the LSAR is maintained and continually updated throughout the design process.

Task Outputs

Task 401 produces the completed LSAR database for the system. As stated previously, the maintenance task analyses for each maintenance-significant item are recorded on the LSA Data Records D and D1. Requirements for any new or critical resources identified as a result of the subtask 3 analyses are recorded on an LSA Data Record E (support or training equipment), LSA Data Record F (facilities), or LSA Data Record G (personnel skill requirements). Transportability issues identified by subtask 7 are entered on LSA Data Record J, and the

---

Maintainability Data Report
Reliability Predictions Report
Failure Mode, Effects, and Criticality Analysis
Maintenance Allocation Chart
Level of Repair Analysis Report
Calibration/Measurement Requirement Summary
Maintenance Plan Report
Human Engineering Design Approach Document
Task and Skill Analysis Report
Training Path System Documentation
Personnel Performance Profiles
Training Support Data
Personnel and Training Requirements
Training Course Proposal
Support Equipment Recommendations Data
Test, Measurement, and Diagnostic Equipment Data
Support Equipment List
Provisioning Parts List
Common Bulk Items List
Tools and Test Equipment List
Recommended Repair Parts List
Depot Maintenance Study
Design Change Notices
Technical Manuals Source Data
Technical Orders Source Data
Operation and Maintenance Instruction Manuals Source Data
Facilities Design Criteria
Facility Design Concepts
Computer Program Test Specification
Computer Resources Integrated Support Data

Fig. 6-4. Data extracted from the LSAR.

provisioning requirements for the system are recorded on LSA Data Records H and H1. The validated LSAR is then used to generate LSA summary reports that provide detailed data on the logistics support resource requirements for the system. Based on the results of the maintenance task analysis process, any alternative design approaches or changes to the support concept that will improve supportability are documented and provided to design engineering for evaluation and incorporation as applicable.

EARLY FIELDING ANALYSIS — TASK 402

The purpose of an early fielding analysis is to analyze the new system in relationship to other systems that already exist in the field. Until this point, planning for resources was limited to the specific requirements of the new system without regard for the needs of existing systems. Additionally, the early fielding analysis addresses the resource needs for the new system when placed in the projected combat environment. Figure 6-5 illustrates the inputs, subtasks, and outputs for Task 402.

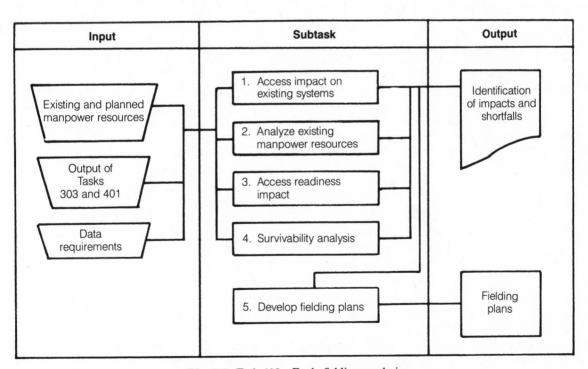

Fig. 6-5. Task 402—Early fielding analysis.

Determination of Logistics Support Resource Requirements

Task Inputs

The unique purpose of Task 402, projecting the impact of the new system on existing support resources, requires a significant amount of input data on other similar systems and the support environment where the new system will be deployed. The contractor may have to rely on the government for a large portion of this input information. If such a need exists, the requirement for this information should be conveyed to the government, at a minimum in the LSA plan, so that the data will be available when needed to support this task. The other inputs for this task come in the form of outputs from Tasks 303 and 401 which identify the resources that will be required to support the system.

Subtasks

Task 402 consists of five subtasks. Subtasks 1 through 4 require specific analyses of the impact of the new system on existing resources and other operational systems. Subtask 5 addresses preparation of fielding plans to deal with implementation of solutions to problems resulting from the analyses of subtasks 1 through 4.

Subtask 1. Assess Impact on Existing Systems Once fielded, the new system will compete for limited support resources with other systems already in operation. The purpose of subtask 1 is to assess how the introduction of the new system in the field will impact the existing support resources such as personnel, maintenance facilities, support equipment, depot workloads, supply support, training facilities, etc. This is not an easy task to accomplish with a fine degree of accuracy because resources are shared and used based on operational scenarios and changing mission requirements. This is especially true at intermediate and depot maintenance levels, where it is sometimes difficult to relate specific resource uses to a specific system. However, there are many cases where even gross estimates prove beneficial. If the new system requires a sizeable increase in a specific resource over the requirements of the system that is being replaced, this issue is a candidate for detailed analysis. For example, if the new system requires twice as much fuel to operate, the fuel distribution system capabilities that the new system must share with existing systems should be analyzed to determine the impact of the new system on the overall fuel capabilities that currently exist. The results of this subtask should identify any changes to existing resource levels necessary to support the new system when fielded so that the effectiveness of existing systems are not degraded.

Subtask 2. Analyze Existing Manpower Resources A special consideration is the availability of adequate manpower to support the new system. Subtask 2 specifically addresses the impact that the new system will have on the pool of available manpower to support both existing systems and the new system. Too much emphasis cannot be placed on this area. Tradeoff analyses should be used to provide feedback to the maintenance task analysis process where necessary to adjust manpower requirements based on limited availability. If the new system significantly degrades the ability of existing systems to perform assigned missions, or if the total requirement for personnel to support both existing systems and the new system exceeds the total available manpower, manpower requirements for the new system should be identified as one of the readiness drivers and treated accordingly throughout the LSA process.

Subtask 3. Assess Readiness Impact The purpose of this subtask is assess the consequences if the resources identified as necessary to support the new system are not available in the quantities required. This "what if" scenario should lead to the identification of alternative approaches to resource requirements or areas of optimization or streamlining which will minimize the impact. Care should be exercised in accomplishing this subtask to not duplicate any analyses that were done in Task 303.

Subtask 4. Survivability Analysis Support resource requirements for a combat environment are much more severe than for peacetime. The purpose of this survivability analysis is to determine unique resource requirements that may be generated when the new system is placed in a combat environment. Items such as predetermined combat spares and battle damage repair procedures and facilities should be considered when appropriate. This analysis should not be a duplication of the survivability analysis of Task 303.

Subtask 5. Develop Fielding Plans An early fielding plan is generated to develop and implement solutions to the problems identified in subtasks 1 through 4. It is essential to the readiness of the new system that any problems or concerns that are raised during the early fielding analysis be addressed prior to deployment. Failure to adequately address these problems will degrade not only the new system, but also existing systems that will have to compete for limited support resources.

Task Outputs

The outputs of Task 402 highlight the impact that the new system will have on existing systems and the existing support resources that must be shared when the new system is fielded. This information must be interjected back into the LSA process so that changes to support requirements can be addressed to develop solutions wherever possible, and must be forwarded to the government so that alternatives can be developed or adjustments to support resources can be planned and implemented.

POST-PRODUCTION SUPPORT ANALYSIS — TASK 403

Production facilities for a new system do not remain operational throughout the life of the system. Therefore, a post-production support analysis is conducted to determine the source of logistics support resources after production ceases. The period of time between the end of production and the disposal of the system may be as much as 20 years and original sources of support resources may not remain available for this complete operational period, so the post-production support problems are not insignificant. Figure 6-6 shows the inputs, subtasks, and outputs of Task 403.

Task Inputs

Inputs for Task 403 consist of information relative to the existing and planned sources of support resources for the new system, anticipated useful life of the system, and projected quantities of resources that will be required to support the system over its useful life. Additionally, any known product improvements that are planned must be considered to adjust the resource requirements when the improvements are incorporated. This input data is normally obtained as outputs from Tasks 201, 401, and 402 or from the government.

Subtasks

There is only one subtask contained in Task 403, but it can be divided into four segments; assessment of the useful life of the new system, identification of potential resource problems, development of alternatives to resolve or avoid these shortage problems, and preparation of a post-production support plan that documents the results of the task. Each segment should be pursued in a step-by-step manner in order to identify potential support problems and propose solutions that can be implemented so that the system does not become ineffective before the end of its useful life. Items to be considered include sources for

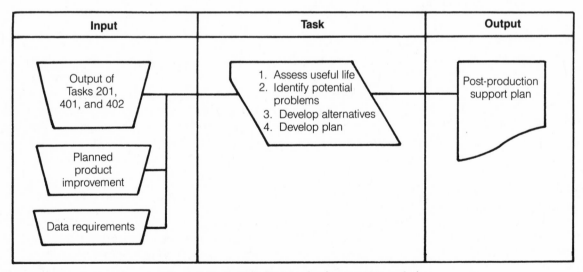

Fig. 6-6. Task 403—Post-production support analysis.

replacement spares and repair parts, maintenance and overhaul facilities, reprocurement data, preplanned product improvement, and configuration management.

Task Outputs

The final step of this task is the preparation of a post-production support plan that assures adequate availability of support resources after production is complete. The plan should identify all the resources that are required to support the system, in at least general terms, and address in detail those items that are projected to cause support problems in the future. Any recommended solutions to projected support resource problems should be highlighted so that planning for implementation can be initiated.

7

Supportability Assessment
Task Section 500

The effectiveness of the overall ILS effort and the adequacy of the LSA program are assessed by actions contained in Task Section 500. There are two types of assessments covered in this task section: assessment of supportability during the development of the new system, and assessment after the system is deployed. Assessment during development is necessary to identify and correct deficiencies prior to fielding the new system. Post-deployment assessment is essential in developing product improvements for the system and in documenting long-term supportability problems and solutions for use on future programs. During the early phases of an acquisition program, test and evaluation may be accomplished using models or simulation to verify the progress toward supportability goals. Towards the end of full-scale development, test and evaluation should be done in an environment that matches as closely as possible the actual environment where the system will be deployed.

SUPPORTABILITY TEST, EVALUATION, AND VERIFICATION — TASK 501

The test, evaluation, and verification of the supportability of a system is a continuous effort. Historically, test and evaluation, if any, have been limited to some testing of the support system just prior to full production. This is unacceptable. The support package for the new system must be repeatedly tested and evaluated throughout the acquisition cycle to verify that the system supportability requirements are being met. Test, evaluation, and verification of support must be accomplished during every phase of the acquisition cycle. Figure 7-1 illustrates the inputs, subtasks, and outputs of Task 501.

Task Inputs

Inputs for Task 501 originate from several sources. The LSA process provides inputs from Tasks 203, 205, and 303 that are the baseline for development of the test strategy and objectives. These task outputs identify the supportability goals and objectives by which the system should be evaluated. The support concepts should be evaluated under the most realistic situations possible to determine if these selected methods are compatible with the final system design. Information on previous tests conducted on similar systems as to the test methodology used and effectiveness of the test results can be used as a guide for developing the test strategy for the current system. What worked, or didn't work, on previous systems should be a key to test development; don't repeat previous mistakes. As supportability tests are conducted, the test results should be input back into the strategy development process for formulation of future tests.

Subtasks

Task 501 contains five subtasks. The first three subtasks address supportability testing during system design and development. Subtasks 4 and 5 deal

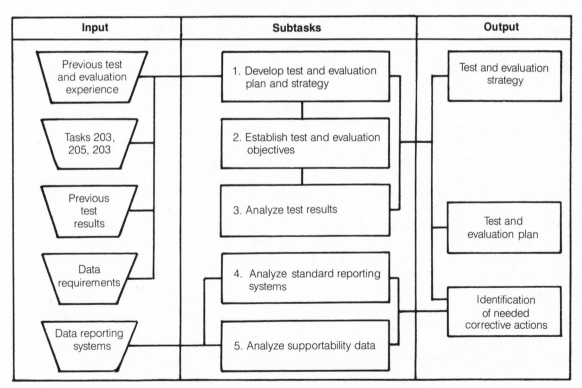

Input	Subtasks	Output
Previous test and evaluation experience	1. Develop test and evaluation plan and strategy	Test and evaluation strategy
Tasks 203, 205, 203	2. Establish test and evaluation objectives	
Previous test results	3. Analyze test results	Test and evaluation plan
Data requirements	4. Analyze standard reporting systems	Identification of needed corrective actions
Data reporting systems	5. Analyze supportability data	

Fig. 7-1. Task 501—Supportability test, evaluation, and verification.

Acceptance Testing
Reliability Development Testing
Reliability Growth Testing
Qualification Testing
First Article Testing
Environmental Stress Screening
System Burn-in Testing
Flight Justification Testing
Development Test and Evaluation
Operational Test and Evaluation
Reliability Qualification Testing
Maintainability Demonstration

Fig. 7-2. Typical development tests.

with analyses and evaluations of the system support after it becomes operational.

Subtask 1. Test and Evaluation Strategy   Prior to the start of each acquisition phase, a strategy for test and evaluation of achievement or progress toward achievement of supportability goals should be developed. The purpose of the plan is to organize test and evaluation efforts to focus on critical supportability areas that should be addressed in the next acquisition phase. The plan should include identification of resources required to accomplish testing, a schedule for accomplishment, and the desired results of the tests. The strategy for the test and evaluation should address how each test fits into the overall verification of system supportability. Many test are conducted during the design process. These tests, some of which are shown in FIG. 7-2, should be considered as part of the supportability testing process, because each test provides information about the performance, reliability, and maintainability of the system. Based on the test results, supportability evaluation and adequacy of the logistics support package developed for the system can be accomplished.

Subtask 2. Test and Evaluation Objectives   Detailed test plans and procedures are developed that implement the results of subtask 1. The first issue to be addressed is development of quantitative goals and objectives to guide testing. Quantitative objectives for the testing must be established in order to facilitate evaluation of system performance and should be documented in detailed testing plans. Figure 7-3 lists typical test plans that are prepared during system design and development. Included in the detailed plans should be availability of resources, data sources, and resource utilization for the support-

Acceptance Test Plan
Qualification Test Plan
Reliability Test Plan
Maintainability Test Plan
Development Test Plan
Integrated Test Plan

Fig. 7-3. Test plans.

1. Correct deficiencies
2. Update system readiness, cost, and resource projections
3. Identify improvements needed to meet readiness goals
4. Identify achievement of contractual goals
5. Update LSAR
6. Database for future acquisitions

Fig. 7-4. Supportability test data uses.

ability portion of each test. As an example, during reliability testing when a failure occurs, the maintenance task prepared as a result of Task 401 should be used to repair the failure. This tests and provides an opportunity for evaluation of the maintenance task and thereby, the supportability aspects for maintenance. The maintainability demonstration is the most comprehensive test and evaluation of the supportability of the system that is conducted by the contractor. This demonstration is designed to evaluate the adequacy and correctness of maintenance tasks, support equipment, training, personnel skills, and spare and repair parts to support the system.

Subtask 3. Analyze Test Results The results of supportability portions of tests are analyzed to identify deficiencies discovered during tests and to verify that corrective actions implemented to correct previously identified deficiencies were adequate to resolve the deficiencies. Figure 7-4 identifies additional uses for supportability test results. This is another opportunity for the LSA program to influence the design to produce a more supportable system.

Subtask 4. Analyze Standard Reporting Systems The supportability of the new system is also evaluated and verified after the system is deployed. Information for evaluation is collected through standard reporting systems in place within each service. The standard reporting systems must be assessed to determine if adequate information will be available through this medium after deployment to conduct an adequate evaluation and verification of supportability. If the standard reporting system is determined to be inadequate, then alternative or supplemental reporting schemes should be considered for implementation.

Subtask 5. Analyze Supportability Data The analysis of supportability data obtained from actual field use of the system can provide significant information for product improvement or support system enhancement. Additionally, a comparative analysis between supportability projections generated during system development and actual field data can provide significant information for use on future acquisition programs to better project cost, supportability, and readiness.

Task Outputs

Task 501 should result in a realistic and viable test and evaluation strategy for system supportability. The strategy should be documented in the LSA plan and corresponding plans for other engineering activities to ensure that every aspect of system test includes provisions for supportability evaluation. Any corrective actions needed to improve supportability that are identified through the testing process should be documented in the LSAR on the LSA Data Record B and should be discussed at program and design reviews for appropriate action and resolution.

8

Supporting Analyses

The success or failure of the logistics support analysis program is dependent on the interaction and dissemination of information from many different disciplines within and outside of the traditional logistics organization. There are several analyses that are performed outside the area of logistics support analysis that have a significant impact on the accuracy and effectiveness of the LSA program. The analyses most commonly included in the umbrella of the LSA program are those performed by reliability and maintainability engineering organizations. The ability of an item of equipment to consistently operate without failure, and its ability to be expeditiously repaired when it does fail are decided factors in the amount of resources that will be required to support the system when it is operational.

There are also analyses that are performed to predict the amount of time that a system will be available to perform its mission, taking into consideration the periods of time it will not be available due to either scheduled or unscheduled maintenance. Studies and analyses are performed to determine if any periodic maintenance can be performed that will prevent failures that create safety hazards for operation or maintenance personnel or improve reliability by replacing items that are prone to failure based on predictable circumstances. Determination of the proper level of maintenance for performance of specific maintenance tasks based on strictly economic considerations provides a method of limiting the long-term cost for maintenance of a system. The analyses discussed in this chapter that support the LSA program include: reliability, maintainability and availability predictions; failure modes, effects, and criticality analysis; reliability centered maintenance analysis; and repair level analysis. Each of these analysis processes contribute to the success of the LSA program in influencing the design for a more supportable system.

RELIABILITY PREDICTIONS

An estimate of the amount of resources that will be required to sustain operation is critical in determining the overall support for a system. One of the key ingredients necessary for developing the range and depth of support resources is a preduction of the reliability of the system design. This is a significant driver for the LSA program and life-cycle costs for the system. Another way of looking at this requirement is to predict the unreliability, or predicted number of failures that will have to be fixed. The more reliable a system, the fewer the failures, and therefore, the fewer resources needed to support operations. Basic system reliability can be expressed in terms of either a failure rate or mean time between failure (MTBF). Calculation of a failure rate is demonstrated in FIG. 8-1. A failure rate is not easily translated into a concept that is usable by the novice, so in most cases, the MTBF is used to convey the reliability of a system. The MTBF is easily calculated, as shown in FIG. 8-2, because it is the reciprocal of the failure rate. The method for conducting reliability predictions varies with the type of equipment under consideration and the status of the design. MIL-STD 756B, Reliability Modeling and Prediction, and MIL-HDBK 338, Electronic Reliability Design Handbook, provide several methods for predicting the reliability of equipment.

For the purposes of this discussion, two typical methods will be presented to illustrate how reliability predictions are developed. The first method, called Parts Count Reliability Prediction, is used in the early stages of design to develop predictions based on the generic failure rates of the anticipated quantity and type of parts to be used in the equipment. The second method, the Part Stress Analysis Prediction, uses the actual design configuration to develop detailed predictions. The parts count method is valuable in developing initial predictions for comparison with existing systems and providing information on the capability of a proposed design meeting basis reliability requirements. This prediction can be used as input to the early LSA process to develop estimates of the resources that will be required to support the system and for conducting tradeoff analyses for different support concepts or maintenance scenarios. Using the parts stress analysis method as the design matures provides detailed information on reliability and identification of specific areas where reliability can be improved. Whenever the stress analysis data becomes available, it should be used to update all logistics analyses to refine support resource estimates. The

$$\lambda \text{ (Failure Rate)} = \frac{\text{Number of Failures}}{\text{Total Operating Time}}$$

Example: If eight failures occurred in 1,000 operating hours:

$$\lambda = \frac{8}{1000}$$
$$\lambda = 0.008$$

Fig. 8-1. Failure rate prediction.

$$MTBF = 1/\lambda$$

Example: If an item had a failure rate of 0.008

$$MTBF = 1/0.008$$
$$MTBF = 125 \text{ hrs.}$$

Fig. 8-2. MTBF calculation.

validity of both methods is dependent on the quality of data used in the predictions and the accuracy of assumptions. These assumptions must be documented and provided to all users of the prediction so that shortcomings or deviations from the assumptions can be identified and quantified. The prediction of failure rates for items of equipment, using either method, begins at the piece part level and is summed to the equipment level. MIL-HDBK 217E, Reliability Prediction of Electronic Equipment, provides detailed instructions and input data for both of these methods.

Formula:

$$\lambda_{EQUIP} = \sum_{i=1}^{i=n} N_i(\lambda_G \pi_Q)$$

Where:

λ_{EQUIP} = Total equipment failure rate (failures/10^6 hr.)
λ_G = Generic failure rate for the ith generic part (failures/10^6 hr.)
π_Q = Quality factor for the ith generic part
N_i = Quantity of ith generic part
n = Number of different generic part categories

MIL-HDBK-217E

Part Type	Failure Rate[1,2]		Quality[2]		Adjusted	Quantity		Total
Transistors (NPN)	0.86	✗	2	=	1.72	✗ 8	=	13.76
Resistors (comp)	0.038	✗	1.5	=	0.057	2		0.114
Resistors (vari)	0.34	✗	1.5	=	0.51	6		3.06
Capacitors (cer)	0.17	✗	1.5	=	0.255	10		2.55
Diodes (gen)	0.14	✗	2	=	0.28	4		1.13
IC (MOS)	0.41	✗	3	=	1.23	12		14.76
Connector	0.15	✗	2.5	=	0.375	1		0.375
Printed board	0.01	✗	3	=	0.03	1		0.03

Total predicted failure rate ($\times 10^{-6}$)   35.769

Predicted MTBF $(1/(35.769)^{10-6})$ =   27,957.16

[1]Failure rates expressed as $\times 10^{-6}$.
[2]Failure rates and quality factors from MIL-HDBK 217E.

Fig. 8-3. Parts count reliability prediction.

Supporting Analyses

Parts Count Reliability Prediction

The parts count method of predicting equipment reliability uses a rather simple formula. Basically, the formula uses the total parts count by types that are used in the equipment and multiplies the quantities of these parts by established generic base failure rates for each part. The formula, illustrated in FIG. 8-3, shows that by using generic failure rates from tables in MIL-HDBK 217E, and anticipated types and quantities of parts, a baseline equipment failure rate can be derived. The quality factor indicates the level of testing and quality control the part manufacturer used when parts were made and the environmental factor adjusts the predicted failure rate based on the intended use of the equipment. Because the parts count method uses generic failure rates, this method of failure rate prediction is not very accurate; however, it can prove extremely useful during the concept phase in developing system level support concepts and requirements estimates. For detailed failure rate prediction, a much more accurate method such as the part stress analysis must be used.

Parts Stress Analysis Prediction

MIL-HDBK 217E contains a series of complex formulas that are used to perform a parts stress analysis reliability prediction. There is a different formula

---

Reliability Worksheet
MIL-HDBK-217E
Monolithic Bipolar and MOS Digital SSI/MSI Devices
(fewer than 100 gates)

Formula:

$$p = Q[C1 \times T \times Y + (C2 + C3) E] L \times 10^{-6}$$

Where:
- p = Device failure rate
- Q = Quality factor (1)
- T = Temperature acceleration factor based on technology (13)
- Y = Voltage derating stress factor (1)
- E = Application environment factor (4)
- C1 = Circuit complexity failure rates based on gate count (0.0077)
- C2 = Circuit complexity failure rates based on gate count (0.0006)
- C3 = Package complexity failure rate (0.01)
- L = Device learning factor (1)

(Example factors obtained from tables in MIL-HDBK 217E)

Calculation:

$$p = Q[C1 \times T \times Y + (C2 + C3)E]L \times 10$$
$$= 0.1425 \times 10^{-6}$$

Predicted failure rate (as computed above) 0.1425×10^{-6}

Fig. 8-4. Parts stress analysis prediction.

tailored for type of part, and each formula considers the electrical stress, operating and extreme temperatures, environment, part quality, and frequency of use of each part type. An example of a stress analysis prediction for a single part is illustrated in FIG. 8-4. This process would be completed for each part for which actual reliability data did not exist or could not be obtained from the manufacturer. The resulting failure rates are then input into formulas that consider the application of the part and whether it operates in a single, dual, parallel, series, and/or redundant mode. This method identifies individual parts and assemblies that drive the equipment reliability up or down. Through the use of the part stress analysis prediction method, reliability engineers produce detailed failure rates for all parts, assemblies, and the total equipment. It must be pointed out that these predictions are just that, statistical predictions. Actual failure rates are not developed until the equipment is built and used for a sufficient length of time to produce field or test data that is based on actual equipment usage.

Figure 8-5 illustrates how failure rates for assemblies are predicted by: 1) determining the failure rate for each type of part used in the assembly; 2) multiplying the part failure rate times the quantity of that part used in the assembly; and 3) summing the results. The MTBF was calculated by taking the reciprocal of the assembly failure rate. The failure rate of the equipment is predicted by adding the failure rates of all the assemblies. This example has been simplified

Item Description	Quantity	Failure Rate	Extended	MTBF
Assembly Level				
Control assembly			16.5925	60268.556
Control card 1	1	1.9956	1.9956	
Control card 2	2	1.4562	2.9124	
Module subassembly	3	3.0582	9.1746	
Multiplexer	1	2.5098	2.5098	
Transceiver Assembly			39.1311	25555.121
Power supply	2	6.8835	13.767	
Transmitter module	4	2.9744	11.8976	
Receiver module	4	3.0861	12.3444	
Audio assembly			1.1221	891186.16
Speaker subassembly	1	1.0684	1.0684	
Interconnection	1	0.0537	0.0537	
System Level				
Communications system			95.9767	10419.195
Control assembly	1	16.5924	16.5924	
Transceiver assembly	2	39.1311	78.2622	
Audio assembly	1	1.1221	1.1221	
Summary				
Predicted Failure Rate			95.9767×10^{-6}	
Predicted MTBF			10419.195 Hours	

Fig. 8-5. Reliability prediction worksheet.

for ease of understanding. In actual practice, the theory for developing failure rate predictions remains the same, but other factors such as duty cycle, derating, and environment are applied that result in a more accurate prediction. The accuracy of this prediction is extremely important, because it is used for several other purposes in addition to identifying areas to increase reliability. The detailed prediction is used as input data for logistics analysis tasks where support resources are developed. Errors in the reliability prediction can distort the results of not only the reliability program, but also the LSA program and ultimately affect the quality of the logistics support of the system when it is fielded.

MAINTAINABILITY PREDICTIONS

The purpose of a maintainability prediction is to determine, using mathematical calculations, if an equipment design will meet the established maintainability goals. The prediction process is also used to identify designs that will not meet the goals. During the concept phase, sufficient information is not available to perform detailed prediction calculations, so predictions may be based on the performance of previous equipment using design changes to modify the result to closely relate to the new design. In order to perform detailed calculations, information such as the maintenance concept, functional block diagrams, identification of replaceable units, and reliability estimates is necessary. Using this information, maintainability engineers can develop predictions for the equipment. As the design matures, the quantity and quality of information increases, allowing further refinement of early predictions. MIL-HDBK 472, Maintainability Prediction, contains instructions on how predictions are accomplished. The measure of the maintainability of a system is the mean time to repair. The generic formula for calculating the MTTR is shown in FIG. 8-6. A separate MTTR for each level of maintenance may be stated as a design requirement for the system. Figure 8-7 shows the results of an MTTR prediction for an electronic assembly. Note that the reliability prediction for each item contained in

$$MTTR = \bar{T}_p + \bar{T}_{FI} + \bar{T}_{FC} + \bar{T}_A + \bar{T}_{CO} + \bar{T}_{ST} = \sum_{m-1}^{m} T_M$$

Where $\bar{T}_p$ = Average preparation time
$\bar{T}_{FI}$ = Average fault isolation time
$\bar{T}_{FC}$ = $\bar{T}_D + \bar{T}_I + \bar{T}_R$
$\bar{T}_D$ = Average disassembly time
$\bar{T}_I$ = Average interchange time
$\bar{T}_R$ = Average reassembly time
$\bar{T}_A$ = Average alignment time
$\bar{T}_{CO}$ = Average checkout time
$\bar{T}_{ST}$ = Average startup time
$\bar{T}_M$ = Average time of the Mth element od MTTR

Fig. 8-6. MTTR formula.

the assembly is used to predict the frequency of the anticipated maintenance actions, which represent those normally associated with the repair of a failed item. This prediction is updated throughout the design process to continually assess the maintainability status of the equipment and to provide information for the decision-making process. The MTTR prediction is an input to the LSA process that is later validated when the actual maintenance task times can be predicted and measures.

AVAILABILITY PREDICTIONS

The combination of the mean time between failure and mean time to repair predictions can be used to predict the amount of time that the system will be available for use when fielded. Availability predictions are useful in conducting tradeoff analyses of different maintenance concepts and system design concepts. There are three different versions of availability predictions; inherent availability, achieved availability, and operational availability, each having slightly different inputs and purposes. These analyses cannot be performed with any accuracy until the necessary inputs are available from reliability and maintainability; however, assumptions or allocations can be used and updated until the actual results from reliability and maintainability predictions are available. The measure of predicted system availability can also be used when evaluating different cost factors for support concepts. In many cases, it has been shown that reaching an acceptable level of availability costs the same as increasing the avail-

---

Item: Electronic assembly   Part Number: 12345-6
Method of Repair: Remove/replace Assy at "O" Level - Remove/replace CCAs at "I" Level

Drawing No.	Nomenclature	Qty (N)	Fail Rate (λ)	(Nλ)	Locate	Isolate	Disay[1]	Intch[2]	Reasy[3]	Ckout[4]	Rp	(Nλ)(R$_p$)
							Organizational Level					
12345-6	Assembly	1	48.0712	48.0712	0.01	0.04	0.08	0.06	0.08	0.01	0.28	13.459936
							Intermediate Level					
12345-6	Assembly	1	48.0712	48.0712	0.05	0.25	0.05	0	0.05	0.25	0.65	31.24628
4685-4	CCA #1	4	7.5437	30.1748	0.01	0.15	0.02	0.02	0.02	0.15	0.37	11.164676
2694-5	CCA #2	2	3.9874	7.9748	0.01	0.15	0.02	0.02	0.02	0.15	0.37	2.950676
6379-4	CCA #3	3	4.3869	13.1607	0.01	0.15	0.02	0.02	0.02	0.15	0.37	4.869459
1693-5	CAA #4	1	2.3476	2.3476	0.01	0.15	0.02	0.02	0.02	0.15	0.37	0.868612
8258-4	CCA #5	2	5.3968	10.7936	0.01	0.15	0.02	0.02	0.02	0.15	0.37	3.993632
8326-5	CCA #6	3	3.6524	10.9572	0.01	0.15	0.02	0.02	0.02	0.15	0.37	4.054164
5274-6	CCA #7	3	1.8643	5.5929	0.01	0.15	0.02	0.02	0.02	0.15	0.37	2.069373

Predicted Mean Time to Repair (MTTR)   0.28 hours at organizational level
0.47 hours at intermediate level
0.75 hours total assembly MTTR

[1]Disassembly.   [2]Interchange.   [3]Reassembly.   [4]Checkout.

Fig. 8-7. MTTR calculation.

ability level by only a few percentage points. For example, the basic support package for a weapon system may cost $10,000. This package is estimated to provide support to repair 90 percent of the predicted system failures that may occur during a typical mission. To increase the scope of the support package so that 95 percent of the predicted failures could be repaired may cost an additional $10,000 for more spares or other items. The question that must be answered is whether or not the 5 percent-increase in availability justifies the 100 percent-increase in the support package costs. Under some circumstances, the costs may be justified; however, in most cases, it is probably better to go with the reasonable availability for a reasonable cost.

Inherent Availability

The prediction of the inherent availability of a system design is the simplest of the three predictions for availability. The purpose of this prediction is to determine the net percentage of time that the system should theoretically be available for its intended use. As shown in FIG. 8-8, the only input data required to perform this prediction are the MTBF and organizational level MTTR, consisting of only corrective maintenance tasks, for the system. The underlying assumptions for this prediction is that whenever a failure occurs, the necessary support (i.e., spares, support and test equipment, personnel, etc.) will be available to perform whatever maintenance is required to return the system to an operational status. Figure 8-8 demonstrates that the inherent availability (A_i) for a system is normally close to 100 percent, because much of the reality of actually performing maintenance on a system is omitted from consideration. The inherent availability calculation does provide a starting point to compare the new system design with other existing systems to determine the adequacy of the maintenance concept and the system's inherent reliability. The A_i figure is normally developed early in the design process and refined until actual data is available.

Formula:

$$A_i = \frac{MTBF}{MTBF + MTTR}$$

Where:

A_i = Inherent availability
MTBF = Mean time between failure
MTTR = Mean time to repair

Example:

If MTBF = 100 hours
MTTR = 0.25 hours

$$A_i = \frac{100}{100 + 0.25} = 0.9975$$

Fig. 8-8. Inherent availability formula.

Formula:

$$A_A = \frac{MTBM}{MTBM + M_{CMT} + M_{PMT}}$$

Where:

A_A	=	Achieved availability
MTBM	=	Mean time between maintenance
M_{CMT}	=	Mean corrective maintenance time
M_{PMT}	=	Mean preventative maintenance time

Fig. 8-9. Achieved availability formula.

Achieved Availability

The calculation of achieved availability (A_a) goes a step beyond that of A_i because this prediction includes the time that will be required to perform preventive maintenance. Figure 8-9 provides the formula for calculating system achieved availability. Note that instead of using the system MTBF, this formula uses the mean time between maintenance (MTBM). The MTBM makes allowances for periods when the system will not be available due to preventive maintenance activities. Also used in the calculation are the mean corrective maintenance times (M_{cmt}) and mean preventive maintenance time (M_{pmt}) for the system. The achieved availability prediction is somewhat more realistic than the inherent availability prediction because it does include all maintenance actions, both corrective and preventive, that will be required to maintain the system. However, the A_a number still does not reflect the real world requirements for maintenance that the system will experience when it becomes operational. If a system does not require any preventive maintenance, the predictions for A_a and A_i should be identical.

Operational Availability

The actual gauge of the availability of a system is what percentage of the time when under actual operating conditions it is available to perform its mission. This is termed operational availability (A_o). Calculation of the actual A_o for many weapon systems is accomplished on a routing basis by the military ser-

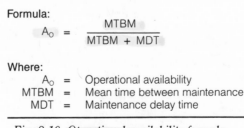

Formula:

$$A_O = \frac{MTBM}{MTBM + MDT}$$

Where:

A_O	=	Operational availability
MTBM	=	Mean time between maintenance
MDT	=	Maintenance delay time

Fig. 8-10. Operational availability formula.

vices as an indicator of how well the systems are actually providing the intended mission support. Detailed recordkeeping is necessary to support calculation of the A_o for a system. The basic formula for calculation of A_o is provided in FIG. 8-10. The key difference between the formula for calculation A_o and other availability measures it that all time over a specific interval is included in the measurement whether the time is operational, maintenance, or downtime awaiting either maintenance or spares. This is the real system availability and shows the actual time, on the average, that a system can be depended on to perform its mission.

As shown in the formula for calculating A_o, the big difference between computing achieved availability and operational availability is the time that is consumed between the time when a failure occurs and when it is returned to service that is not due to active maintenance. This maintenance downtime can be due to a lack of spare parts or tools and support equipment, or it can be due to improperly trained personnel or insufficient numbers of personnel to support the volume of maintenance at a given maintenance level. These are all areas where the logistics support analysis process should be able to circumvent these types of problems, thereby increasing operational availability for the system.

FAILURE MODES, EFFECTS, AND CRITICALITY ANALYSIS

The identification of all the probable ways that parts, assemblies, and the equipment may fail, the causes for each failure, and the effect that the failure will have on the capability for the equipment to perform its mission provide a valuable tool for reliability engineers. A FMECA, developed in accordance with Task 204 and MIL-STD 1629, Failure Modes, Effects, and Criticality Analysis, is a complete analysis of each level of the equipment. Using the FMECA, reliability engineers identify each possible failure mode of the equipment. A failure mode is something that occurs, such as a part failing, causing the equipment to malfunction. A single part can have several failure modes. Failure modes are actual failures, not symptoms of failures. For example, if you put the key in the ignition of your car, turn it, and nothing happens, that is a failure symptom. The actual failure would be a dead battery, faulty ignition switch, etc. Turning the key and nothing happening is only a failure indicator. The FMECA also provides information of failure indicators, or how users know when a failure has occurred.

Other information developed by a FMECA includes: predictions of the percentage of occurrence of each failure mode for a part; a description of what caused the failure; the effect that the failure will have on the capability of the equipment to perform its mission; identification of any safety or other type hazard that the failure will cause; identification of methods required to fault-isolate the failure; and corrective action required to fix the failure. MIL-STD 1629 contains detailed tasks that describe the techniques reliability engineers use to conduct and document a FMECA, and MIL-HDBK 338 contains further in-

Failure Mode Effects and Criticality Analysis
MIL-STD 1629A

System ① _____
Indenture Level ② _____
Reference Drawing ③ _____
Mission ④ _____

Date _____
Sheet ___ Of ___
Compiled by _____
Approved by _____

Identification Number	Item/Functional Identification (Nomenclature)	Function	Failure Modes and Causes	Mission Phase/ Operational Mode	Failure Effects			Failure Detection Method	Compensating Provision	Severity Class	Remarks
					Local Effects	Next Higher Level	End Effects				
⑤	⑥	⑦	⑧	⑨	⑩	⑪	⑫	⑬	⑭	⑮	⑯

1. Identification of the end item using either name or part number.
2. Indenture level of the item being analyzed.
3. Drawing number of the engineering drawing being used as reference for the analysis.
4. Identification of the function of the item being analyzed.
5. Identification number for the function being analyzed using either a functional group code, per MIL-STD 780, or an LSCAN, per MIL-STD 1388-2A. For traceability with other ILS activities, it is recommended that the LSCAN be used.
6. Identification of the item or function contained in the item identified by note 3, above, that is being analyzed.
7. Statement of the function performed by the item being analyzed.
8. List all possible failures of the item being analyzed. There can be many failures of a single item listed here. Remember that the failures are of the item identified in column 6.
9. Identify the phase of the operation or mission when the failure is predicted to occur, i.e., start-up, peak operation, etc.
10. Identify what will happen to the item being analyzed when the failure occurs.
11. Identify what will happen to the next higher assembly-level item when the failure occurs.
12. Identify what will happen to the end item when the failure occurs.
13. Identify how the operator will know when the failure occurs.
14. Identify design provisions that will permit nullifying the effect of the failure on system operation, i.e., redundancy, reset, etc.
15. Assign the appropriate classification for the severity of the consequences if the failure occurs.
   Category I is catastrophic, including loss of equipment or death of personnel.
   Category II is critical, including severe injury to personnel or damage to equipment.
   Category III is marginal, including minor injury or damage to equipment.
   Category IV is minor, no serious injury or damage, but still requires unscheduled maintenance.
16. Record additional pertinent information as required.

Fig. 8-11. FMECA worksheet.

formation on developing FMECA data. Figure 8-11 is an example of a FMECA worksheet with a description of the information that is recorded on the worksheet.

Later in the text, the FMECA will be referenced as input information for other design analysis activities. These activities include maintainability, testability, maintenance planning, safety, and supportability. The FMECA is an integral part of the process that identifies requirements for logistics support resources. As with the part stress analysis, the results of the FMECA are widely used by other disciplines in addition to reliability engineering. The accuracy of the FMECA is a must in order to not cause a flow down of erroneous data to other analyses. The FMECA is a direct input to the logistics support analysis process as part of the identification of necessary maintenance tasks. The results of the FMECA are recorded in the logistics database as an integral part of the logistics support analysis record for each maintenance significant item in the system. Without this key input, the LSA process would be hampered in having any influence on the system design in order to increase system supportability.

RELIABILITY-CENTERED MAINTENANCE ANALYSIS

The purpose of reliability-centered maintenance (RCM) is to develop a scheduled maintenance program that increases the availability of an item of equipment by identifying failures or potential failures before they degrade equipment effectiveness. An RCM analysis is conducted to determine what maintenance tasks would provide an increased equipment reliability over the life of the equipment based on a logical selection criteria. This analysis technique is applicable to any equipment development program. MIL-STD 2173, Application of Reliability-Centered Maintenance to Naval Aircraft, Weapon Systems and Support Equipment, contains detailed instructions on how to conduct an RCM analysis.

Preventive Maintenance

Maintenance tasks that are performed on a scheduled periodic basis to prevent failures while an equipment is in operation are termed preventive maintenance tasks which should not be confused with other scheduled maintenance tasks that are required to sustain operation such as lubrications or adjustments. Preventive maintenance tasks can be divided into two categories: scheduled inspections and scheduled removals. A scheduled inspection can be accomplished at any level of maintenance to identify failures that have occurred or impending failures. Scheduled removals are conducted to recondition items that have reached a predetermined usage or that have reached an anticipated statistical useful life. Maintenance tasks resulting from scheduled inspections are either on-condition or failure-finding tasks. Scheduled removals generate either scheduled rework tasks or discard of the removed item. The purposes of on-condition, rework, and discard tasks are to prevent single-point failures and fail-

Scheduled inspections:
1. On-condition task—A scheduled inspection, test, or measurement to determine whether an item is in, or will remain in, a satisfactory condition until the next scheduled inspection.
2. Failure-finding task—A scheduled inspection of a hidden function item to find functional failures that have already occurred but were not evident to the operating crew.

Scheduled removals:
1. Rework task—Scheduled removal of units of an item to perform whatever maintenance tasks are necessary to ensure that the item meets its defined condition and performance standards.
2. Discard task—Scheduled removal of an item to the card the item or one of its parts at a specified life limit.

Fig. 8-12. Maintenance task descriptions.

ure-finding tasks are to prevent multiple failures. Figure 8-12 describes each of these tasks in detail.

Analysis Process

The RCM analysis process considers the significant items that comprise an equipment. It uses information generated by the FMECA to identify the items that are most critical to the reliability of the equipment and where a failure would have the greatest effect on availability. Figure 8-13 illustrates the analysis

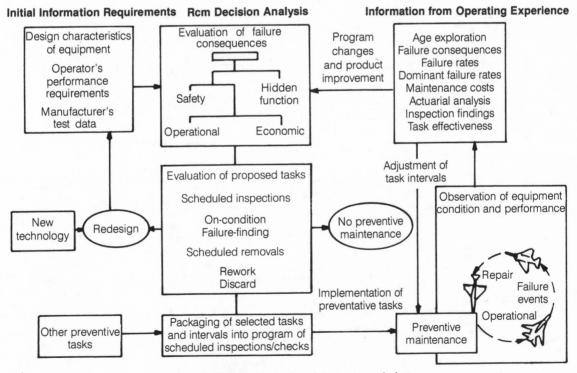

Fig. 8-13. Reliability-centered maintenance analysis process.

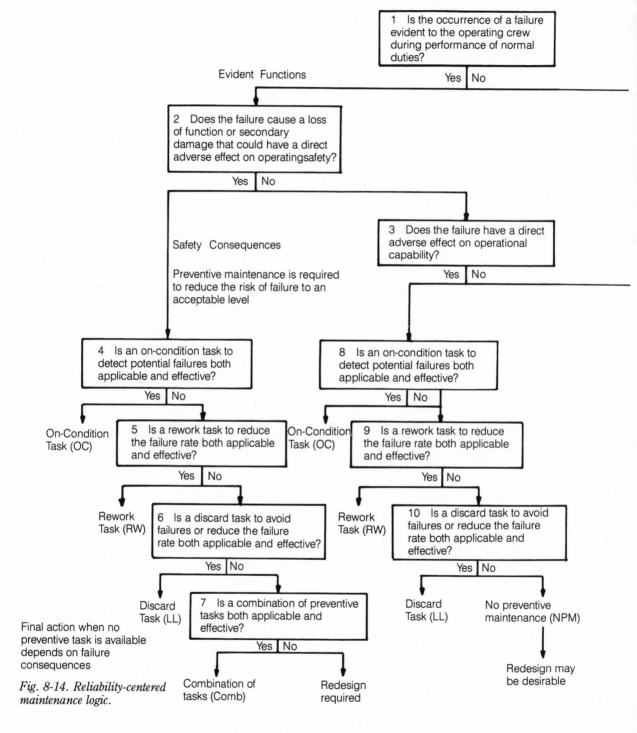

Fig. 8-14. Reliability-centered maintenance logic.

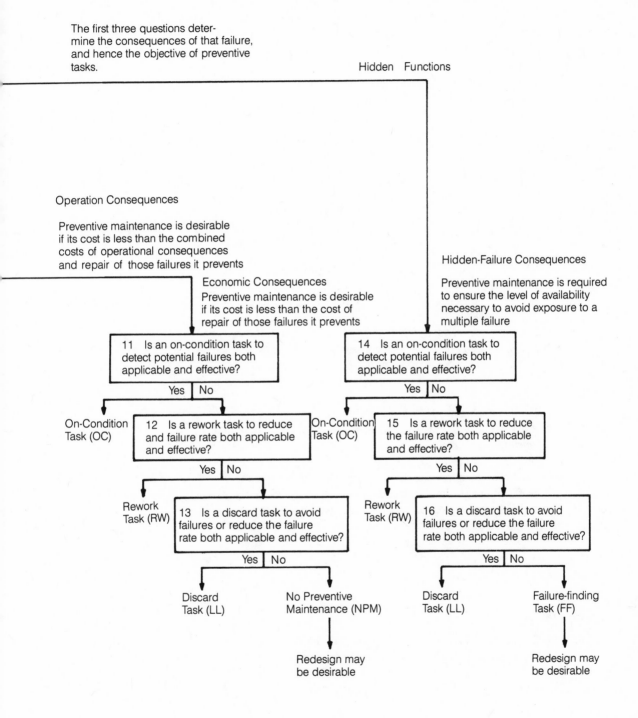

The first three questions determine the consequences of that failure, and hence the objective of preventive tasks.

Hidden Functions

Operation Consequences

Preventive maintenance is desirable if its cost is less than the combined costs of operational consequences and repair of those failures it prevents

Hidden-Failure Consequences

Preventive maintenance is required to ensure the level of availability necessary to avoid exposure to a multiple failure

Economic Consequences

Preventive maintenance is desirable if its cost is less than the cost of repair of those failures it prevents

11 Is an on-condition task to detect potential failures both applicable and effective?

14 Is an on-condition task to detect potential failures both applicable and effective?

Yes | No

Yes | No

On-Condition Task (OC)

12 Is a rework task to reduce and failure rate both applicable and effective?

On-Condition Task (OC)

15 Is a rework task to reduce the failure rate both applicable and effective?

Yes | No

Yes | No

Rework Task (RW)

13 Is a discard task to avoid failures or reduce the failure rate both applicable and effective?

Rework Task (RW)

16 Is a discard task to avoid failures or reduce the failure rate both applicable and effective?

Yes | No

Yes | No

Discard Task (LL)

No Preventive Maintenance (NPM)

Discard Task (LL)

Failure-finding Task (FF)

Redesign may be desirable

Redesign may be desirable

process and shows how both design and field data are used during the analysis process to identify preventive maintenance tasks. The analysis has proven to be effective in planning preventive maintenance programs for new systems during the development process and when upgrading an existing maintenance program for a system that has experienced significant field use.

Decision Logic

The key to the RCM analysis is the RCM decision logic shown in FIG. 8-14. Using this decision tree as a guide, a complete analysis of each significant item can be conducted. The results of the analysis provide a clear decision as to what preventive maintenance tasks should be developed to support a system. As shown in the decision diagram, there is a step-by-step process consisting of yes or no questions that lead the analyst to decide which type of task, if any, is required. In cases where no clearcut information is available for making the decision, MIL-STD 2173 provides default answers that can be used to complete the analysis. The sixteen questions that lead to an RCM decision are the summary output for recording the results of the analysis process. This iterative process is used to evaluate each maintenance significant item to determine if a preventive maintenance task is warranted. The consolidated results of the RCM analysis process forms the preventive maintenance program for the system. Note that the decisions are divided into four areas: safety, operational, economic, and hidden failure detection. Each area is related to the activities of several ILS disciplines that should be involved in the RCM analysis process.

Age Exploration

The RCM process does not cease when the system is fielded. A continuing analysis of the preventive maintenance program is conducted to identify areas for improvement. This extension of the process is called age exploration. Because many preventive maintenance programs are initially planned and implemented using insufficient data, this technique is necessary to achieve the maximum benefits of RCM. Age exploration is a systematic gathering of actual field operation data that is used to refine the preventive maintenance program. Each service has established data gathering systems that are used to accumulate sufficient field data to thoroughly review and refine the preventive maintenance program.

Documentation

MIL-STD 2173 contains a set of eight data sheets that are used to record the results of the RCM analysis process. RCM Worksheet Number 1 provides a summary of the results for a specific item and is shown in FIG. 8-15. Note that block number 4 contains the answers to the applicable sixteen questions of the

RCM Worksheet No. 1	Summary Data		g) Revision No./Date	l) Page ____ Of ____
a) System/Subsystem Nomenclature		d) Reference Drawing	h) Prepared by/Date	
b) LSCAN/WUC		e) Identure Level	j) Reviewed by/Date	
		f) End Item Nomenclature/Type, Model, Series		

1) Item LSCAN/ WUC	2) Item Nomenclature	3) List the Functional Mode Code (FFMC)	4) RCM Logic Question Answers (Y or N) 1 2 3 4 5 6 7 8 9 10 11 12 13 14 15 16	5) Description of Maintenance Requirements From RCM Task Worksheets	6) Task Number	7) Inspection Interval (Packaged)	8) LSA Task Code

Fig. 8-15. RCM worksheet.

decision tree. The other seven worksheets provide detailed backup for the summary contained on this worksheet. This information is also documented in the LSAR database as will be discussed in Chapter 9.

REPAIR LEVEL ANALYSIS

There are several different names given to this type of analysis: Repair Level Analysis (RLA), Optimum Repair Level Analysis (ORLA), Network

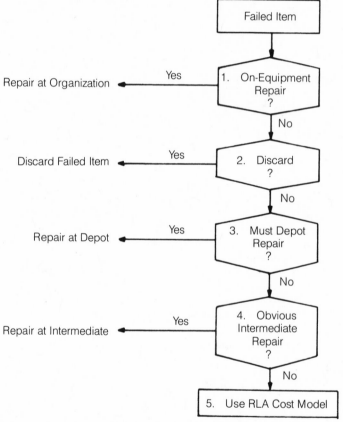

NOTES:

1. Corrective maintenance can be performed without removing the item from the system.
2. Discard-at-failure versus repair analysis indicates it is more cost-effective to discard than to repair the item.
3. Repair must be accomplished at the depot level for reasons of technical complexity, high skill-level requirements, or sophisticated facility requirements.
4. Repair at the intermediate level is obvious if skills and support equipment required to accomplish repair are available and also required to perform other intermediate-level tasks.
5. There is no overriding reason for accomplishment of repair at intermediate or depot levels. Use RLA model to determine which level is most cost-effective.

Fig. 8-16. Repair level analysis decision tree.

Repair Level Analysis (NRLA), or Level of Repair Analysis (LORA); however, the basic concept for which they were developed is the same. An RLA is used to evaluate maintenance actions to determine if it is cost-effective and where the task can be accomplished most cost-effectively. The easiest way to explain how an RLA works is to refer to the decision tree in FIG. 8-16. As illustrated by the decision tree, there are actually five decisions made in the RLA process: 1) "O" level repair; 2) discard at point of failure; 3) repair at depot; 4) repair at "I" level; 5) use of RLA model to determine level cost-effectiveness. Three of the decisions are based on factors not directly related to cost, and two use cost as the determining factor. The source for identification of maintenance tasks to be used as input to the RLA process is the maintenance task analysis. Additional information required to complete an accurate and reliable RLA are shown in FIG. 8-17. The use of an RLA in the concept and DEMVAL phases may not be appropriate unless the user can quantify the uncertainties and risks involved. An RLA is most effective when used during FSD when adequate information is available; however, if it is used in the later stages of FSD, the results may be too late to be useful. Therefore, the RLA should be used as soon as possible, depending on the availability of input information.

Organization Level Repair

The most desirable place to perform maintenance is at the organizational level. If all maintenance were done at "O" level, there would be no requirement

---

Maintenance Task Analysis
   Maintenance task identification
   Manhours required per task
   Materials required per repair
Other Sources
   MTBF
   System operating hours
   Life expectancy
   Number of systems in operation
   Number of locations performing maintenance
   Unit cost
   Quantity per end item
   Projected cost of
      Support equipment
      Support equipment maintenance
      Technical documentation
      TRaining
      Spares
      PHS&T
      Labor
   Number of days for repair turnaround
   Safety-level days of supply

Fig. 8-17. Repair level analysis input data.

for "I" and "D" level maintenance resources, which would significantly reduce the cost for maintenance. Conversely, it is not realistic to propose that each organization have the capability to completely repair every failure that would occur (refer to the example of maintenance tasks in chapter 5). The image of an M1 Tank moving out on the battlefield towing a trailer full of repair parts and test equipment is pretty scary; therefore, there must be a reasonable basis for determining what maintenance tasks should be done where. The key to identifying the tasks that should be performed by "O" level maintenance is to have a detailed knowledge of the existing capabilities of the proposed user. The tools, test capabilities, training and availability of personnel, and facilities that are available are used to determine if a task can and should be accomplished at "O" level. If everything needed to accomplish the tasks is at "O" level, it is obvious that is where the task should be performed.

Discard at Point of Failure

It may be more economical to discard an item when it fails rather than repair it. This decision is based on a comparison of the cost to repair an item with the relative cost to buy a replacement. There are several methods used to determine this. Figure 8-18 illustrates the basic philosophy that is used in making this decision. This method compares the relative value of a repaired item with the cost to buy a replacement. The factor "N" is a predetermined acceptance

Formula:

If $(MTBF_2/MTBF_1)\ N \leq \dfrac{(L + M)}{P}$ then discard

Where:

$$
\begin{aligned}
MTBF_1 &= \text{MTBF of new item} \\
MTBF_2 &= \text{MTBF of repaired item} \\
N &= \text{Predetermined acceptance level} \\
L &= \text{Labor required to repair item} \\
M &= \text{Material required to repair item} \\
P &= \text{Unit price of new item}
\end{aligned}
$$

Examples:	A	B	C
$MTBF_1$	1,000	1,000	1,000
$MTBF_2$	1,000	800	600
L	100	20	40
M	100	40	80
P	200	500	200
N	60%	60%	50%
Computation Results	$0.60 \leq 1.0$	$0.48 \leq 0.12$	$0.30 \leq 0.60$
Decision	Discard	Repair	Discard

Fig. 8-18. Discard versus repair criteria.

level, either supplied by the government or set by the contractor, that is used to establish a criteria for derating the value of a repaired item. Basically, it creates an acceptance criteria of a discard decision that states that if the cost for repair exceeds a given percent of the cost of a new item, the decision should be to discard the failed item.

Depot Repair

Some repair tasks must be accomplished at depot level due to the technical complexity of the item, high skill level requirements to accomplish the maintenance task, or requirements for sophisticated facilities. When such requirements exist, the decision to repair at depot level overrides all other concerns. Maintenance planning must consider such requirements and establish design criteria early in the equipment design to minimize the need for depot maintenance as much as possible.

Intermediate Repair

Maximum use of existing skills and support equipment at intermediate level to accomplish maintenance tasks will reduce the cost of repairs. When repairs can be supported at intermediate level, without additional resources, such a repair decision is obvious.

RLA Model

When there is no overriding reason that dictates accomplishment of a maintenance task at a specific maintenance level, the decision can be made on purely

---

Formula:

$$DC = SE + SEM + TD + TNG + SS + PS + RP + L$$
$$IC = SE + SEM + TD + TNG + S + L$$

Where:

SE	=	Support equipment
SEM	=	Support equipment maintenance
TD	=	Technical documentation
TNG	=	Training
SS	=	Safety stock
S	=	Shipping/stocking spares
PS	=	PHS&T of failed items
RP	=	Repair pipeline
L	=	Labor required to repair item
DC	=	Depot costs
IC	=	Intermediate costs

Fig. 8-19. Intermediate versus depot repair analysis.

Example

Item: Control Assembly
Cost: $5,000
QPEI: 2

\# Aircraft: 500
\# Squadrons: 20 (25 Aircraft/Squadron)

Life Expectancy: 10 years
Flight Hours/Month: 20
Flight Hours Between Failure: 10

Decision Tree Results: 60% Repairs On Equipment
                                      5% Discard
                                      10% Depot Must Repair
                                      10% Obvious Field Repair
                                      15% RLA Model

RLA Repairs per Month: 300

$$\frac{\text{\# Aircraft} \times \text{Flight Hrs/Mo.}}{\text{Flight Hrs Between Failures}} \times \text{QPEI} \times \text{\% Tasks Model} = \text{Repairs/Mo.}$$

$$\frac{500 \times 20}{10} \times 2 \times .15 = 300$$

Fig. 8-20. Intermediate versus depot repair analysis.

economic considerations. The RLA model is designed to determine which maintenance level will provide the most cost-effective alternative to performing a maintenance task over the life of an item of equipment. There are several RLA models that can be used for this purpose. In most cases, the models are computerized to efficiently handle the amount of data and calculations that must be made to prepare a complete RLA for an entire weapon system. Figures 8-19 through 8-25 are examples of how an RLA would be used to determine where repairs of a single item would be accomplished. Figure 8-19 provides the basic formulas that are used to compute the costs for repair at depot and intermediate

---

SE	=	$50,000
SEM	=	Negligible
TNG	=	$5,000
TD	=	None
PHS&T for Failed Item	=	$150
Safety Stock Level	=	15 Days
Repair TAT	=	60 Days
Labor Cost	=	$12 per Hour
Average Manhours per Repair	=	2.5 Hour

Fig. 8-21. Depot model data.

SE = $100,000 per Squadron
SEM = 1% per Year
TNG = $30,000 per Squadron
TD = $100,000
Repair TAT = 8 Days
Cost of Stocking Parts = $120 per Repair
Cost of Labor = $5 per Hour
Average Manhours per Repair = 2.5

Fig. 8-22. Intermediate model data.

levels. The RLA uses cost as the determining factor for where a repair will be accomplished. Although the two formulas contain similar components, the costs may vary between levels as is shown in subsequent figures. Figure 8-20 shows the input information that will be used in the RLA computations. The decision tree results show the percentage of maintenance tasks (15 percent for the control assembly, not the entire system, that are being modeled. The remaining 85 percent have been assigned to a specific level based on the results of the decision tree. Number of repairs per month, calculated as indicated in FIG. 8-20, indicates the volume of repairs that must be accomplished.

Figure 8-21 provides specific input information for the depot level model, and FIG. 8-22 provides specific input information for the intermediate level model. Figure 8-23 shows the values, either given or computed, for the depot level model, and FIG. 8-24 provides similar values for the intermediate level mode. Figure 8-25 is a comparison of the values for each model. This analysis

SE = $50,000
SEM = 0
TD = $5,000
SS = $750,000

Repairables/Month × Safety Level × Unit Price = SS
300 × 0.5 (15 Days) × 5,000 = $750,000

PS = $5,400,000

Repairables/Month × # Month Expectancy × Cost to Package & Ship = PS
300 × 120 × 150 = 5,400,000

RP = $3,000,000

Repairables/Month × TAT × Unit Price = RP
300 × 2 (Month) × 5,000 = 3,000,000

L = $1,080,000

Repairables/Month × # Months × Labor Rate × Hrs/Repair = L
300 × 120 × 12 × 2.5 = 1,080,000

Fig. 8-23. Depot level computations.

SE = 2,000,000

    Cost of PSE × # of Squadrons = SE
      100,000 ×   20   = 2,000,000

SEM = 200,000

    Cost of PSE × Maintenance Cost % × Years Used × # of Squadrons = SEM
      100,000 ×   0.01   ×   10   ×   20   = 200,000

TD = 100,000
TNG = 600,000

    Unit TNG Cost × # of Squadrons = TNG
      30,000   ×   20   = 600,000

 S = 4,320,000

    Cost of Stocking parts × Failure/Month × # Months = S
         120   ×   300   ×   120   = 4,320,000

 L = 450,000

    Failures/Month × # Months × Labor Cost × Hours/Repair = L
        300   ×   120   ×   5   ×   2.5   = 450,000

Fig. 8-24. Intermediate level computations.

shows that, based on purely economic factors, the repairs should be accomplished at intermediate level. It is interesting to note that in this example the cost of additional spares and shipping of items to depot for repair are the driving factors that lead to the decision to repair at intermediate level. The sensitivity of models for conducting tradeoff comparisons between alternatives must also be considered. Figure 8-26 shows that if the reliability of the control assembly

Element	Intermediate	Depot
SE	2,000,000	50,000
SEM	200,000	0
TD	100,000	0
TNG	600,000	5,000
S	4,320,000	N/A
SS	N/A	750,000
PS	N/A	5,400,000
RP	N/A	3,000,000
L	450,000	1,080,000
Total	$7,670,000	$10,285,000

Fig. 8-25. Intermediate vs. depot analysis.

Element	Intermediate	Depot
SE	2,000,000	50,000
SEM	200,000	0
TD	100,000	0
TNG	600,000	5,000
S	2,160,000	N/A
SS	N/A	375,000
PS	N/A	2,700,000
RP	N/A	1,500,000
L	225,000	540,000
Total	5,285,000	5,170,000

Fig. 8-26. Intermediate vs. depot analysis (increased reliability).

could be doubled, from 1 failure per 10 flight hours to 1 failure per 20 flight hours, the results of the RLA model would indicate that the repairs should be accomplished at depot level, and the total cost for either level would be significantly less than the costs determined in FIG. 8-25.

The RLA is a useful tool when trying to determine where repairs should be accomplished based on cost and it can also be used to make tradeoff decisions of proposed alternative support approaches. The RLA can be a complex task when modeling an entire weapon system and, therefore, should be done by computer. MIL-STD 1390, Level of Repair, provides a detailed process for accomplishing an RLA. The formulas contained in this document are comprehensive, but give specific guidance as to how an RLA should be conducted.

9

LSA Record

The results of the logistics support analysis process are recorded in a single database comprised of logistics support analysis records (LSAR). The purpose of the LSAR is to provide a standardized method for compiling and storing logistics and logistics related engineering data. This fulfills the fourth purpose of LSA program, which is to maintain a single database for all logistics data. The LSAR allows all relative supportability information to be used in an organized and uniform manner to identify and develop logistics support resource requirements. A key point is that the LSAR only reports the results of the LSA process, it does not constitute a standalone analysis. LSA tasks must be completed in order for LSAR data to be generated. Additionally, many LSA tasks and subtasks can be done without producing any data that are recorded in the LSAR. A common misconception is that the quantity of LSAR data records generated is an indicator of the progress of the LSA program. The LSAR is only a tool for gathering logistics related data for further analysis and completing LSA program requirements of documenting support requirements and related supportability data. The iterative cycle for generating, reviewing, and updating the LSAR, and the creation of reports from the LSAR database is shown in FIG. 9-1. MIL-STD 1388-2A, DOD Requirements for a Logistics Support Analysis Record, contains a detailed description of the LSAR process, data requirements of LSAR data records, definitions for data elements, and standard summary reports that are generated from the LSAR database. Additional discussions of the LSAR process will address individual data records, data element selection and definition, methods for using the LSAR, automatic data processing requirements, and preparation of summary reports from the LSAR database.

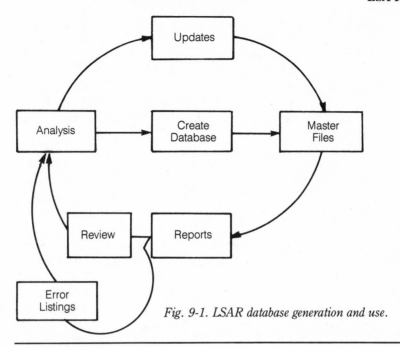

Fig. 9-1. LSAR database generation and use.

LSA Data Record	Purpose and Use
A	System level operation and maintenance parameters
B	R&M characteristics for system and each maintenance significant item
B1	Failure modes and effects analysis for system and each maintenance significant item
B2	Criticality of each failure mode and maintainability data for system and each maintenance significant item
C	Summary of each operation and maintenance task required for support of system and each maintenance significant item
D	Detailed narrative of operation or maintenance task for system or maintenance significant item
D1	Listing of all tools and materials required to support operation or maintenance task
E	Identifies requirement for a specific item of support equipment or training material
E1	Continuation of Data Record E for preparation of SERD
E2	Identifies requirement for off-line testing and automatic test equipment
F	Identifies requirement for a specific new or upgraded facility
G	Identifies requirement for a specific new or upgraded facility
H	Identifies specific part or tool used in the system
H1	Provides information about the use of a part in the system design
J	Identifies transportability requirements for the system

Fig. 9-2. LSA data records.

DATA RECORDS

The LSAR database is actually made up of a series of 15 different data records. Each data record, described in FIG. 9-2, has a specific function and requires definitive data that is produced as a result of analysis required by one or more of the LSA tasks contained in MIL-STD 1388-1A. Although each data record is significantly different in purpose and content, there are certain similarities. Each data record is a series of 80 card column lines with each line having a distinct three-digit identifier in the first three card columns, which allows easy computer layout and entry and creates a standard data transfer medium so that information can be readily communicated between computerized databases. Additionally, each data record contains one or more key data fields common throughout each set of data records for a particular item. A set of data records is normally prepared for each maintenance significant item contained in a system. Figure 9-3 shows that LSA data records A thru J are normally required for the system level, while lower levels of the system require selected records. Nonrepairable items normally only require preparation of LSA data records H and H1 for identification of spare and repair parts requirements. A detailed description of each LSA data record including purpose, key data elements, and use for preparation of standard summary reports is provided in the following paragraphs.

Data Record A, Operation and Maintenance Requirements

Data Record A, shown in FIG. 9-4, is used to record information related to the planned operation and maintenance of the system. This data record is normally completed by the government and provided to the contractor, or it is prepared jointly at the initial LSA guidance conference. The information contained on the data record should reflect the requirements of the product specification for operation and maintenance. Key items of information contained in LSA Data Record A are shown in FIG. 9-5. This information is used as the benchmark for

Hardware Level	LSA Data Records														
	A	B	B1	B2	C	D	D1	E	E1	E2	F	G	H	H1	J
System	A	A	A	A	A	A	A	O	O	O	A	A	A	A	A
Subsystem	A	A	A	A	A	A	A	O	O	O	A	A	A	A	O
Assembly	A	A	A	A	A	A	A	O	O	O	O	O	A	A	N
Part	N	N	N	N	N	N	N	N	N	N	N	N	A	A	N
Tools/SE	N	N	N	N	N	N	N	O	O	O	N	N	A	A	N

A = generally applicable
O = dependent on program requirements
N = generally not applicable

Fig. 9-3. LSA data record application matrix.

comparison with the results of the summary of the detailed analysis for each maintenance significant item of the system. Normally, only one Data Record A is required for an LSA program. In cases where differing operational or maintenance requirements are placed on subsystems, such as on an aircraft, a separate Data Record A may be required for each subsystem. After the initial Data Record A is completed, there are normally very few additions or corrections to this record unless the operating or support parameters are changed.

Data Record B, Item Reliability and Maintainability Characteristics

A Data Record B is prepared for each repairable or maintenance significant item in the system. This includes system, subsystems, components, assemblies, subassemblies, etc. Data Record B describes the function of the item, the proposed maintenance concept for that item, and any design constraints placed on the item. Reliability and maintainability characteristics, summaries of the FMECA and RCM analysis, maintainability predictions, and other logistic evaluations are documented on Data Record B as illustrated in FIG. 9-6. The key purpose of Data Record B is to summarize the results of the maintenance analysis of the item being considered and provide quantified justification as to whether the item meets all specification requirements. The logistics considerations of the item, illustrated in FIG. 9-7, serve to highlight areas where specification criteria are not met and possible redesign is required. This quantitative information gives logistics engineers the opportunity to input to design engineers to influence the final design. Here is where the iterative LSA process is most evident. The design is continually analyzed until each logistics consideration not meeting specification requirements is either resolved or taken to the point where design limitations preclude meeting specifications. The logistics consideration data reflected on Data Record B should be the starting point for each LSA review. In theory, if all the considerations are being met, the design should be as supportable as possible and no redesign should be required. The bottom portion of Data Record B provides logistics engineers with an area to highlight design problems or other considerations that are identified for further analysis or needs for improving overall performance or supportability.

Data Record B1, Failure Modes and Effects Analysis

The results of the failure modes and effects analysis performed by reliability engineers in accordance with MIL-STD 1629 are recorded on Data Record B1. This data record, shown in FIG. 9-8, contains three distinct sections for recording failure data which are described in FIG. 9-9. An entry in one section requires corresponding entries in the remaining sections. The failure modes are used to identify maintenance requirements. The effect of each failure mode on the next higher assembly level is significant in determining the severity of the failure in terms of safety and detriment to system operation. The method of

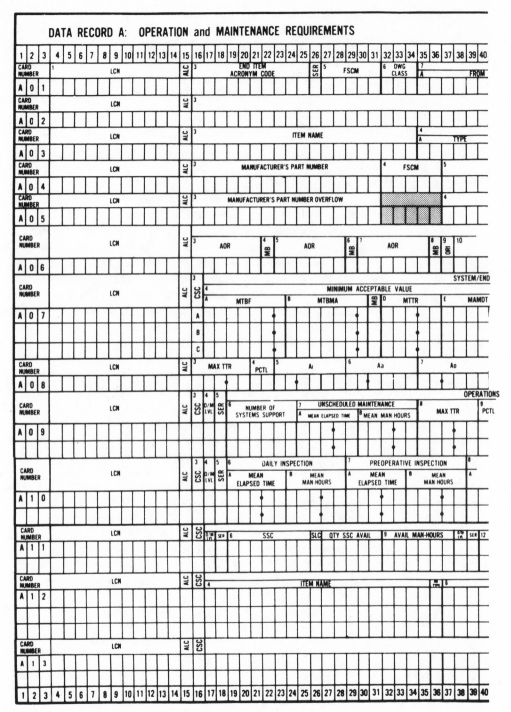

Fig. 9-4. LSA Data Record A.

DATE _____ PAGE _____ OF _____

SUBMITTED BY _____ EXT _____

| 41 | 42 | 43 | 44 | 45 | 46 | 47 | 48 | 49 | 50 | 51 | 52 | 53 | 54 | 55 | 56 | 57 | 58 | 59 | 60 | 61 | 62 | 63 | 64 | 65 | 66 | 67 | 68 | 69 | 70 | 71 | 72 | 73 | 74 | 75 | 76 | 77 | 78 | 79 | 80 |

SERIAL NUMBER EFFECTIVITY   B   TO   8   **USABLE ON CODE**   U C

USABLE ON CODE   U C

ITEM DESIGNATOR CODE   5 **CONVERSION FACTOR**   U C
B   MODEL   SERIES D   SUFFIX

DRAWING NUMBER   6 **FSCM**   7 **WUC/TM FGC**   U C

DRAWING NUMBER OVERFLOW   U C

OPERATIONAL DATA   U C

| ANNUAL NUMBER OF MISSIONS | 11 ANNUAL OPERATING DAYS | 12 MEAN MISSION DURATION | 13 MB | 14 MODE OF TRANSPORT | 15 TOTAL SYSTEMS SUPPORTED | 16 CREW SIZE | 17 NUMBER OF OPERATING LOCATIONS |

ITEM RAM CHARACTERISTICS   U C

5 **BEST OPERATIONAL CAPABILITY**

| A | MTBF | B | MTBMA | MB | D | MTTR | E | MAMDT |

8 **ALDT**   U C

AND MAINTENANCE LEVEL REQUIREMENTS   U C

| 10 **MAN-HOUR PER OPERATING HOUR** | | 11 **ANNUAL MAN-HOURS** | | 12 **TURNAROUND** | |
| A SCHEDULED | B UNSCHEDULED | A SCHEDULED | B UNSCHEDULED | A MEAN ELAPSED TIME | B MEAN MAN-HOURS |

POST-OPERATIVE INSPECTION   9 **PERIODIC INSPECTION**   10 **MISSION PROFILE CHANGE**   U C

| MEAN ELAPSED TIME | B MEAN MAN-HOURS | A MEAN ELAPSED TIME | B MEAN MAN-HOURS | A MEAN ELAPSED TIME | B MEAN MAN-HOURS |

MANPOWER AND SKILL CONSTRAINTS   U C

| SSC | SLC | QTY SSC AVAIL | 15 AVAIL MAN-HOURS | O/M I/R | SER | 18 SSC | SLC | QTY SSC AVAIL | 21 AVAIL MAN-HOURS |

TRANSPORTABILITY INTEROPERABILITY REQUIREMENTS
NATIONAL STOCK NUMBER/REFERENCE NUMBER   7 **FSCM**   U C

ADDITIONAL SPECIFICATIONS/REQUIREMENTS   U C

| 41 | 42 | 43 | 44 | 45 | 46 | 47 | 48 | 49 | 50 | 51 | 52 | 53 | 54 | 55 | 56 | 57 | 58 | 59 | 60 | 61 | 62 | 63 | 64 | 65 | 66 | 67 | 68 | 69 | 70 | 71 | 72 | 73 | 74 | 75 | 76 | 77 | 78 | 79 | 80 |

RELEASE 3

- Mission and Operation Data
- Mean Time Between Failure
- Mean Time Between Maintenance Action
- Mean Time to Repair
- Number of Operational Systems Supported
- Annual Scheduled Maintenance Manhours
- Annual Unscheduled Maintenance Manhours
- Manpower and Skills Required for Maintenance

Fig. 9-5. LSA Data Record A key information.

detecting each failure provides input to planning for incorporation of built-in test or external methods for testing the item being analyzed. The combination of these three pieces of information allows detailed analysis of ways to improve system availability for rapid detection of failures and start of corrective maintenance actions.

By incorporating the reporting of the FMEA into the LSAR database, all relevant design failure information is maintained in a coordinated format, and the need for a standalone reliability report is eliminated. A Data Record B1 is normally prepared as a companion to each Data Record B and supports the summary entries in the reliability section. Reliability engineers should have access to the LSA database for direct entry of the reliability data into this section to streamline collection of all relevant data. Reliability related reports can be generated from this file to fulfill reporting requirements.

Data Record B2, Criticality and Maintainability Analyses

The results of the criticality analysis portion of the FMECA and also maintainability analyses on each item are recorded on Data Record B2. This information, as shown in FIG. 9-10, is used to evaluate the need for maintenance tasks and to accumulate maintenance task times for future maintainability analyses. There is a direct link between the entries of maintainability information on Data Record B2 and detailed maintenance task analysis information that will be discussed on subsequent data records. For each entry on Data Record B2, there must be a corresponding Data Record C, D, and D1. This provides an audit trail, shown in FIG. 9-11, to ensure that each failure mode of the maintenance significant items is fully addressed by appropriate maintenance tasks to repair each potential failure mode. Additionally, the criticality information allows failure modes to be ranked by probability of occurrences and potential for causing system level failures.

The combination of entries on Data Records B1 and B2 that are summed on Data Record B provide a complete input for detailed logistics analysis of the probable failure modes and criticality of the failures in conjunction with the maintainability aspects and give logistics engineers the information necessary to identify all tasks that will be required to maintain the system.

Data Record C, Operation and Maintenance Task Summary

Data Record C is used to document the identification of all operation and maintenance tasks required to support an item. A separate data record is prepared for each repairable or maintenance significant item and is paired with the corresponding Data Records B, B1, and B2. Data Record C, shown in FIG. 9-12, lists each maintenance task required to support the item for which the record is prepared. Additionally, Data Record C summarizes the significant support requirements for maintenance as shown in FIG. 9-13. One of the key items of information contained on Data Record C is the maintenance task code for each maintenance task. The maintenance task code, illustrated in FIG. 9-14, is a seven-digit code that uniquely identifies each maintenance task. The combination of task code and logistics support analysis control number forms an identifier for specific tasks that cannot be duplicated anywhere else in the LSAR.

As will be shown later when LSA Data Record H1 is discussed, the maintenance task code must be in concert with the source, maintenance, and recoverability code assigned to the item under analysis so that spare and repair parts can be procured and stocked at appropriate locations to support maintenance. Additionally, the technical manuals that describe the maintenance tasks for the item must be based on the task code so that the necessary directions for performance of maintenance are reflected in the applicable organizational level or intermediate level technical manual.

Data Record D, Operation and Maintenance Task Analysis

A step-by-step detailed narrative description of each operation or maintenance task identified on Data Record C is documented using Data Record D. An example of Data Record D is shown in FIG. 9-15. If a Data Record C identifies a requirement for twenty different operation or maintenance tasks for an item, then a separate Data Record D is prepared for each task. As illustrated in FIG. 9-16, the data record is used to document the task narrative, number, and required skill specialty codes of personnel necessary to perform the task, and the elapsed and total times required to perform each sequential step of the task. The information contained on the Data Record D provides virtually everything that is required to prepare technical manual data for maintenance of the item. The task narrative should be detailed to the level that technical writers can transfer the information from the Data Record D directly into final technical manual format with little or no additional research. This ensures continuity between the maintenance tasks analysis process and the output of the technical manual effort.

Data Record D1, Personnel and Support Requirements

The narrative identification of support requirements contained on Data Record D is recorded in tabular form on a companion Data Record D1, shown in

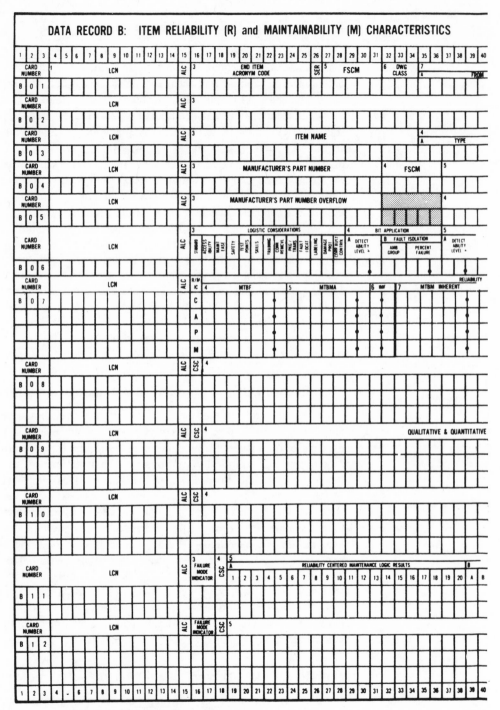

Fig. 9-6. LSA Data Record B.

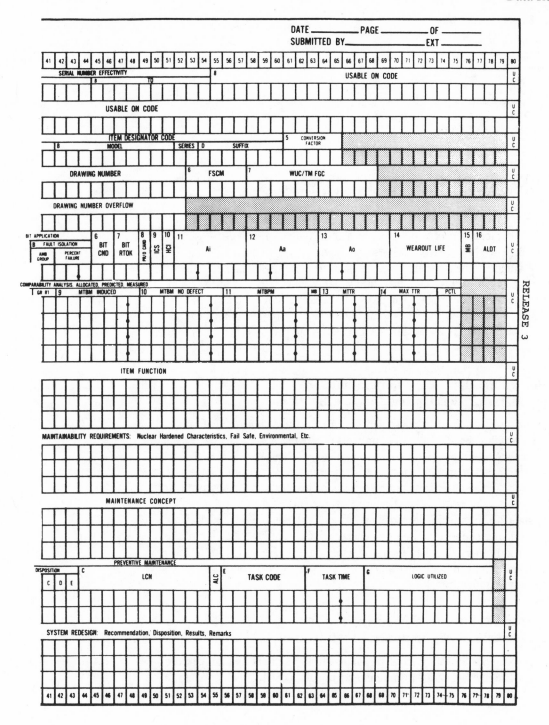

Standardization
Accessibility
Maintenance Ease
Safety
Test Points
Skills
Training
Ease of Connector Removal
Packaging and Transportation
Fault Location
Labeling
Self-Protection After Failure
Corrosion/Rust Control

Fig. 9-7. Logistics considerations,
LSA Data Record B.

FIG. 9-18. This tabulation of requirements allows computerized processing of data for summary into top support levels. As shown in FIG. 9-17, Data Record D1 includes a summary of the personnel and skill requirements to perform the task, corresponding maintenance task times, and materials in the form of support equipment or spares and repair parts. The information contained on Data Record D1 is combined with corresponding data for all other maintenance and operation tasks to identify and justify the logistics support resources required to support the system.

Data Record E, Support Equipment and Training Material Description and Justification

Data Record E is used to consolidate all the pertinent information generated by the maintenance task analysis process relative to the use or need for a specific item of support equipment or training material. This data record lists all the tasks, by logistics support analysis control number and maintenance task code, that require the use of the item and provides justification for procuring or authorizing use of the item. A Data Record E, shown in FIG. 9-19, is prepared for each nonstandard or special item of support or test equipment and training material needed to support operation or maintenance. The identification of the requirement to prepare this data record is found on Data Record C in the card blocks that indicate that either special support equipment or training is required to support a maintenance task.

Data Record E1, Support Equipment and Training Material Designation and Justification

The purpose of the Data Record E1, shown in FIG. 9-20, is to automate the preparation of support equipment recommendation data (SERD). Historically, a SERD is the document that the government uses as detailed justification for procurement of support equipment. Preparation of the SERD prior to use of Data Record E1 was a laborious and often confusing task due to the lack of traceable maintenance information. Data Record E1 solves this problem because it contains all the pertinent information necessary to completely identify the need for the item of support equipment and the source for either the manufacture or purchase of the support equipment. Using the LSAR database to prepare this document enables the logistics engineer to have complete supporting documentation available throughout the preparation process in the form of detailed maintenance tasks requiring use of the item.

Data Record E2, Unit Under Test Description and Justification

Data Record E2 is used to record detailed information pertaining to testing of assemblies after removal from the system and use of automated test programs. The purpose of this data record is to consolidate all references in the maintenance task narrative on Data Record D into a single requirement for a specific test program set (TPS) or other need for using automatic test equipment for fault isolation or testing. Data Record E2, illustrated in FIG. 9-21, identifies the unit under test (UUT), the type of testing to be accomplished, test parameters, and TPS requirements.

Data Record F, Facility Description and Justification

Requirements for special facilities required to support operation, maintenance, or training identified on Data Record C are documented using Data Record F. The data record, shown in FIG. 9-22, contains identification of all the tasks the facility is required to support, a technical description of the facility, and complete rationale and justification for using the facility. A Data Record F is prepared for each new or modified facility required to support maintenance of the system.

Data Record G, Skill Evaluation and Justification

Data Record G is used to document the need for new or modified personnel skills to support maintenance of the new equipment. A data record is prepared for each new or modified skill. Figure 9-23 shows the data record includes identification of tasks to be accomplished, personnel qualifications, training requirements, and a detailed justification for the new or modified skill. The information required to complete Data Record G is extracted from Data Records C, D, and D1, as applicable, to completely describe the actual training that is required for the new or modified skill.

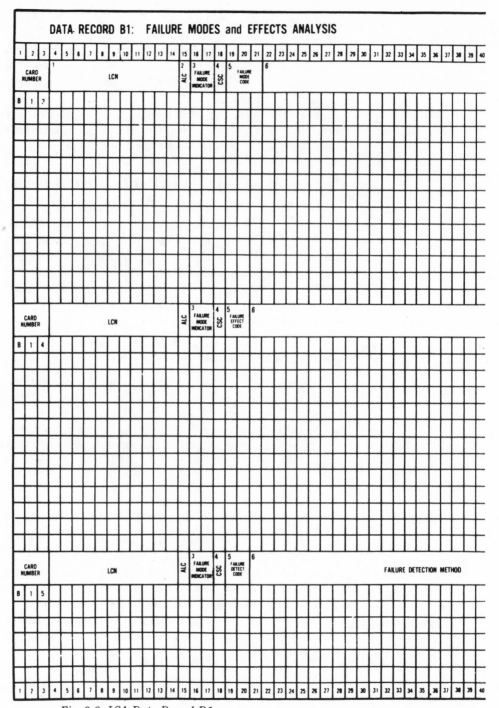

Fig. 9-8. LSA Data Record B1.

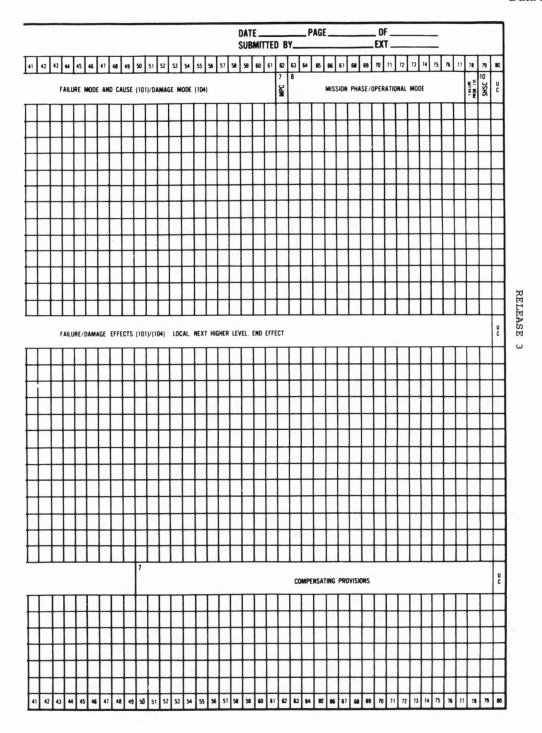

DATE _____ PAGE _____ OF _____
SUBMITTED BY _____ EXT _____

RELEASE 3

- Failure mode and cause/damage effect
- Failure/damage effect - local/next higher assembly/system level
- Failure detection methods

Fig. 9-9. Reliability analysis information.

Data Record H, Support Items Identification

Provisioning documentation for the system is prepared using Data Records H and H1. The purpose of provisioning documentation is to identify the range and depth of spare and repair parts that will be required to support operation or maintenance of the system. A Data Record H is prepared for each unique item or part used in a system. This data record, shown in FIG. 9-24, contains all the cataloging information necessary to identify the part, such as name, commercial and government entity code (CAGE), price, national stock number (NSN), that does not change with different applications of the part. Only one Data Record H is prepared for each part, regardless of how many times the part is used in a system.

Data Record H1, Support Items Identification (Application Related)

All provisioning information related to the specific application of a part in a system is documented on the Data Record H1. Also included on the data record is information pertaining to technical manuals and engineering changes. As shown in FIG. 9-25, the Data Record H1 contains the source, maintenance and recoverability (SMR) code, maintenance factors, quantities per assembly and end item, and other information about part usage. A Data Record H1 is prepared for each application or each part in a system. For example, if a valve is used ten times in a system, one Data Record H is prepared to record cataloging information about the valve, and ten Data Record H1s are prepared to document each use of the valve. A Data Record H1 should be prepared for each item listed on each Data Record D1. It is important that the item category codes assigned to a part on both the Data Record H1 and Data Record D1 match exactly.

Data Record J, Transportability Engineering Characteristics

Information about the transportability characteristics of an item are documented using Data Record J. As shown in FIG. 9-26, the data record addresses the physical movement requirements of the system. Because a Data Record J is prepared for each transportable portion of a system, in many cases, only one data record is required for a complete program. This information is used by the government to plan for transporting the system when delivered and for preparing mobility requirements for deployment.

Data Record Relationships

There are many interrelationships between LSA data records. Maintenance engineering and the maintenance task analysis process deal with Data Records B, B1, B2, C, D, and D1, simultaneously. These data records must be considered as a single entity. The Data Record B series identifies the need for a maintenance task, Data Record C identifies what tasks are to be performed, and Data Records D and D1 contain the actual tasks and support resource requirements. This chain of actions is necessary to ensure that all required maintenance tasks and support resource requirements are identified. Data Records E, E1, E2, F, and G support the maintenance engineering data records because they contain consolidated information and justification for decisions made during the task analysis process. The provisioning data records are dependent on the data in Data Record D1 for identification of all parts and other items required to support maintenance. Figure 9-27 shows the relationship between data records and how decisions made by one activity affect another.

Data Record Requirements

The number of data records required to document the results of an LSA program can be overwhelming. Determining exactly how many are required is not a simple task, but the magnitude of the project can be approximated. A general philosophy for estimating the number of data records that will be required for a program is given in FIG. 9-28. Using information from past programs or similar systems, the contractor should be able to determine, within reasonable tolerances, the scope of the LSA data record effort for a given program. When an LSA program is tailored, the data requirements are also tailored to document only the pertinent information that is generated by the analyses. The data requirements for a specific program should be in concert with the overall program requirements. Generation of data merely for the purpose of having a large stack of paper at the end of a program is not the intent of LSAR. It should be remembered that the LSAR only documents the results of the LSA process.

Data Elements

The last subject to be discussed in relation to data records is the detailed data requirements that must be prepared for each record. A review of the data records previously discussed shows that there are numerous data elements contained on each sheet. Several of the data elements are repeated from sheet

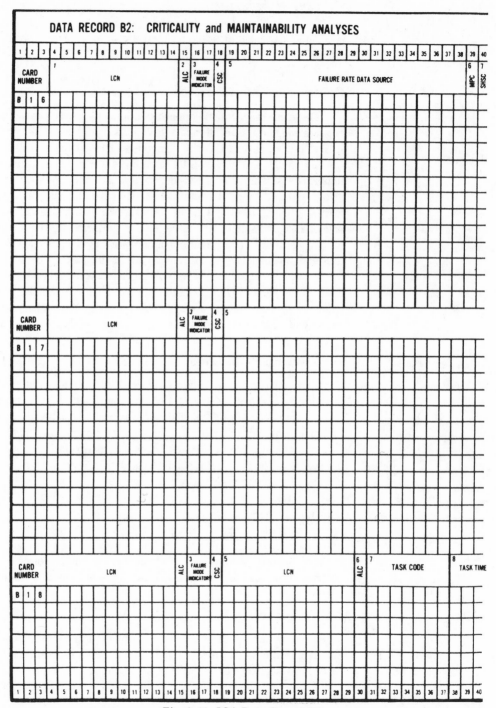

Fig. 9-10. LSA Data Record B2.

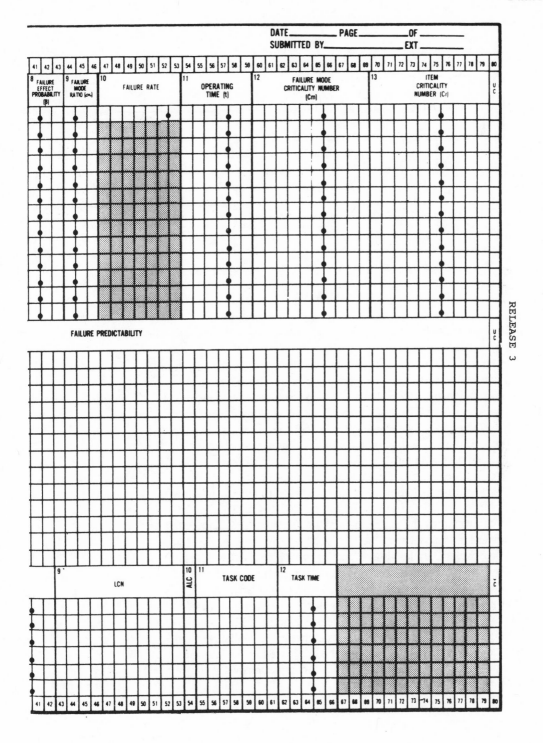

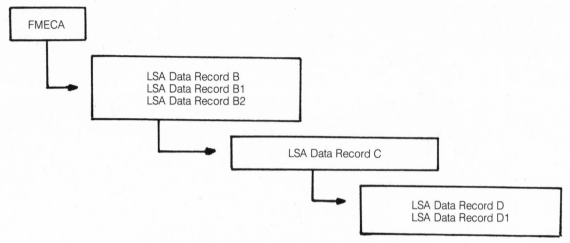

Fig. 9-11. Audit trail from FMECA to maintenance task.

to sheet; however, many are unique and must be generated specifically for a data record. MIL-STD 1388-2A provides complete information on how each data element of each data record is to be completed. The instructions are formatted as shown in FIG. 9-29 and identify the data record card, block and title where the entry is to be made, the data element description number that can be referenced for information about correct data entries, and formatting instructions for the entry. Appendix F, MIL-STD 1388-2A, is a data element dictionary that defines and describes each data element in the LSAR system. Because the LSAR was developed to address the requirements of all services, and each service has unique requirements for data reporting, no LSAR will ever require that every data element be completed on all data records.

DD Form 1949-1, LSAR Data Selection Sheet, is used to identify the data elements required for a specific program. DD Form 1949-1 is a two-part, 16-page form that is completed by the government and provided to the contractor either with a request for proposal or at the LSA guidance conference. Part I is for all data records, except Data Records H and H1, which are at Part II. This form addresses every data element block on each data record, one at a time, and identifies if the data element is required for the program. Part I, page 1 of DD Form 1949-1 is shown in FIG. 9-30. Many data blocks, indicated by a triangle in the righthand column, are required for data processing of the LSAR. It is recommended that detailed instructions on what data elements are to be used and selection criteria for variables in data elements be addressed in the LSA program plan. This provides logistics engineers with a comprehensive guide for completing LSAR requirements.

USING THE LSAR

The LSAR database is designed to be used to meet the goals of the LSA program, not just created and filed away. As shown previously, the LSAR provides a consistent and controlled method of collecting, analyzing, and disseminating logistics related design information. The files should be used by all ILS disciplines throughout the program to develop the detailed support plans and requirements for the system. It is important to understand how the LSAR is to be used when a program starts so that the methods for use can be identified and understood by all concerned. There are four basic areas that must be understood before any real benefit can be obtained from the LSAR. These four areas are: LSA control numbers, LSA candidates, LSA summary reports, and LSA data processing systems.

LSA Control Numbers

The LSAR process generates a tremendous amount of paper and data. The method for controlling data records is the LSA control number (LSACN) which is a unique identifier assigned to each maintenance significant item in the system. Each LSA data record pertaining to an item in the system is assigned the same LSACN, thereby providing the ability to automatically process information about a particular item or group of items. The LSACN is the key field in card columns 4 through 14 of Data records A, B, B1, B2, C, D, D1, E, E1, E2, F, G, and J, and card columns 21 through 31 of Data Record H1. The only data record that does not require assignment of an LSACN is LSA Data Record H, because this record is used as a reference for all appearances of an item in the system, regardless of indenture or use.

There are three methods commonly used for LSACN assignment: classical, modified classical, and sequential. Figure 9-31 shows how the classical method is used to assign an LSACN for each item and how the indenture level dictates the number of digits used. The classical method provides the most traceability from lower to higher levels of indenture. One of the problems with using the classical method is that a maximum of eleven digits can be used for an LSACN. Because many larger systems require indentures that will exceed assignment of specific groups of the LSACN to an indenture level, the modified classical or sequential methods must be used. When either of these two methods are used for LSACN assignment, the traceability of lower level assemblies to the top assembly is harder to maintain. The key points to remember about LSACN assignment are that no two maintenance significant items can have the same number, and numbers should not be reused or switched from item to item due to confusion with controlling assignment. Detailed directions for assignment of LSACNs is contained in appendix D of MIL-STD 1388-2A.

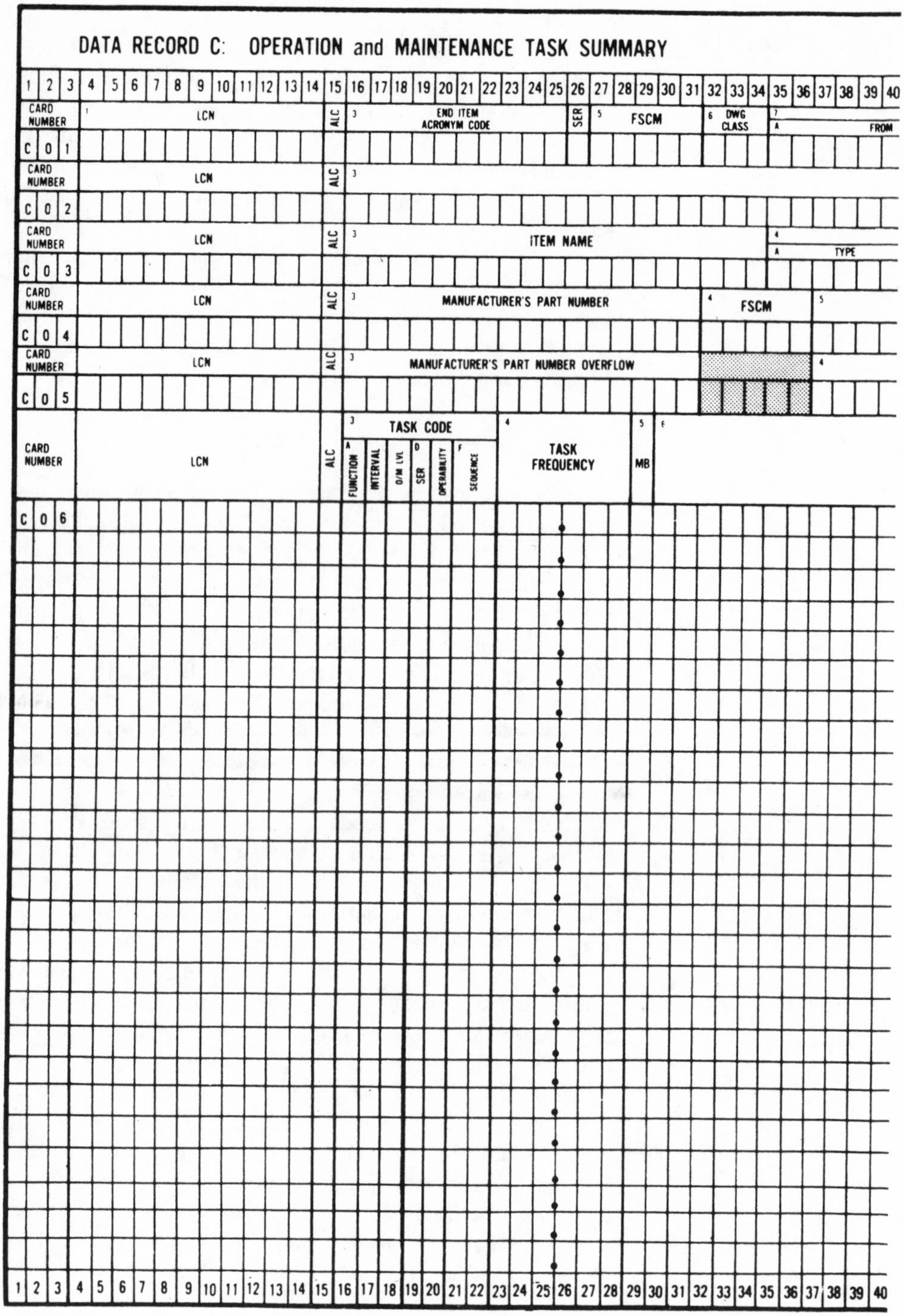

DATA RECORD C: OPERATION and MAINTENANCE TASK SUMMARY

1 2 3 4 5 6 7 8 9 10 11 12 13 14 15 16 17 18 19 20 21 22 23 24 25 26 27 28 29 30 31 32 33 34 35 36 37 38 39 40

CARD NUMBER | 1 LCN | ALC | 3 END ITEM ACRONYM CODE | SER | 5 FSCM | 6 DWG CLASS | 7 A FROM

C 0 1

CARD NUMBER | LCN | ALC | 3

C 0 2

CARD NUMBER | LCN | ALC | 3 ITEM NAME | 4 A TYPE

C 0 3

CARD NUMBER | LCN | ALC | 3 MANUFACTURER'S PART NUMBER | 4 FSCM | 5

C 0 4

CARD NUMBER | LCN | ALC | 3 MANUFACTURER'S PART NUMBER OVERFLOW | 4

C 0 5

CARD NUMBER | LCN | ALC | 3 TASK CODE (A FUNCTION, INTERVAL, O/M LVL, D SER, OPERABILITY, F SEQUENCE) | 4 TASK FREQUENCY | 5 MB | 6

C 0 6

1 2 3 4 5 6 7 8 9 10 11 12 13 14 15 16 17 18 19 20 21 22 23 24 25 26 27 28 29 30 31 32 33 34 35 36 37 38 39 40

Fig. 9-12. LSA Data Record C.

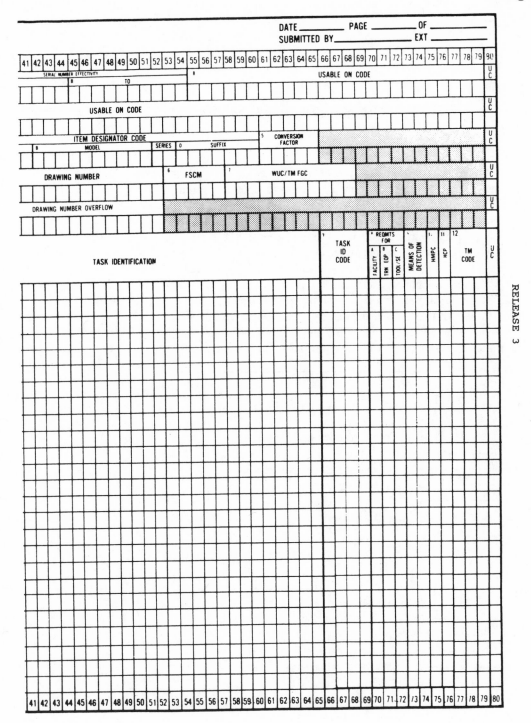

- Maintenance task code
- Task frequency
- Task identification
- Facility requirements
- Training requirements
- Special tools requirements

Fig. 9-13. Significant LSA Data Record C entries.

LSA Candidates

Maintenance engineers begin the LSA process by identifying the elements of the system that are candidates for analysis. This breakdown of the system is normally referred to as an LSA candidate list. The candidate list identifies each part of the system that should be considered for further analysis through the LSA process. The primary source for identification of maintenance significant items is the FMECA performed by reliability engineers, because it identifies all the items in the system and their corresponding failure modes. As the analysis process progresses, the preliminary candidate list is expended as the lower level assemblies and items are identified through further analysis. Eventually, every item in the system that requires maintenance or is involved with the operation of the system is identified as a candidate. This does not mean that a 100-percent identification of every part in the system is required. Nonrepairable

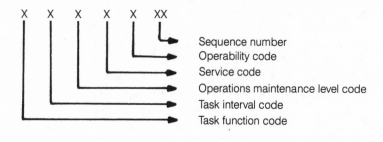

Example:

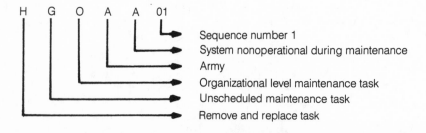

Fig. 9-14. Maintenance task code.

assemblies, piece parts, and materials used to manufacture items are not normally included in the candidate list. In theory, a complete set of LSA data records will be prepared for each item on the candidate list. Figure 9-32 shows the format and content of a typical LSA candidate list. The government may require that a preliminary list be prepared and submitted as a part of the contractor's proposal package. The candidate list is maintained and updated throughout the LSA program as a guide for ensuring that all maintenance significant items in the system are addressed by the analysis process.

LSA Summary Reports

The data contained in the LSAR is used to determine the logistics resources required to support the system. It is also used to identify needs for design changes to increase supportability. The government has prepared a set of computer generated reports that summarize key information contained in the LSAR database. These reports, referred to as LSA summary reports, provide detailed information from the LSAR database in a usable and relevant format. Reports can be generated that identify the most time-consuming or critical maintenance tasks, personnel and skill requirements, training requirements, maintenance allocation charts, and requirements for support and test equipment. LSA summary reports also generate all provisioning documentation for the system. Figure 9-33 lists the standard LSA summary reports. A complete description and example of each report is contained in appendix A of MIL-STD 1388-2A.

Historically, the logistics organization has been required to submit a large number of reports specified by a contract data requirements list (CDRL). Many of the LSA summary reports are designed to fulfill submittal of these contractually required documents, thereby eliminating redundancy of effort for creating both LSA summary reports and standalone CDRL documents.

Appendix E of MIL-STD 1388-2A contains a matrix that cross references standard CDRL requirements with LSA summary reports. Appendix E of MIL-STD 1388-2A also contains a matrix that identifies which LSA data record entries are necessary in order to produce specific LSA summary reports. By selecting which reports are needed to fulfill contractual requirements and working backwards through which data records are required to produce the reports, the scope of detailed data elements that will be required to meet the needs of the program can be identified. This tailoring process can eliminate generation of information that is not necessary and reduce the amount of effort required for completing data records.

LSA Data Processing Systems

The LSAR that is generated by the LSA process normally consists of thousands of individual LSA data records. Therefore, the data records are designed

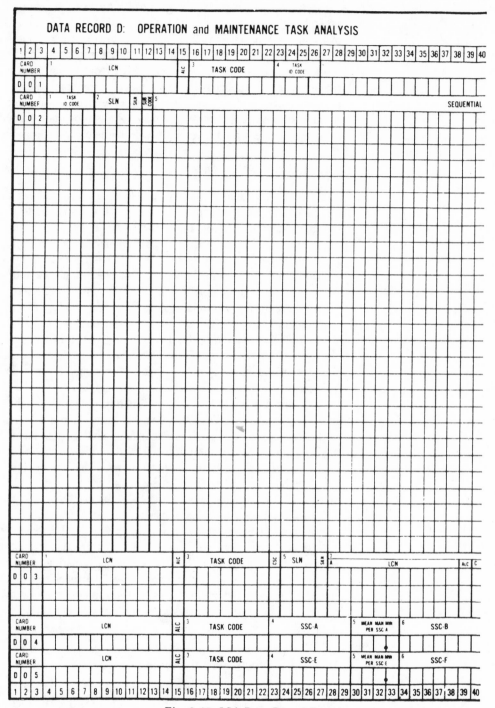

Fig. 9-15. LSA Data Record D.

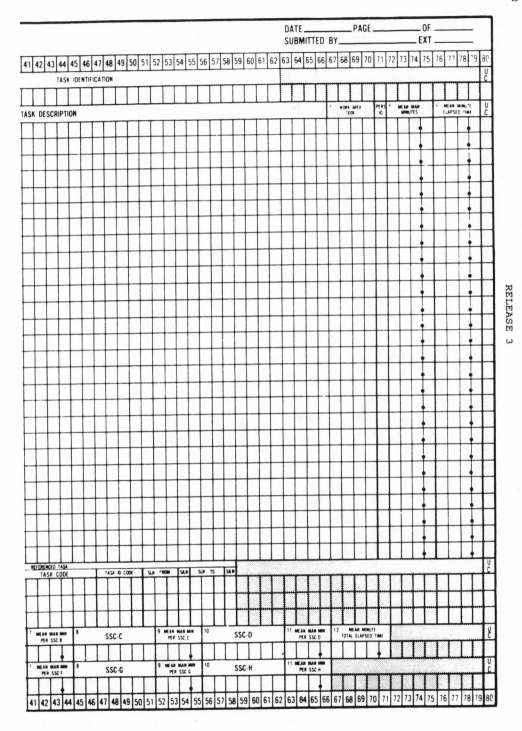

- Maintenance task code
- Sequential task narrative
- Actual time to perform maintenance task
- Elapsed time to perform maintenance task
- Identification of person(s) by skill level

Fig. 9-16. Significant LSA Data Record D information.

to be handled and processed using computers to optimize efficiency and produce the previously described LSA summary reports. Selection of the appropriate computer hardware and software for LSA data processing for a specific program depends on many variables that cannot be adequately addressed in the limited space available in this text. However, there are factors, shown in FIG. 9-34, that must be considered when selecting a computer system. Every program's and company's requirements for computer systems are different; therefore, there are no hard and fast answers. The right answer for one company may not be for another. For the purpose of this discussion, the general alternatives to processing LSA data will be presented. There are two basic steps in processing LSA data: first, building the LSAR database and, second, generating LSA summary reports. These steps can be accomplished manually, totally automated, or a combination of the two. The specific method selected depends on the factors provided in FIG. 9-35.

Building the Database   To build the LSA database, information contained on each LSA data record must be entered into a computer. The two most common methods for accomplishing this task are: to have logistics engineers annotate the information on worksheets and then have the information transferred to a database by data entry personnel or to have logistics engineers enter the information directly into the computer database through display terminals. The current trend is to use the latter method using an interactive software system. Such software is available from several companies that provide both software and training to aid in building the database. The advantage of using this method is inherent with computer applications where the person entering the data has the ability to review and correct errors, help features aid in choosing the correct entries, and built-in error checks that eliminate faulty data entries. Any software used for this purpose should have the ability to create the standard format LSA data records for use in generation of LSA summary reports. Any software selected for this purpose should first be validated by the government using the procedures outlined in MIL-STD 1388-2A.

Generating LSA Summary Reports   The U.S. Army Material Command, Material Readiness Support Activity (MRSA), Lexington, Kentucky, is responsible for maintenance of the Joint Service LSAR ADP system. This software system is available upon request to be used in processing LSA data. The purpose of the Joint Service LSAR ADP system is to standardize the generation of the LSA summary reports described previously in this chapter. This software does not provide the ability to build the initial LSA database; it only generates reports after the database has been built. The MRSA software, as it is commonly called, operates on a mainframe computer in the batch mode. Detailed specifications for an application and assistance for loading the programs on a computer mainframe should be coordinated with the appropriate agency.

The process for generating summary reports using the MRSA software is done in three steps as shown in FIG. 9-36. The first step is to import the existing LSA database from wherever it was created. This step is referred to as the update process for creating the most current database. The software uses this imported database to create three separate internal working databases for use in generating reports. These internal working databases are the LSA Control Number Master File that consists of information from the Data Records A thru G and J; the Parts Master File created for the Data Records H and H1; and the Task Narrative Master File extracted from the Data Record D. All LSA summary reports are generated from one or more of these three files.

The next step in generating summary reports is to prepare selection cards for each required report. A selection card consists of a single 80-card column set of instructions used by the summary report generator to actually select the data that is to be displayed in the report. A separate selection card is required for each report. All report selection cards have mandatory fields that must be entered for a report to be generated. Additionally, most selection cards have optional or variable entries that modify or tailor the report generated. In most cases, it is not sufficient to ask for a specific report, because of the variables available. This is a significant point when a company is trying to produce reports that meet the government's requirements. Specifics concerning the requirements for each report should be thoroughly discussed and understood at the LSA guidance conference in order to prevent unnecessary report preparation and delays in meeting contractual requirements. One point to be remembered when selecting summary reports is that most reports require the key data fields on source LSA data records to have the necessary entries in order for the reports to run. These key fields are not the ones that are annotated on DD Form 1949-1 as mandatory for data processing.

- Predicted or measured task elapsed time
- Summary of personnel requirements by skill level
- Training requirements and location
- Support equipment requirements
- Part number of spares/repair parts/tools
- Quantity required per task
- Item category code of spares/repair parts/tools

Fig. 9-17. Data Record D1 information.

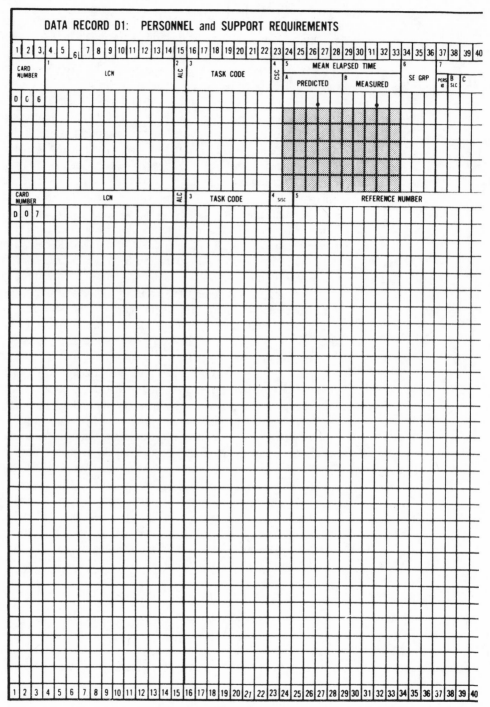

Fig. 9-18. LSA Data Record D1.

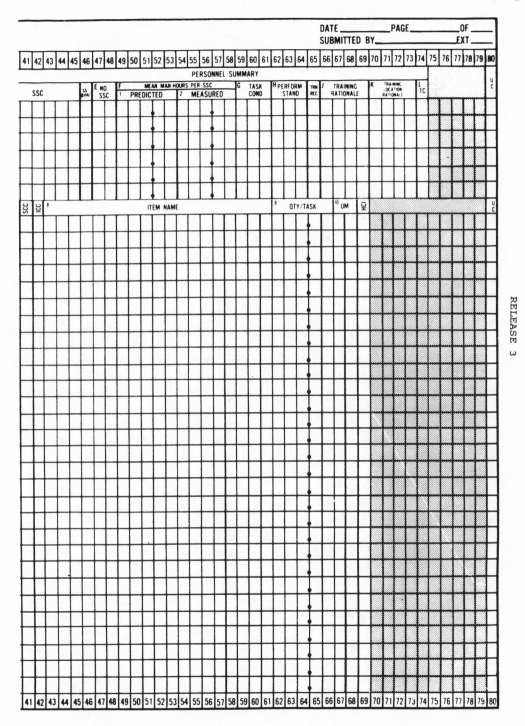

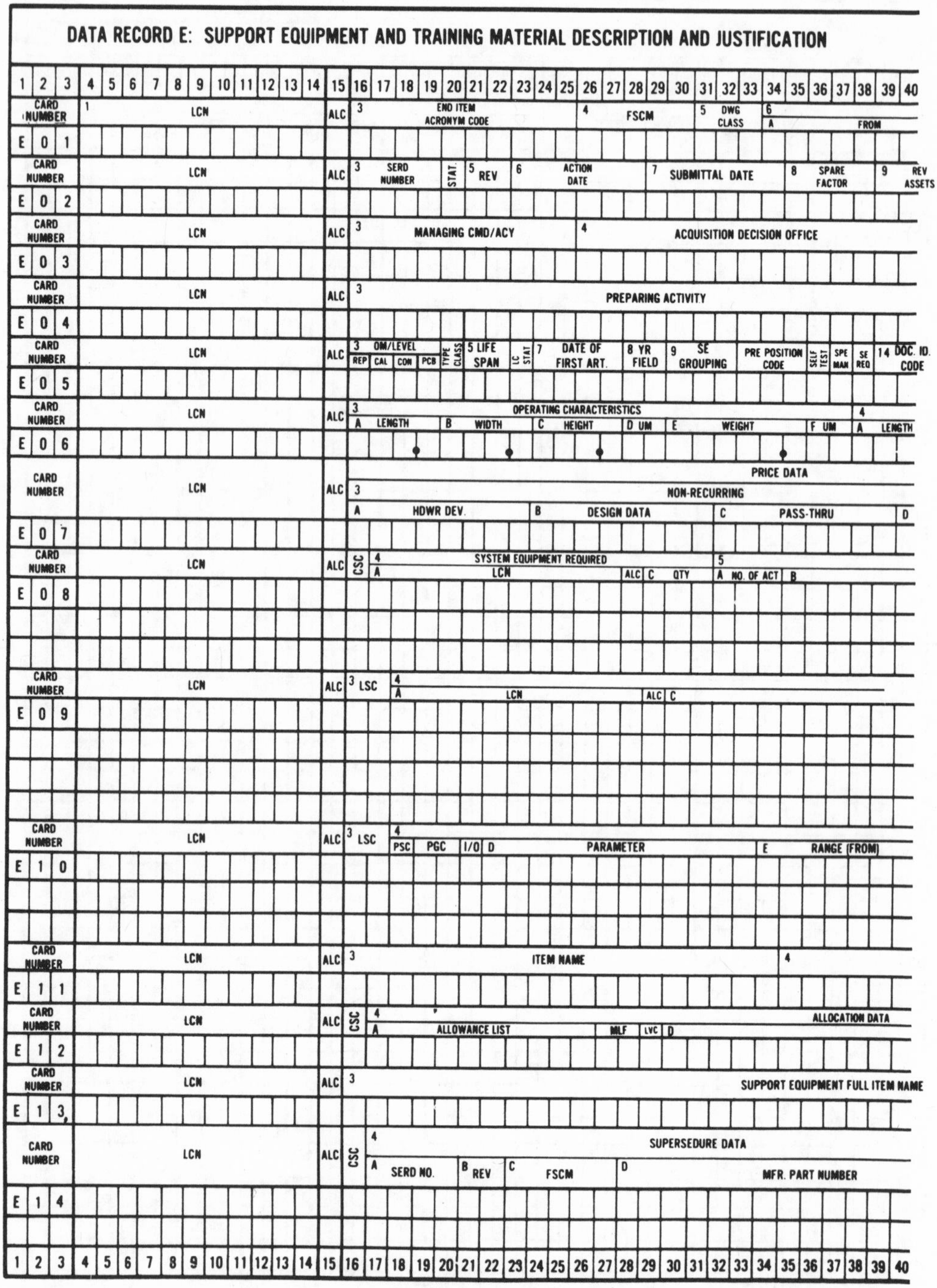

DATA RECORD E: SUPPORT EQUIPMENT AND TRAINING MATERIAL DESCRIPTION AND JUSTIFICATION

| 1 | 2 | 3 | 4 | 5 | 6 | 7 | 8 | 9 | 10 | 11 | 12 | 13 | 14 | 15 | 16 | 17 | 18 | 19 | 20 | 21 | 22 | 23 | 24 | 25 | 26 | 27 | 28 | 29 | 30 | 31 | 32 | 33 | 34 | 35 | 36 | 37 | 38 | 39 | 40 |

A blank grid form with the following labeled card rows:

- **CARD NUMBER** / LCN / ALC | E 0 1 — 1, 3 END ITEM ACRONYM CODE, 4 FSCM, 5 DWG CLASS, 6 A FROM
- **CARD NUMBER** / LCN / ALC | E 0 2 — 3 SERD NUMBER, STAT, 5 REV, 6 ACTION DATE, 7 SUBMITTAL DATE, 8 SPARE FACTOR, 9 REV ASSETS
- **CARD NUMBER** / LCN / ALC | E 0 3 — 3 MANAGING CMD/ACY, 4 ACQUISITION DECISION OFFICE
- **CARD NUMBER** / LCN / ALC | E 0 4 — 3 PREPARING ACTIVITY
- **CARD NUMBER** / LCN / ALC | E 0 5 — 3 OM/LEVEL (REP, CAL, CON, PCB), TYPE CLASS, 5 LIFE SPAN, LC STAT, 7 DATE OF FIRST ART., 8 YR FIELD, 9 SE GROUPING, PRE POSITION CODE, SELF TEST, SPE MAN, SE REQ, 14 DOC. ID. CODE
- **CARD NUMBER** / LCN / ALC | E 0 6 — 3 OPERATING CHARACTERISTICS: A LENGTH, B WIDTH, C HEIGHT, D UM, E WEIGHT, F UM, 4 A LENGTH
- **CARD NUMBER** / LCN / ALC | E 0 7 — 3 PRICE DATA / NON-RECURRING: A HDWR DEV., B DESIGN DATA, C PASS-THRU, D
- **CARD NUMBER** / LCN / ALC | E 0 8 — CSC, 4 SYSTEM EQUIPMENT REQUIRED: A LCN, ALC, C, QTY, 5 A NO. OF ACT, B
- **CARD NUMBER** / LCN / ALC | E 0 9 — 3 LSC, 4 A LCN, ALC, C
- **CARD NUMBER** / LCN / ALC | E 1 0 — 3 LSC, 4 PSC, PGC, I/O, D, PARAMETER, E RANGE (FROM)
- **CARD NUMBER** / LCN / ALC | E 1 1 — 3 ITEM NAME, 4
- **CARD NUMBER** / LCN / ALC | E 1 2 — CSC, 4 A ALLOWANCE LIST, MLF, LVC, D, ALLOCATION DATA
- **CARD NUMBER** / LCN / ALC | E 1 3 — 3 SUPPORT EQUIPMENT FULL ITEM NAME
- **CARD NUMBER** / LCN / ALC | E 1 4 — CSC, 4 SUPERSEDURE DATA: A SERD NO., B REV, C FSCM, D, MFR. PART NUMBER

| 1 | 2 | 3 | 4 | 5 | 6 | 7 | 8 | 9 | 10 | 11 | 12 | 13 | 14 | 15 | 16 | 17 | 18 | 19 | 20 | 21 | 22 | 23 | 24 | 25 | 26 | 27 | 28 | 29 | 30 | 31 | 32 | 33 | 34 | 35 | 36 | 37 | 38 | 39 | 40 |

Fig. 9-19. LSA Data Record E.

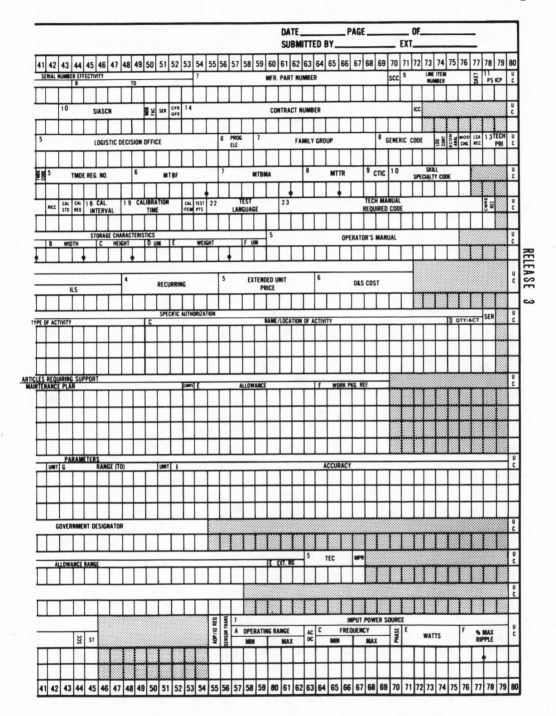

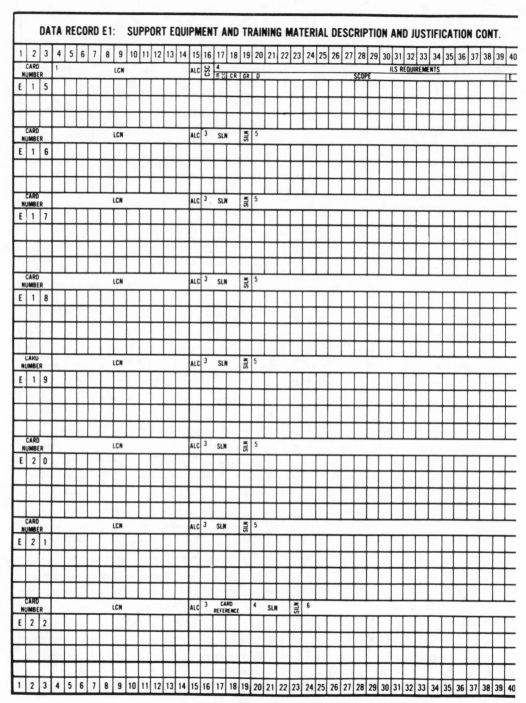

Fig. 9-20. LSA Data Record E1.

DATE_____ PAGE_____ OF_____

SUBMITTED BY_____ EXT_____

| 41 | 42 | 43 | 44 | 45 | 46 | 47 | 48 | 49 | 50 | 51 | 52 | 53 | 54 | 55 | 56 | 57 | 58 | 59 | 60 | 61 | 62 | 63 | 64 | 65 | 66 | 67 | 68 | 69 | 70 | 71 | 72 | 73 | 74 | 75 | 76 | 77 | 78 | 79 | 80 |

DESIGN DATA

EST. PRICE | CR | GR | D | SCOPE | E | EST PRICE | U C

ADDITIONAL SKILLS AND SPECIAL TRAINING REQUIREMENTS — U C

FUNCTIONAL ANALYSIS — U C

SE NON-PROLIFERATION EFFORTS — U C

DESCRIPTION AND FUNCTION — U C

JUSTIFICATION — U C

INSTALLATION FACTORS OR OTHER FACILITIES — U C

EXPLANATION — U C

| 41 | 42 | 43 | 44 | 45 | 46 | 47 | 48 | 49 | 50 | 51 | 52 | 53 | 54 | 55 | 56 | 57 | 58 | 59 | 60 | 61 | 62 | 63 | 64 | 65 | 66 | 67 | 68 | 69 | 70 | 71 | 72 | 73 | 74 | 75 | 76 | 77 | 78 | 79 | 80 |

RELEASE 3

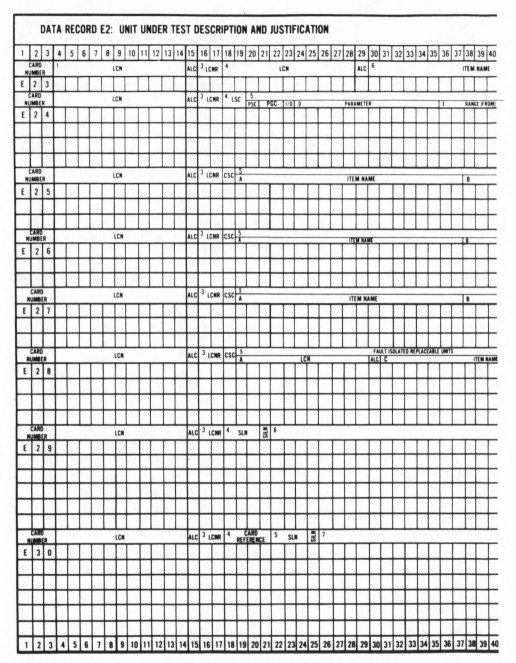

Fig. 9-21. LSA Data Record E2.

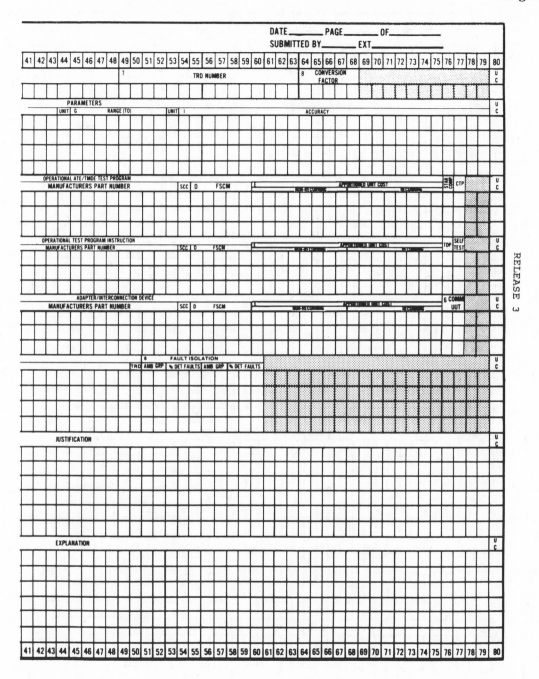

RELEASE 3

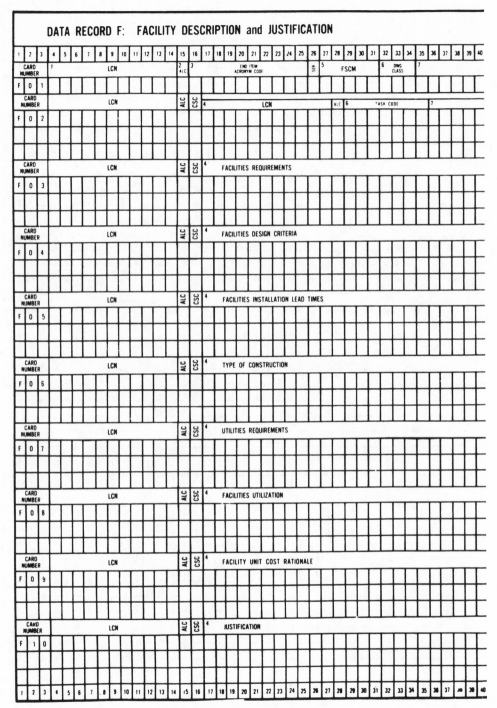

Fig. 9-22. LSA Data Record F.

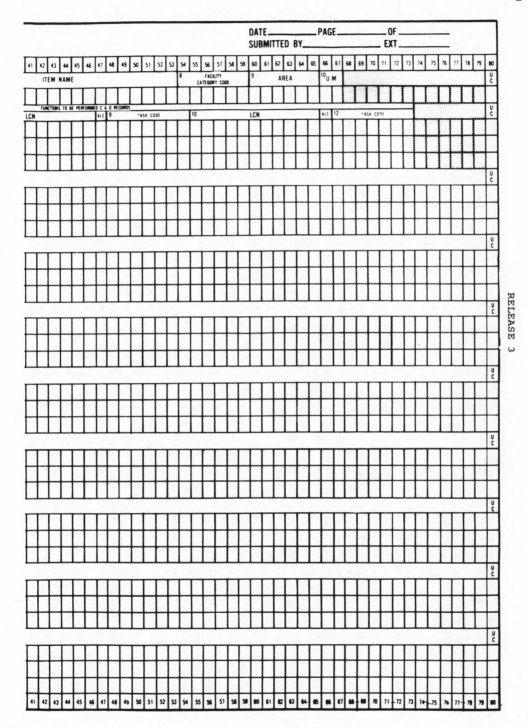

RELEASE 3

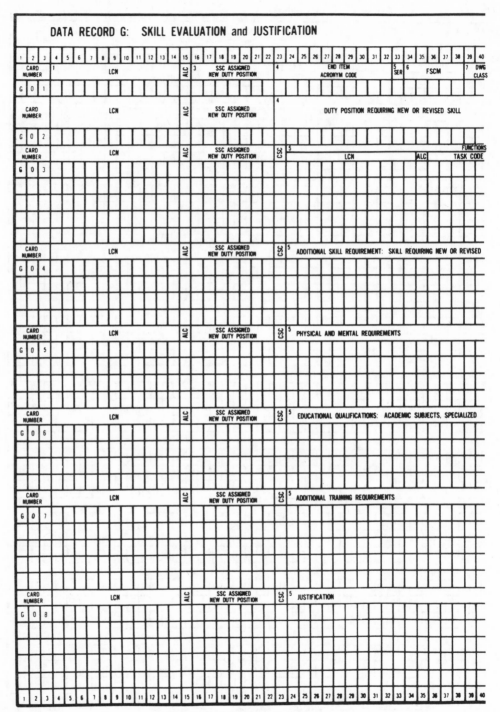

Fig. 9-23. LSA Data Record G.

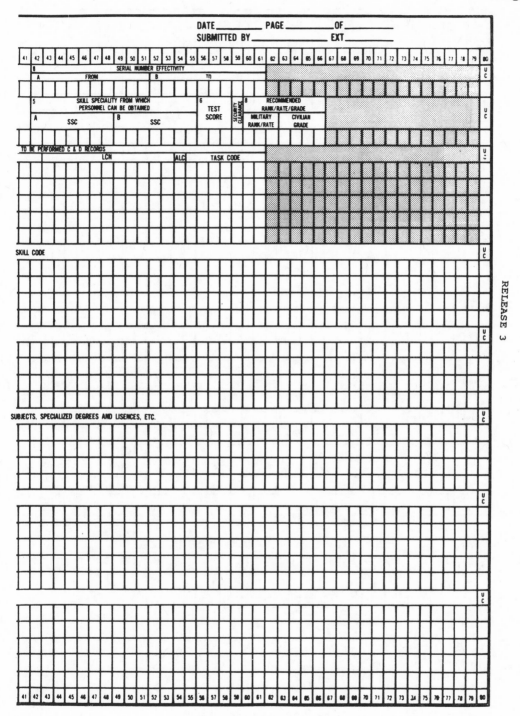

DATA RECORD H: SUPPORT ITEMS IDENTIFICATION

1	2	3	4	5	6	7	8	9	10	11	12	13	14	15	16	17	18	19	20	21	22	23	24	25	26	27	28	29	30	31	32	33	34	35	36	37	38	39	40

Row H 0 1:
CARD NUMBER | REFERENCE NUMBER (1) | SCC (2) | PSIC (3) | FSCM (4) | RNCC (5) | PPSL (6) | RNVC (7) | DAC (8) | (9)

Row H 0 2:
CARD NUMBER | REFERENCE NUMBER | SCC | PSIC | REFERENCE NUMBER OVERFLOW (4) | (5)

Row H 0 3:
CARD NUMBER | REFERENCE NUMBER | SCC | PSIC | CSC (4) | (5) | ADDITIONAL

Row H 0 4:
CARD NUMBER | REFERENCE NUMBER | SCC | PSIC | CSC (4) | UM PRICE (5) | (6) A | LOT FROM

Row H 0 5:
CARD NUMBER | REFERENCE NUMBER | SCC | PSIC | BASIS OF ISSUE (4) | QTY AUTH | EI | LVL | CTRL | (5)

Row H 0 6:
CARD NUMBER | REFERENCE NUMBER | SCC | PSIC | CSC (4) | PACKAGING CATEGORY CODE (5) | MTH PRES (6) | CD (7) | PRES MATL (8) | WRAP MATL (9) | CUSH MATL (10) | CT (11) | UNIT CONT (12)
Rows: A, B, C

Row H 0 7:
CARD NUMBER | REFERENCE NUMBER | SCC | PSIC | CSC (4) | UC LVL (5) | CONTAINER NSN (6) FSC / NIIN | OPI (7) (8)
Rows: A, B, C

Row H 0 8:
CARD NUMBER | REFERENCE NUMBER | SCC | PSIC | CSC (4) | (5)
Rows: A, B, C

1	2	3	4	5	6	7	8	9	10	11	12	13	14	15	16	17	18	19	20	21	22	23	24	25	26	27	28	29	30	31	32	33	34	35	36	37	38	39	40

Fig. 9-24. LSA Data Record H.

DATE _____ PAGE _____ OF _____
SUBMITTED BY _____ EXT _____

41	42	43	44	45	46	47	48	49	50	51	52	53	54	55	56	57	58	59	60	61	62	63	64	65	66	67	68	69	70	71	72	73	74	75	76	77	78	79	80

ITEM NAME

	10 PTD SELECT									11 QUP	12 TOTAL QUANTITY RECOMMENDED	13 PLT	14 SMCC	15 PLCC	16 SMIC	17 HCI	18 PMIC	U C

PTD SELECT sub-columns: LL TI | PPL | SF PPL | CB IL | RIL | IS IL | PCL | TT EL | SC PL | DC N

NSN RELATED DATA

PREFIX	FSC	NIIN	SUFFIX	6 UI	7 UI PRICE	8 UI CONVERSION FACTOR	9 SL	10 SLAC	U C

REFERENCE NUMBER

	6 FSCM	7 RNCC	8 RNVC	9 MAOT	10 MAC	PS/PC	ADP EC	AIC A	AIC B	14 AIC QTY	IMC	15 DSR/R A	16 DSR/R B	U C

QUANTITY

B	TO	7 CPC	8 TUC	9 PUC	10 FY	11 UM	12 CTIC	13 AMC	14 AMSC	15 FSCM	16 FSCM	17 FSCM	18 FSCM	U C

BASIS OF ISSUE

QTY AUTH	EI	LVL	CTRL	6 QTY AUTH	EI	LVL	CTRL	U C

13 INT CONT	14 ICQ	15 DOP	16 SPEC MKG	17 UNIT PACK WEIGHT	18 UNIT PACK SIZE			19 SPI NO	20 SPI REV	21 PK CD			U C

UNIT PACK SIZE sub-columns: L | W | D
PK CD sub-columns: A | B | C/X

UNIT SIZE

L	W	H	9 UNIT WEIGHT	10 FSCM	11 HC	12 SUPPLEMENTAL PACKAGING DATA	U C

SUPPLEMENTAL PACKAGING DATA OVERFLOW

																										U C

41	42	43	44	45	46	47	48	49	50	51	52	53	54	55	56	57	58	59	60	61	62	63	64	65	66	67	68	69	70	71	72	73	74	75	76	77	78	79	80

DATA RECORD H1: SUPPORT ITEMS IDENTIFICATION (APPLICATION RELATED)

Fig. 9-25. LSA Data Record H1.

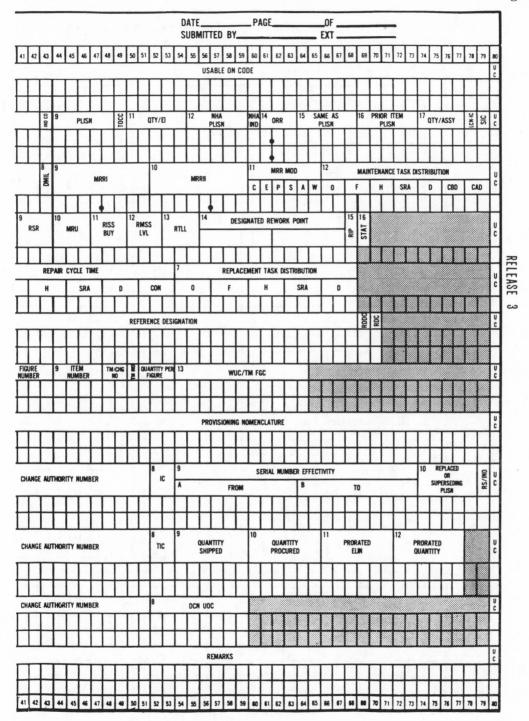

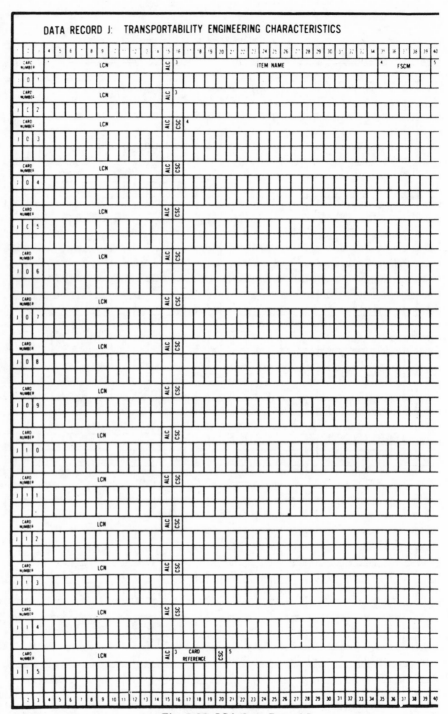

Fig. 9-26. LSA Data Record J.

DATE _____ PAGE _____ OF _____
SUBMITTED BY _____ EXT _____

| 41 | 42 | 43 | 44 | 45 | 46 | 47 | 48 | 49 | 50 | 51 | 52 | 53 | 54 | 55 | 56 | 57 | 58 | 59 | 60 | 61 | 62 | 63 | 64 | 65 | 66 | 67 | 68 | 69 | 70 | 71 | 72 | 73 | 74 | 75 | 76 | 77 | 78 | 79 | 80 |

DRAWING NUMBER · USEABLE ON CODE

USEABLE ON CODE · U C

ITEM DESCRIPTION · U C

DOD DEVELOPING AGENCY · U C

ITEM IDENTIFICATION · U C

SHIPPING MODES · U C

SHIPPING DIMENSIONS · U C

TOTAL NUMBER AND TYPE OF AXLES · U C

MAXIMUM AXLE LOAD · U C

GROUND CONTACT LENGTH · U C

GROUND CONTACT AREA · U C

SPECIAL SHIPPING REQUIREMENTS · U C

TIEDOWN PROVISIONS · U C

LIFTING PROVISIONS · U C

REMARKS/OVERFLOW · U C

| 41 | 42 | 43 | 44 | 45 | 46 | 47 | 48 | 49 | 50 | 51 | 52 | 53 | 54 | 55 | 56 | 57 | 58 | 59 | 60 | 61 | 62 | 63 | 64 | 65 | 66 | 67 | 68 | 69 | 70 | 71 | 72 | 73 | 74 | 75 | 76 | 77 | 78 | 79 | 80 |

RELEASE 3

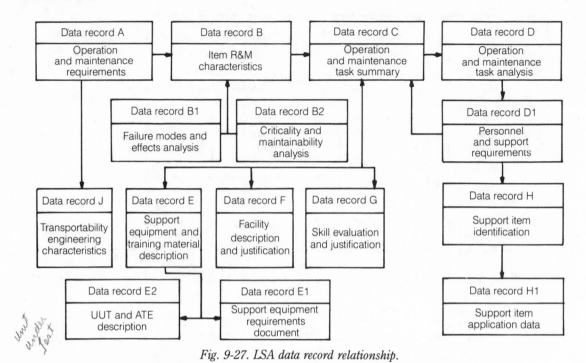

Fig. 9-27. LSA data record relationship.

Data record	Estimating rationale
A	One data record per program unless directed otherwise.
B, B1, B2, C	One data record required for each repairable or maintenance-significant item.
D, D1	One data record required for each maintenance task listed on the corresponding Data Record C. At a minimum, plan for tasks for fault isolation, remove and replace, and repair for each item.
E, E1, E2, F, G	As required to document need and justification for support and test equipment, facilities, or personnel skills.
H	One data record for each unique part used in the system.
H1	One data record for every application of every part used in the system.
J	As required to document system transportability requirements. At least one per system.

Fig. 9-28. Data record estimating.

Card A01, Block 1.   Logistics Support Analysis Control Number

DED 197   11 × L −

This data element is mandatory for LSAR ADP processing. Enter the LCN of the item for which the data record is being prepared. The LCN will be the same for all cards of the data record.

Fig. 9-29. Data element layout.

160

PART I		LSAR DATA SELECTION SHEET	Form Approved OMB No. 0704-0188 Exp. Date: June 30, 1986
CARD/ BLOCK NUMBER	**DED NO.**	**DATA ELEMENT NAME**	**REQUIRED**
		LSAR DATA RECORD A	
01-1	197	LOGISTIC SUPPORT ANALYSIS CONTROL NUMBER (Applies to complete A Record) ▲	
01-2	023	ALTERNATE LSA CONTROL NUMBER CODE (Applies to complete A Record as needed) ▲	
01-3	106	END ITEM ACRONYM CODE	
01-4	414	SERVICE DESIGNATOR CODE	
01-5	139	FEDERAL SUPPLY CODE FOR MANUFACTURERS	
01-6	098	DRAWING CLASSIFICATION	
01-7	411	SERIAL NUMBER EFFECTIVITY	
01-8	536	USABLE ON CODE ▲	
	536	OPTION 1	
	536	OPTION 2	
	536	OPTION 3	
01-9	535	UPDATE CODE (Applies to complete A Record) ▲	
02-3	536	USABLE ON CODE ▲	
03-3	181	ITEM NAME	
03-4	178	ITEM DESIGNATOR CODE	
03-5	069	CONVERSION FACTOR	
04-3	213	MANUFACTURER'S PART NUMBER	
04-4	139	FEDERAL SUPPLY CODE FOR MANUFACTURERS	
04-5	099	DRAWING NUMBER	
04-6	139	FEDERAL SUPPLY CODE FOR MANUFACTURERS	
04-7	545	WORK UNIT CODE / TECHNICAL MANUAL FUNCTIONAL GROUP CODE	
05-3	214	MANUFACTURER'S PART NUMBER OVERFLOW	
05-4	100	DRAWING NUMBER OVERFLOW	
06-3,5,7	029	ANNUAL OPERATING REQUIREMENTS	
06-4,6,8	244	MEASUREMENT BASE	
06-9	285	OPERATIONAL REQUIREMENT INDICATOR	
06-10	027	ANNUAL NUMBER OF MISSIONS	
06-11	028	ANNUAL OPERATING DAYS	
06-12	234	MEAN MISSION DURATION	
06-13	244	MEASUREMENT BASE	
06-14	254	MODE OF TRANSPORT	
06-15	499	TOTAL SYSTEMS SUPPORTED	
06-16	073	CREW SIZE	
06-17	268	NUMBER OF OPERATING LOCATIONS	
07-3	051	CARD SEQUENCING CODE ▲	
07-4	248	MINIMUM ACCEPTABLE VALUE	
07-4A	235	MEAN TIME BETWEEN FAILURES	
07-4B	236	MEAN TIME BETWEEN MAINTENANCE ACTIONS	
07-4C	244	MEASUREMENT BASE	
07-4D	241	MEAN TIME TO REPAIR	
07-4E	219	MEAN ACTIVE MAINTENANCE DOWNTIME	
07-5	039	BEST OPERATIONAL CAPABILITY	
07-5A	235	MEAN TIME BETWEN FAILURES	
07-5B	236	MEAN TIME BETWEEN MAINTENANCE ACTIONS	
07-5C	244	MEASUREMENT BASE	
07-5D	241	MEAN TIME TO REPAIR	
07-5E	219	MEAN ACTIVE MAINTENANCE DOWNTIME	
08-3	218	MAXIMUM TIME TO REAPIR	
08-4	312	PERCENTILE	
08-5	158	INHERENT AVAILABILITY	
08-6	003	ACHIEVED AVAILABILITY	
08-7	283	OPERATIONAL AVAILABILITY	
08-8	015	ADMINISTRATIVE AND LOGISTIC DELAY TIME	

DD Form 1949-1, 84 JUL   *Previous editions are obsolete*   ▲   Required for automated processing

Part I, Page 1

Fig. 9-30. DD Form 1949-1.

LSA Record

A complete understanding of all the aspects of running each report is required to assure the proper information needed to run a report in the database. Otherwise, it may not be possible to generate required reports. Detailed preparation instructions for selection cards and identification of key data fields are contained in the Joint Service LSAR ADP System Functional Operating Instructions that are provided by MRSA with the software system.

The last step is generating LSA summary reports is initiation of the report software where the system uses the prepared selection cards to select data from one or more of the master files to produce the actual reports. As can be

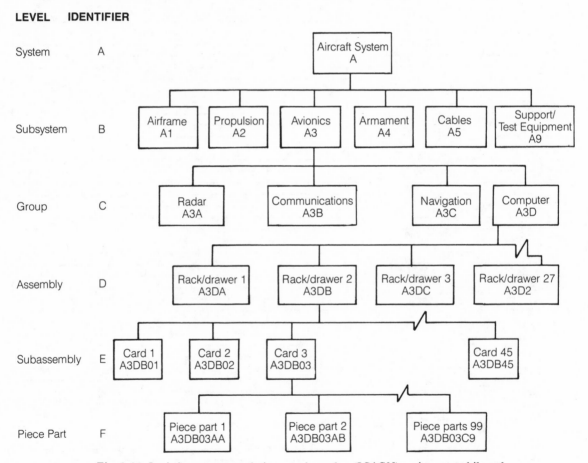

Fig. 9-31. Logistics support analysis control number (LSACN) assignment philosophy.

LSACN	Item Name	Part Number
A	System	133-2
AA	Subsystem 1	133-2-1
AAA	Assembly 1	388-2
AAAA	Subassembly 1	388-2-1
AAAAA	Part 1	RCR07G100JS
AAAAB	Part 2	JANTX2N2222A
AAAAC	Part 3	MS1950-2
AAAB	Subassembly 2	399-294
AAABA	Part 4	399-294-1
AAABB	Part 5	399-294-2
AAB	Assembly 2	76487
AABA	Subassembly 3	5847
AABAA	Part 6	366628
AABAB	Part 7	14532
AABB	Subassembly 4	46632
AB	Subsystem 2	133-2-2
ABB	Assembly 3	24435-1
ABC	Assembly 4	24435-2
AC	Subsystem 3	133-2-3
AD	Subsystem 4	133-2-4
ADA	SubAssembly 5	74001
ADAA	Subassembly 5	AGR9756
ADAAA	Part 8	MS38510-155
ADAAB	Part 9	MS38510-2
ADAAC	Part 10	392006
AE	Subsystem 5	133-2-5

Fig. 9-32. LSA candidate list.

seen, the process for generating reports using the MRSA software system can be time-consuming; however, it does provide a company with a viable alternative for meeting contractual requirements. The other alternative for generating summary reports is to use one of the available off-the-shelf LSA data systems offered by subcontract of consultant firms. These systems normally provide a complete turnkey ability for both upfront database preparation and actual report generation. As shown in FIG. 9-37, this type of system usually streamlines LSA data processing. There are considerations in choosing this type of system over the MRSA software system. A few of these concerns are acquisition and setup costs, maintenance, computer hardware compatibility and availability, and training requirements. The decision as to which alternative to choose should be based on a complete evaluation of current and future company needs, investment versus return, and overall computer plans of the company. Selection of either alternative will represent a significant investment of time, manpower, and capital, so any decision must be based on the particular needs of the company; however, efficient and effective collection, analysis, and use of LSA data provides an invaluable tool in meeting the goals of the LSA program.

LSA-001	Direct Annual Maintenance Manhours by Skill Specialty Code and Level of Maintenance
LSA-002	Personnel and Skill Summary
LSA-003	Maintenance Summary
LSA-004	Maintenance Allocation Summary
LSA-005	Support Item Utilization
LSA-006	Critical Maintenance Task Summary
LSA-007	Support Equipment Requirements by Skill Specialty Code and Level of Maintenance
LSA-008	Support Item Validation
LSA-009	Support Item List
LSA-010	Parts Standardization Summary
LSA-011	Requirements for Special Training Device
LSA-012	Requirements for Facility
LSA-013	Support Equipment Grouping Number Utilization
LSA-014	Training Task List
LSA-015	Sequential Task Description
LSA-016	Preliminary Maintenance Allocation Summary
LSA-017	Preliminary Maintenance Allocation Summary - Tool Page
LSA-019	Maintenance Task Analysis Validation
LSA-020	Tool and Test Equipment Requirements
LSA-021	Task Referencing List
LSA-022	Referenced Task List
LSA-023	Maintenance Plan, Summary
LSA-024	Maintenance Plan
LSA-025	Packaging Requirements Data
LSA-026	Packaging Development Data
LSA-027	Failure, Maintenance Rate Summary
LSA-028	Reference Number/Additional Reference Number Cross-Reference List
LSA-029	Repair Parts List
LSA-030	Special Tools List
LSA-031	Part Number/National Stock Number/Reference Designation Cross Reference Index
LSA-032	DLSC Submittals
LSA-034	Stockage List Type-Four Report
LSA-036	Provisioning Requirements
LSA-040	Components of End Item List
LSA-041	Basic Issue Items List
LSA-042	Additional Authorization List
LSA-043	Expendable/Durable Supplies and Materials List
LSA-045	Stockage List Type-Three Report
LSA-050	Reliability Centered Maintenance Summary
LSA-051	Reliability Summary - Redesign
LSA-052	Criticality Analysis Summary
LSA-053	Maintainability Summary - Level of Repair
LSA-054	Failure Mode Analysis Summary
LSA-055	Failure Mode Detection Summary
LSA-060	LCN Master File
LSA-061	Parts Master File
LSA-070	Support Equipment Recommendation Data (SERD)
LSA-072	Rest Measurement and Diagnostic Equipment (TMDE) Requirements Summary Report

Fig. 9-33. LSA summary reports.

LSA-074	Support Equipment Tool List
LSA-075	LSAR MANPRINT Report
LSA-077	Depot Maintenance Interservice Data Summary
LSA-080	Bill of Materials
LSA-100	Chronolog
LSA-101	Transaction Edit Results - Selection Cards
LSA-102	Transaction Edit Results - LCN Master
LSA-103	Transaction Edit Results - Parts Master
LSA-104	Transaction Edit Results - Task Narrative Master
LSA-105	Key Field Change Transactions
LSA-106	Reference Number Discrepancy List
LSA-107	LCN-Task Identification Code Cross-Reference
LSA-108	Critical Data Changes
LSA-109	Unidentified Transactions
LSA-150	Provisioning Error List
LSA-151	Provisioning Parts List Index
LSA-152	PLISN Assignment/Reassignment
LSA-154	Provisioning Parts Breakout Summary
LSA-155	Recommended Spare Parts List for Spares Acquisition Integrated with Production

Fig. 9-33. Continued.

Fig. 9-34. Factors for selection of computer systems.

- Computer systems already available
- Size of development program
- Existing data available for use
- Estimated size of LSAR database
- Anticipated number of users
- Budget and schedule constraints

Fig. 9-35. Factors for selection of data processing method.

- Cost and schedule of preparation
- Availability of automated data processing system
- Development hardware complexity
- Acquisition cycle
- Delivery schedule and requirements
- Design stability
- Compatibility with other LSAR systems

Correlation of Tasks, Data Records, and Reports   One of the difficult situations facing the logistics engineer is to determine exactly what LSA tasks produce information for which data records that will allow generation of that LSA summary reports. This is especially critical when trying to develop detailed LSA requirements and at the same time attempting to limit the effort necessary to complete program requirements. In general terms, the only LSA tasks that produce data for the LSAR are Tasks 205, 301, 401, and 501. The outputs of these tasks can be subdivided further into specific subtasks that have

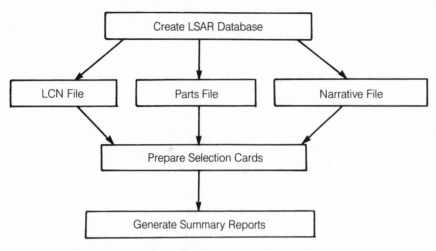

Fig. 9-36. Standard LSA summary report generation steps.

inputs to specific data records. This is not to say that other tasks do not contribute information to the LSAR, but the outputs of other tasks are used as inputs to the tasks that do output data for the LSAR, rather than having direct inputs to the LSAR. Figure 9-38 illustrates the interrelationships between LSA tasks, LSA data records, and LSA summary reports.

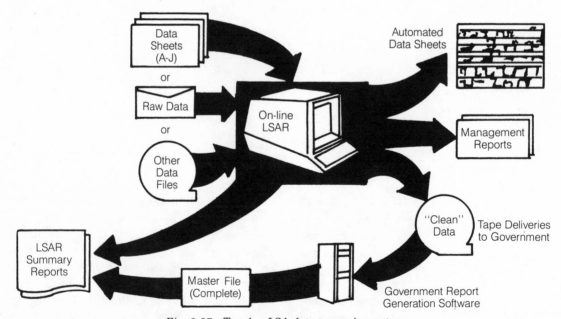

Fig. 9-37. Turnkey LSA data processing system.

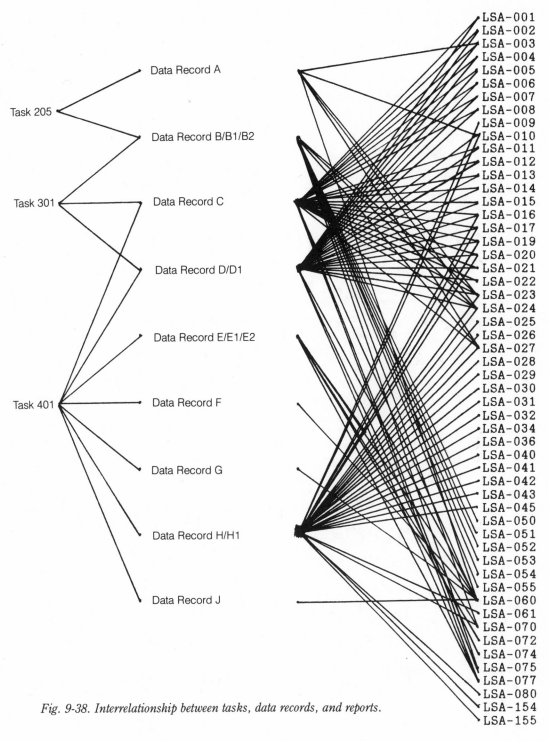

Fig. 9-38. Interrelationship between tasks, data records, and reports.

10

Life Cycle Cost

The ultimate cost of ownership, life cycle cost (LCC), of the system being designed is probably the most important and most misunderstood aspect of the design process. Determining exactly what costs of ownership the new system will incur from concept through disposal and identifying how the design can be changed to minimize costs is very difficult. This difficulty results from inadequate information, inaccurate predictions, and events unforeseen during the design process. However, life cycle cost should be a primary concern throughout the design and acquisition process. The LSA program, and especially the LSAR database, when used properly should provide a significant amount of valuable input data for the life cycle costing effort. The combination of thorough planning, coordination, and organization can meld the LSA process and the LCC process into a mutually supportive and interactive analysis that will result in the best support possible for the lower life cycle cost.

LIFE CYCLE COST ELEMENTS

The prediction of the total costs that will be incurred throughout the life of a system, or any other equipment, serves an important role in the acquisition process. The total life cycle cost of a system encompasses every conceivable direct and indirect cost that will be related to the acquisition, operation, support, and disposal of the system. This is an extremely useful tool during the acquisition process when determining the best alternatives for design configurations, operation concepts, maintenance concept, production schemes, and logistics support concepts and policies. MIL-HDBK 259, Life Cycle Cost in Navy Acquisitions, provides a detailed description of the applications for life cycle cost analysis.

Cost Elements

Determination of the predicted total life cycle cost is accomplished by combining all of the relevant cost elements associated with the costs incurred for acquisition, operation and support, and disposal of a system. These costs, both direct and indirect, reflect the government's cost of ownership. Figure 10-1 shows the relative portion that each of these elements contributes to total life-cycle cost. The figure illustrates the often overlooked fact that the majority of costs for a system are due to operation and support costs rather than acquisition costs. This is why it is of utmost importance that every effort be made during the acquisition process to design a system that optimizes total life cycle cost rather than acquisition cost.

Acquisition Costs

All costs incurred by the government from the start of the concept phase until the end of the production phase are normally considered acquisition costs. This includes funds expended both internally and externally by the government, not just the funds paid to contractors to design and develop the system. Acquisition costs are further divided into research and development (R&D) costs and investment costs as shown in FIG. 10-2.

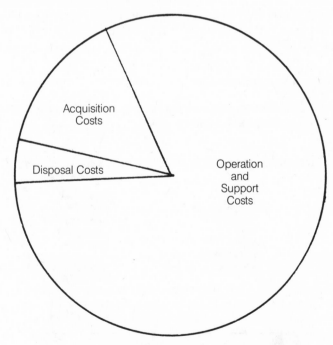

Fig. 10-1. Element contributions to total life cycle cost.

Life Cycle Cost

Research and Development Costs

The costs incurred by the government during the concept, demonstration and validation, and full-scale development phases of the acquisition process are categorized as R&D costs. The result of R&D is completion of the detailed documentation (e.g., engineering drawings, specifications, plans) necessary to enter the production phase. All costs associated with the R&D effort to include planning, management, engineering, test, evaluation, special equipment, and facilities, whether incurred by the government or contractors make up this cost element.

Investment Costs

The costs of actually producing the system, procuring and developing the necessary initial support, and establishing an initial operating capability are considered investment costs. This includes the cost of building the system, logistics planning, initial spare and repair parts, training operation, maintenance and supervisor personnel, support and test equipment, documentation, maintenance facilities, and initial PHS&T. Investment costs many times overshadow other life cycle costs and distort the perspective of attempting to reduce costs because they are considered to be the price paid by the government to contractors to build a system. Procurement contracts can exceed a billion dollars, which seems like an enormous amount of money, but it represents only a small percentage of the total cost that the government will pay for ownership of the system over its complete life cycle.

Operation and Support Costs

The largest percentage of costs incurred over the life cycle of a system are due to operation and support (O&S) costs. Included in O&S costs are direct

Research and Development Costs	Investment Costs
Planning	Production
Management	Planning
Engineering	Management
Test	Initial spares
Evaluation	Training
Equipment	Support equipment
Facilities	Technical manuals
	Engineering
	Test
	Facilities
	Initial PHS&T

Fig. 10-2. Acquisition costs.

and indirect costs necessary to sustain the system. Figure 10-3 illustrates typical O&S costs elements.

Direct O&S Costs Any cost that has a direct relationship to the operation or support of a system is considered a direct cost. Costs for personnel include operators, maintenance personnel, and supervisors, both military and civilian, who are responsible for the operation or maintenance of the system or components. This can include support personnel who are directly related to the mission scenario of the system. A subelement of personnel cost is the cost of specific training related to operation and maintenance of the system, which can be either initial skill specialty code (SSC)-related training, on-the-job training, or sustainment training. Consumables are any items that are required to sustain operation or maintenance (e.g., fuel, lubricants, maintenance materials, expendable supplies, or repair parts). The purchase of spare parts needed to replace initial provisioned items or increase the range and depth of spares is a direct cost. The cost of maintenance of support and test equipment and procurement of replacement items is also a direct cost. Any facility costs that are incurred for support of operation or maintenance activities are direct, but this does not include the construction or modification costs, which are considered an investment cost. Facility costs also include the cost of water, power, and other utilities directly related to maintenance or operations.

Maintenance of supplies and equipment is a direct cost, but the labor requirements for maintenance are included in personnel costs and should not be duplicated in this cost element. PHS&T costs include all movements of the system due to operation or maintenance needs after initial delivery, and the movement of spares and repair parts between maintenance facilities, supply facilities, and the user. Technical data is initially procured as an investment cost; however, the maintenance and updating of the data is a direct O&S cost. Supply management costs are attributed to the unique spare and repair parts of the system that must be stocked to support operations or maintenance. These costs are incurred at all levels of supply, from organizational to depot, and also include the administrative costs of maintaining DLSC and National Inventory Control Point

Direct Costs	Indirect Costs
Personnel	Personnel
Consumables	Facilities
Replacement spares	Training
Support equipment	
Facilities	
Maintenance	
PHS&T	
Technical data	
Supply management	
Modifications	

Fig. 10-3. Operation and support costs.

(NICP) records for the items. All engineering changes and other modifications to the system that occur after deployment are direct O&S costs. Modification costs are considered sustaining investment costs that are necessary to enhance the reliability, maintainability, supportability, or operational capabilities of the system.

Indirect O&S Costs Those costs that are incurred for relevant services, support personnel, and noninvestment items that are necessary to sustain operations or maintenance, but cannot be directly related to a specific system, are categorized as indirect O&S costs. These costs can include a broad range of cost elements such as military installation facilities, medical facilities, maintenance of real estate, and initial training costs. Personnel costs classified as indirect may include medical personnel, initial training instructors, and personnel administration and management. Indirect facility costs consist of real property maintenance and upkeep, installation maintenance, base exchanges and commissaries, and other facilities that are required to indirectly support either the personnel or operation and maintenance of the system. Initial training cannot be attributed to a specific system, but it is required to produce trained operation and maintenance personnel.

Disposal A cost element that is often ignored is the cost of disposing of a system as it becomes obsolete or is replaced. In some instances, the equipment may have salvage or resale value which may offset the cost of disposal; however, costs can be incurred. Figure 10-4 shows typical costs that occur during disposal. Spare and repair parts that are unique to the system being disposed must be purged from the active supply inventory, which may constitute a significant expense. If the system, such as an aircraft, has many lines of supply that must be disposed of, then the cost for such an operation should be identified. PHS&T costs are incurred to physically move the system from its operational sites to a disposal site. As a part of the disposal effort, the data collected during the life cycle of the system must be closed and dispositioned. Significant data related to operations, reliability, maintainability, performance, or other information that has other uses is reviewed and forwarded to the appropriate destination.

If the system is to be sold as foreign military sales (FMS) or redistributed to other users, refurbishment or overhaul may be required. A portion of this cost may be recouped after transfer; however, portions may be charged as a part of disposal. Demilitarization is the act of rendering an item useless for mili-

---

Inventory closeout
PHS&T
Data management
Refurbishment
Demilitarization
Waste management

Fig. 10-4. Disposal costs.

tary purposes. Government regulations require that certain classes of items be demilitarized before disposal. If the system being disposed of requires such actions, then the costs are accrued as disposal costs. Systems, or their components, that contain dangerous or hazardous materials require special handling for disposal. If the item contains nuclear materials or dangerous chemicals, the disposal process may be lengthy and very costly. Such costs may have a significant impact on the predicted life cycle cost.

LIFE CYCLE COST MODELS

Life cycle cost models are, by nature, extremely complex if they are to be of any useful value. As previously described, there are a myriad of cost factors that must be considered when attempting to predict the life cycle cost of a system. Therefore, all modeling should be done by computer because of the number of possible elements and variable inputs and to provide a method of making tradeoff analyses. There are several LCC models available for use by contractors; however, each service has a preferred method that should be used. In each case, the models have been developed to address specific situations related to life cycle cost and proper use depends on an understanding of the intent of the model. Some models are actually a series of submodels that address certain aspects of the life cycle.

Modeling Concept

The basic concept of life cycle cost modeling is illustrated in FIG. 10-5. Each of the major cost elements can be expanded to include several hundred subelements and variables. Figure 10-6 shows how the concept of FIG. 10-5 can be expanded using only the subelements identified in the previous section of this chapter. This refinement process can be repeated until the resulting model contains elements that address every cost that can be associated with a system. That is why it is important to use computer models for this task.

Model Characteristics   If a life cycle cost model is to be a useful tool in analyzing the total cost of a system, it should contain certain characteristics.

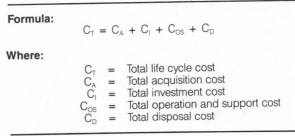

Formula:
$$C_T = C_A + C_I + C_{OS} + C_D$$

Where:

C_T = Total life cycle cost
C_A = Total acquisition cost
C_I = Total investment cost
C_{OS} = Total operation and support cost
C_D = Total disposal cost

Fig. 10-5. Life cycle cost modeling concept.

Life Cycle Cost

MIL-HDBK 259 contains a list of desired LCC model characteristics, which are shown in FIG. 10-7. Regardless of the type or origin of the model chosen, it should be capable of providing comparisons and evaluations for tradeoff analyses of alternative options, identification of risks, and establishing a baseline for sensitivity analyses throughout the acquisition process.

Modeling Problems   When LCC models are used as a tool for making critical design and support decisions, problems can occur that distort the model utility. These problems should be considered when choosing the model and interpreting the resulting predictions. Common problems include: use of invalid

Formula:

$$C_T = C_{RP} + C_{RM} + C_{REV} + C_{REQ} + C_{RF} + C_{IPR} + C_{IPN} + C_{IM} + C_{IS} + C_{ISE} + C_{TM} + C_{IE} + C_{IF} + C_{IP} + C_{ODP} + C_{OC} + C_{ORS} + C_{OSE} + C_{ODF} + C_{ODM} + C_{OP} + C_{OTD} + C_{OSM} + C_{OM} + C_{OIP} + C_{OIF} + C_{OIT} + C_{DI} + C_{DP} + C_{DDM} + C_{DR} + C_{DD} + C_{DW}$$

Where:

C_T	=	Total life cycle cost
C_{RP}	=	R&D planning costs
C_{RM}	=	R&D management costs
C_{REV}	=	R&D evaluation costs
C_{REQ}	=	R&D equipment costs
C_{RF}	=	R&D facilities costs
C_{IPR}	=	Investment production costs
C_{IPN}	=	Investment planning costs
C_{IM}	=	Investment management costs
C_{IS}	=	Initial spares costs
C_{ISE}	=	Initial support equipment costs
C_{TM}	=	Technical manual costs
C_{IE}	=	Investment engineering costs
C_{IF}	=	Investment facilities costs
C_{IP}	=	Initial PHS&T costs
C_{ODP}	=	O&S direct personnel costs
C_{OC}	=	O&S consumables costs
C_{ORS}	=	O&S replacement spares costs
C_{OSE}	=	O&S support equipment costs
C_{ODF}	=	O&S direct facilities costs
C_{ODM}	=	O&S direct maintenance costs
C_{OP}	=	O&S PHS&T costs
C_{OTD}	=	O&S technical data costs
C_{OSM}	=	O&S supply management costs
C_{OM}	=	O&S modification costs
C_{OIP}	=	O&S indirect personnel costs
C_{OIF}	=	O&S indirect facilities costs
C_{OIT}	=	O&S indirect training costs
C_{DI}	=	Disposal inventory closeout costs
C_{DP}	=	Disposal PHS&T
C_{DDM}	=	Disposal data management costs
C_{DR}	=	Disposal refurbishment costs
C_{DD}	=	Disposal demilitarization costs
C_{DW}	=	Disposal waste management costs

Fig. 10-6. Basic life cycle cost model.

assumptions when insufficient data exists; changes in production schedule or order quantities; lack of uniformity in categorizing cost elements; inadequate description of the life cycle; use of obsolete data; inappropriate cost element structure; and use inaccurate inflation or discount rates. Any combination of these problems can invalidate the results of a LCC model. Another common problem associated with using the results of LCC models is for analysts to focus too much attention of the cost aspects rather than the limited availability of some critical resources. Sometimes cost may not be the driving factor for making critical support decisions; it may be the optimum use of limited critical resources.

Data Sources   LCC modeling requires an enormous amount of input data from many different sources in order to produce a reasonable prediction. Figure 10-8 shows typical data sources for LCC modeling. Much of the data comes from the government through direct or indirect sources. The Office of Management and Budget (OMB) provided current and projected costs for government cost elements. The Defense Logistics Agency (DLA) can be a source for data related to projected supply and maintenance activities. Other significant information from the government includes the force structure of the military; when and where the system will be deployed, and operational scenarios. Contractor supplied information is the result of analyses and data collection efforts by several engineering and logistics support disciplines, all coordinated and guided through the LSA program.

In cases where valid data does not exist, the contractor must develop ground rules for assumptions to be used until the actual data is available. It should be pointed out that the majority of the costs predicted for the system will occur after the contract for development and production is complete, so the

---

1. The model should be useful to the acquisition management process as well as to the review process.
2. The model should be sensitive to management control factors, design changes, and varied operational and logistics support scenarios.
3. All significant cost drivers that are relevant to the issue under consideration should be incorporated into the model as clearly as possible.
4. The development, alteration, updating, and operation of the model should be as inexpensive as possible.
5. The model should be sensitive to design parameters or acquisition characteristics that affect the cost of investment alternatives.
6. Valid, relevant input data should be readily available.
7. The model should be flexible and capable of accommodating the growing complexity of an acquisition; and it should allow for adjustment of inflation, discounting, and learning curve factors.
8. The model should be separated into interactive modules for easier modification.
9. Inputs and outputs should be expressed in terms that are familiar to users and that can be verified to ensure credibility.
10. Outputs should be reliable; i.e., results should be repeatable.

Fig. 10-7. Life cycle cost model characteristics.

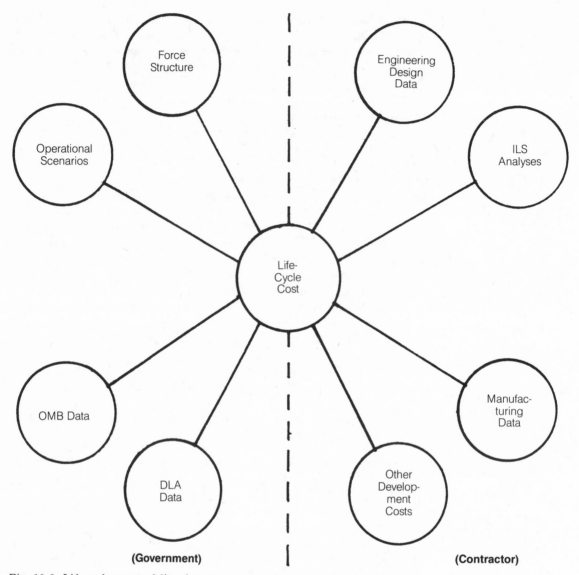

Fig. 10-8. Life cycle cost modeling data sources.

contractor must rely heavily on the LSAR database for much of the data to predict the operation and support and disposal costs for the system. During the concept phase, the quantity and quality of detailed design data is limited, so the bulk of information used for modeling must come from assumptions or estimates. As the design matures near the end of full-scale development, the data should be much more accurate making the LCC model results as precise as possible.

Estimating Techniques

There are three accepted techniques for estimating life cycle costs when data for modeling is not available. These techniques are analogy, parametric, and engineering estimating. MIL-HDBK 259 contains a detailed explanation of these techniques and their application. Each method has varying degrees of application to the phases of a system life cycle and can be used independently or interactively to produce estimates of the predicted life cycle cost.

Life Cycle Cost Prediction

Predicting the life cycle cost of a system is not easily accomplished. In fact, creating a model that accurately addresses all the facets of potential costs that contribute to the total life cycle cost of a system is extremely difficult. However, a comprehensive prediction should be conducted for each system during design to identify the significant cost drivers that will most probably affect life cycle cost. Using the results of the prediction, design engineers have the information needed to address and either eliminate or attempt to minimize the impact of the system cost drivers. In actual practice, predicting the life cycle cost for a system is normally done using one of many available complex models. A problem that can be encountered using one of these off-the-shelf models is that many require detailed input data in order to be useful. Additionally, it is important for the user to understand the relationship between different cost elements and how each can contribute to the life cycle cost of a system. Many times the most insignificant appearing item of input data can have tremendous impact on the final predicted cost. The following paragraphs describe the philosophy of constructing a model, selecting input information, actual life cycle cost calculations, and how model sensitivities can be used to identify cost drivers.

Background

For illustration purposes, assume that a life cycle cost model is being constructed from scratch to identify cost drivers for a system currently being designed. Because available information is limited to specification requirements and historical data from a previous similar system, several assumptions need to be made to make any model applicable. A brief description of the system use and deployment program to be modeled is given in FIG. 10-9. An interesting point to make is that the detailed design of the system has virtually no impact on the life cycle cost other than the cost of the design and the attributes of the design as related to operation and supportability issues.

THE MODEL

When constructing a life cycle cost model during the design process, emphasis must be placed on producing results that can be used to identify cost drivers that impact the total system cost. Many of the indirect costs noted previously are significant in determining the overall ownership costs to be borne by the user; however, these indirect costs will not change in proportion to the system design. Therefore, for the sake of keeping the model as simple as possible, these costs can be eliminated from a model designed to identify cost drivers. Additionally, a majority of the life cycle cost prediction will be based on assumptions. By qualifying the assumptions that are used in a model and basing the assumptions on known limits or relevant past history of similar systems, the credibility of the model can be increased. Because the largest percentage of life cycle costs are incurred during the operation and support of a system, and not during acquisition, a model should address these costs for identification of design features or support concepts that drive the overall system cost. Figure 10-10 identifies typical costs and other elements that should be included in a simple life cycle cost model.

Background Information

Product Description	The product being designed is a multi-service radar system that will be installed in various aircraft. The total quantity of 1,000 systems will be procured. Systems will be delivered over 7 years. A 2-year development period will be required to design and test the system prior to production. The system should have an MTBF of not less than 500 hours.
Maintenance Concept	The system, once deployed, will be maintained using the standard three-level maintenance concept. Sufficient spares and repair parts will be procured to support 100 percent removal and replacement of failed units at organizational level. An estimated 80 percent of failures will be repaired at intermediate level with the remaining 20 percent requiring depot repair. Estimated MTTR for the system is 15 minutes at organization, 30 minutes at intermediate, and 4 hours at depot.
Operation	Annual operating hours are estimated to be 2,000 hours per system per year. The system will require a dedicated operator. There will be 24 sites where organizational maintenance will be performed, 8 intermediate maintenance sites, and 2 depot maintenance sites. Staffing of maintenance technicians will be 8 technicians at each organizational site, 3 technicians at each intermediate site, and 2 technicians at each depot.
Training	All operators and maintenance technicians will require formal training. Duration of training courses will be 80 hours for operators and 160 hours for maintenance technicians.

Fig. 10-9. Example model input information.

Model Input Parameters

The parameters chosen for input to a model should be completely documented, including the rationale for assumptions. In many cases, the use of assumptions allows establishment of a baseline costing that can be updated as more accurate information becomes available. The results of many analyses performed by reliability, maintainability, and logistics engineers form the basis for life cycle costing. Much of the data is directly transferable from the LSAR database to the LCC model. In other cases, the government may be the only source for accurate input parameters. When no input data is available, the use of a completely documented assumption allows the model to be completed and provides a starting point for refinement of the model. For this discussion, the input parameters for the model being constructed are shown in FIG. 10-11. A similar process should be used whenever conducting a life cycle prediction.

Production System Unit Cost The cost for a production system is a significant input parameter to a life cycle cost model, because this cost repre-

---

- R&D Nonrecurring Engineering Costs
- Cost for Testing
- Technical Data
- Production System Unit Cost
- Initial Provisioning and Cost of Spare/Repair Parts
- Cost of Support Equipment By Maintenance Level
- Inventory Management Cost
- Number of System Operators
- Number of Maintenance Technicians By Maintenance Level
- Initial Transportation Cost
- Average Labor Costs for Operator and Maintenance Personnel
- Estimated Annual Operating Hours
- Predicted Mean Time Between Failure
- Service to Flight Ratio
- Mean Time to Repair at Each Maintenance Level
- Percent of Failures Repaired at Each Maintenance Level
- Training Time for Operator and Maintenance Technician
- Training Support Cost
- Personnel Turnover Rate
- Number of Maintenance Sites By Maintenance Level
- Allocation of System Costs
- Estimated Cost of Replenishment Parts By Maintenance Level
- Cost for Support Equipment Maintenance
- Packaging Costs
- Transportation Costs
- Cost of Facilities for Operation and Each Maintenance Level
- Operator Allocation
- Maintenance Technician Allocation
- Initial Training Program Costs
- Estimated Annual Cost Escalation Rate
- Quantity To Be Produced
- Delivery Schedule
- System Operation Schedule

Fig. 10-10. Life cycle cost model elements.

Production System Unit Cost	$200,000
Estimated Annual System Operating Hours	2,000 hours per system
Predicted Mean Time Between Failure	500 hours
Service to Operation Ratio	1.25
Predicted Mean Time To Repair - Organization	15 minutes
Predicted Mean Time To Repair - Intermediate	30 minutes
Predicted Mean Time To Repair - Depot	4 hours
Failures Requiring Organization Remove/Replace	100%
Percent Failures Repaired at Intermediate	80%
Percent Failures Repaired to Depot	20%
R&D Nonrecurring Engineering	$2,000,000
Cost of 1st Article Testing	$150,000
R&D Technical Data	$500,000
Logistics Technical Data	$300,000
Cost of O&S Technical Data	$200 per repair
Cost for Initial Provisioning	40,000
Cost of Initial Investment Spares/Repair Parts	$500,000
Cost of Replenishment Spares - Organizational	0.1% of system cost
Cost of Replenishment Spares - Intermediate	1.0% of system cost
Cost of Replenishment Spares - Depot	5.0% of system cost
Inventory Management Cost	5% of spares value per year
Number of Systems Operators	1 per system
Number of Maintenance Technicians - Organization	8 per site
Number of Maintenance Technicians - Intermediate	3 per site
Number of Maintenance Technicians - Depot	2 per site
Number of Maintenance Sites - Organizational	24 sites
Number of Maintenance Sites - Intermediate	8 sites
Number of Maintenance Sites - Depot	2 sites
Labor Cost - Operator	$12 per hour
Labor Cost - Maintenance Technician	$14 per hour
Initial Training Program Cost	$60,000 per course
Training Time per Operator	80 hours
Training Time per Maintenance Technician	160 hours
Training Support Cost	$2,500 per student
Personnel Turnover Rate	15% per year
Support Equipment Cost - Organizational Level	$25,000
Support Equipment Cost - Intermediate Level	$50,000
Support Equipment Cost - Depot Level	$75,000
Cost of Support Equipment Maintenance	10% of acquisition cost per year of operation
Initial Transportation Cost	3% of spares cost
Packaging Cost	$20 per one-way shipment
Transportation Cost	$100 per one-way shipment
Facilities Cost - Operation	5.0% of system cost
Facilities Cost - Organizational Maintenance	0.5% of system cost
Facilities Cost - Intermediate Maintenance	2.0% of system cost
Facilities Cost - Depot Maintenance	4.0% of system cost
Percent of Operator Allocation	100%
Percent of Maintenance Technician Allocation	100%
Allocation of System Costs	15%
Annual Cost Escalation Rate	6% per year

Fig. 10-11. Life cycle cost model input parameters.

sents a large percentage of the acquisition cost for the system. Additionally, as will be shown, a percentage of unit cost is often used to predict other costs in the absence of actual input information. It should be pointed out that this is the cost of a production unit and not an engineering or preproduction unit. A production unit normally costs much less because of the standard manufacturing processes used. This number may vary when procurement is through options of differing quantities or in different time periods. A weighted average unit cost may be developed for the purposes of life cycle cost modeling to provide a more accurate prediction.

Estimated Annual System Operating Hours   The estimated number of annual operating hours for the system is a critical input parameter. This figure is used in conjunction with other input factors to determine the cost of logistics support resources that will be required to support operation and maintenance. The government should be requested to provide this number for life cycle cost prediction. Another source for operating hours is data on a previous or similar system having the same or similar mission scenario.

Predicted Mean Time between Failure   The predicted system MTBF is used in conjunction with the estimated operating hours to determine the number of failures that are predicted to occur each year. The predicted number of failures is then used to identify support resource requirements. Initially, the minimum required system MTBF contained in the product specification can be used as input to the model. As the design matures, reliability engineers develop a detailed MTBF prediction that should be used to refine the life cycle cost prediction.

Service to Operation Ratio   The service to operation ratio is an input parameter that is often overlooked when selecting input parameters for a life cycle cost model. This parameter is used to adjust the predicted operating hours to account for the pre-operation and post-operation maintenance that is performed on the system. While the system is not actually performing its mission during this time, it is still experiencing usage that must be accounted for to accurately predict the total operating time of the system. For airborne equipment, similar adjustments can be made using parameters such as service to flight ratio. The actual number used should be based on historical information for similar systems or inputs from the government. Near the completion of the design process, logistics engineers should calculate the actual time that is predicted to be used for preventive maintenance so it can be used to further refine the prediction.

Predicted Mean Time to Repair   The minimum mean time to repair for each maintenance level is normally contained in the product specification. As the design matures, maintainability engineers calculate predicted mean time to repair based on the actual system design. The calculated figures should be used when available. The times used in FIG. 10-1 are typical for electronic systems. When the LSAR database information is adequate to support further refinement of the prediction, actual predicted or measured task times can be used in conjunction with task frequencies to replace these estimates.

Percent Failures Repaired by Maintenance Level Predicting the percentage of repairs accomplished by each maintenance level can be difficult at the beginning of a design program; however, information from similar systems should prove to be valuable when constructing a model. The results of a repair level analysis provides definitive inputs for these parameters and should be used as the information becomes available. Again, the LSAR database eventually should be used to give the most accurate data inputs to the calculation.

R&D Nonrecurring Engineering The cost for R&D nonrecurring engineering should be easily determined, because it is normally the price that the government pays a contractor for all engineering efforts, starting with the concept phase and ending at the close of full-scale development. Most contracts are firm-fixed price, which determines the exact parameter to be used. The cost of the LSA program, if not considered a separate cost subelement, is part of this engineering cost.

Cost of 1st Article Testing The cost for all the testing that a system must complete to become qualified for production can be extracted from the total price of the full-scale development contract. This information may or may not be included as a separate parameter in the life cycle cost model, depending on the level of testing required, who is to perform the testing, and the impact that the testing can have on total life cycle cost.

R&D Technical Data A separate input parameter for technical data prepared by the contractor during full-scale development allows cost to be segregated for engineering and nonengineering efforts. This parameter, like the 1st article testing, may or may not be applicable to a specific application. Engineering test plans, test reports, studies, and analyses can all be included in R&D technical data. Engineering drawings, schematics, parts lists, and specifications are also considered R&D technical data.

Logistics Technical Data The input parameter for logistics technical data addresses the requirement for documentation to support the operation and maintenance of the system. This parameter can be limited to the cost of technical manuals, or it can be expanded to include the results of analyses and studies conducted to identify cost drivers for logistics support resources. The actual input information should be available from the full-scale development contract. If not included in nonrecurring engineering costs, the cost of the total LSA program could be attributed to the effort necessary to produce the logistics technical data.

Cost of Operation and Support Technical Data The operation and support technical data input parameter is different from the R&D and logistics technical data in that it is an identification of the cost that will be incurred to document operation and support actions after the system is deployed. At a minimum, it addresses the maintenance of technical data prepared during acquisition, such as technical manual changes and updates, change orders, and the administrative costs associated with processing the technical information. It also includes the time required to record and report each maintenance action, collect the data at a central point, and perform analyses to identify failure trends or necessary redesign efforts. An accurate input parameter should be obtained from the government or should be based on historical data.

Cost for Initial Provisioning The cost for identification of required spare and repair parts and the development of documentation should be included as a standalone input parameter rather than being amortized over the cost of spares. This parameter should be obtained from the full-scale development contract. The reason that the cost of initial provisioning is included in the model is to identify a separate cost that will be incurred if the system must be reprovisioned because of redesign.

Cost of Initial Investment Spares and Repair Parts The range and depth of spares and repair parts initially procured as a result of the provisioning activity must be identified as a separate cost item. This represents the costs necessary to create a pipeline of spares and repair parts required to support maintenance. The input parameter during the early stages of design may be expressed as a percentage of total production system unit cost; however, this is not desirable. The recommended spares provisioning lists generated from the LSAR database provide much more detailed information to be used in the prediction. Actual data of expenditures for spares can be obtained from separate provisioned item orders that are additions to the original full-scale development contract, but these are normally only available long after the LCC estimating has been completed.

Cost of Replenishment Spares The cost for replenishment spares needed to supplement or replace initial investment spares is determined by the maintenance actions required. Historical information may be available to develop a percentage based on unit cost that can be used initially for prediction. In the late stages of the full-scale development phase, the results of the detailed maintenance task analysis recorded in the LSAR, coupled with the mean time between failure to predict the frequency of task occurrence, can be used to more accurately predict the cost of spares per maintenance action. The input parameters used in FIG. 10-11 are for purposes of illustration only.

Inventory Management Cost The cost for managing the spares inventory is normally determined as a percentage of total spares value as the spares are procured. While it may seem that this is a minor cost, the usage rate of spares and a design that requires high levels of replenishment spares can generate a requirement for management expenses that will impact the overall life cycle cost. This cost is normally expressed as a percentage of spares value per year. The exact input parameter may be developed using historical data or can be requested from the government.

Number of System Operators and Maintenance Technicians The cost for personnel required to operate and maintain the system can be one of the larger costs incurred during the life cycle. The number of personnel can normally be obtained from the mission scenario or the government. When a new system is being developed, the results of the maintenance task analysis may be used to determine the staffing levels required to support maintenance. LSA summary reports can be used to provide the recommended number of direct maintenance hours required by skill and maintenance level. Because this cost is one of the big contributors to operation and support costs, using the LSAR database to determine the estimated labor required can be extremely beneficial in refining the LCC estimate. The parameters in FIG. 10-11 are for illustration purposes only.

Number of Maintenance Sites   The proposed maintenance concept and mission scenario should provide the number of sites where maintenance at all levels will be performed. This information should also be available from the government. The number of maintenance sites is necessary to determine requirements for sets of support equipment, facilities costs, and minimum staffing requirements.

Labor Costs   Hourly labor rates are required to predict the costs for personnel that will be incurred for operation and maintenance of the system. This prediction can be argued by stating that military personnel are paid by the month, not by the hour, and that they are to be considered an available resource. However, if the personnel required to support operation and maintenance are treated as a captive resource, one of the larger life cycle cost drivers will be ignored. Labor rates used are normally a composite of military grades or are determined by the specific rank of the individuals who will be performing operation and maintenance tasks. Input parameters should be requested from the government.

Initial Training Program Cost   The cost for development of each required training program is included to identify costs necessary to train the initial operation and maintenance personnel. The input parameters for training courses may be available in the full-scale development contract. If the government is to provide training, a per student factor can be used to estimate the costs.

Training Time   The amount of time required to train operator and maintenance personnel should be identified as a separate cost. This allows tradeoffs to be conducted to determine the impact of changing training courses. Training course lengths are normally determined by the complexity of the system and the standard military training program. Input parameters should be requested from the government.

Training Support Cost   The costs that are incurred to train each operator or maintenance technician are identified to determine the impact of changing required personnel staffing. Input parameters are normally based on government information or historical data from similar training courses.

Personnel Turnover Rate   The turnover rate of military personnel must be considered when predicting life cycle cost. The predicted personnel turnover rate can have a significant impact on total life cycle cost by requiring additional training of replacement personnel. The actual turnover rate to be used in the prediction should be requested from the government.

Support Equipment Cost The cost of support equipment required at each maintenance level must be included in the prediction. Cost of support equipment is normally a combination of general-purpose and special test equipment. It can also include common and peculiar hand tools. The actual support equipment requirements are normally determined as an output of the detailed maintenance task analysis that is summed into several LSA summary reports. Costs for standard items of support equipment can be obtained from available government documents. Costs for certain contractor supplied support equipment can normally be extracted from the full-scale development contract.

Cost of Support Equipment Maintenance The cost incurred for maintenance of support equipment cannot be overlooked. For large developmental programs where significant amounts of special support equipment are developed specifically for the program, a separate supplemental program dedicated to support equipment may be required. A separate LCC prediction may be required or necessary for these special items. For the purpose of this discussion, the cost of support equipment maintenance is expressed as a percentage of the acquisition cost of support equipment.

Initial Transportation Cost The transportation costs for spares is included in the life cycle cost prediction, because it is dependent on the quantity of spares procured. Determination of the exact cost transportation of spares is difficult without a detailed analysis of the shipping cost for each item, so it is normally expressed as a percentage, based on historical data, of spares value. If spares transportation becomes a significant concern, selected data can be obtained from the LSAR database identifying the factors needed to develop a detailed estimate.

Packaging and Transportation Costs Identification of the costs that will be incurred for packaging and transportation of failed spares from the point of failure to the appropriate maintenance facility and then back to a supply facility when repaired must be included in the life cycle cost prediction. This cost is dependent on the number of predicted failures, different maintenance sites, and maintenance concept. The costs for packaging and transportation can have an impact on the repair level analysis and on total life cycle cost. A somewhat complex submodule can be developed using a combination of maintenance tasks, task frequency, maintenance concept, and spares packaging information to generate more detailed information when needed.

Facilities Cost Determination of the cost for facilities necessary to support operation and maintenance of a system is difficult to pinpoint. The reason for this difficulty is that, in most instances, facilities are not dedicated to supporting one system. Therefore, the actual input parameters for facilities may never be known without detailed after-production data. Annual maintenance tasks or manpower estimates for each maintenance level could be used to develop a somewhat defensible projection of the space required to support maintenance. This information of space requirements could then be translated into a distinct facility projection. Historical data on similar systems or a system being replaced by the new system being designed may be used if available. Otherwise, a percentage of system unit cost may be used.

Percent of Operator and Maintenance Technician Allocation In some instances, operator or maintenance personnel may not be 100 percent dedicated to supporting a single system or system type. When this occurs, a percent allocation of the time that these persons are supporting the system should be developed to more accurately predict the life cycle cost of the system. As will be shown in later sections of this chapter, personnel costs can comprise a significant portion of the total cost for supporting a system.

Allocation of System Costs As with personnel, other resources necessary to support the operation or maintenance of the system may not be dedicated. Examples of these resources include support equipment and facilities. When these resources are identified, a percentage of the total cost of the resources should be allocated to the system being modeled to refine the life cycle cost prediction.

Escalation Rate (Annual Cost) Life cycle cost models are normally based on constant year dollars to provide a base for comparing cost elements. However, because most systems have an extended life expectancy of up to 20 years, it is important to include an escalation rate factor in the prediction to identify the actual ownership costs that will be incurred throughout the life of the system. Normally this factor highlights the increased cost that will result from operating and supporting the system over an extended period of time.

Delivery and Operation Schedule A key input parameter to the life cycle cost model is the schedule of when systems will be delivered to the government and when the systems will actually be placed into operation. Exact delivery dates of the system should be available from the production contract

System Delivery and Operational Schedule		
Year	**Operational Quantity**	**Delivery Quantity**
FY88	0	0
FY89	0	0
FY90	40	20
FY91	90	70
FY92	150	230
FY93	220	450
FY94	220	580
FY95	220	800
FY96	60	940
FY97	0	1,000
FY98	0	1,000
FY99	0	1,000

Fig. 10-12. System delivery and operation schedule.

because delivery dates and quantities are contractually stated therein. The schedule of when systems are to be placed into operation should be obtained from the government. For the purposes of this example, a delivery and operational schedule is given in FIG. 10-12.

Calculating Life Cycle Cost

The calculations for life cycle cost of the system described in FIG. 10-9 address the acquisition costs for a system followed by the first 10 years of operation and support costs. As stated previously, a life cycle cost model is extremely complex; therefore, the example provided in this section is, by necessity, abbreviated because of space limitations. The input parameters provided in FIG. 10-11 and the delivery and operation schedule in FIG. 10-12 are used for calculation of the predicted life cycle cost of the system. System acquisition costs have been divided into research and development costs and investment costs for purposes of illustration. Operation and support costs are calculated beginning with scheduled first unit operation and continuing through the tenth year of system operation.

Research and Development Costs

The calculation of R&D costs should be fairly straightforward for the contractor identifiable costs during full-scale development. Figure 10-13 shows costs spread over 2 years, which is the time allotted for R&D efforts. R&D efforts must be completed before production can begin. Testing is entered in only the second year on the premise that testing cannot begin until late in the R&D process.

Investment Costs

Production costs for the system are combined with the cost of establishing initial logistics support for the system to calculate investment costs shown in FIG. 10-14. For purposes of illustration, production costs are calculated by multi-

Life Cycle Cost Prediction
Research and Development Costs ($ × 1,000)

Cost Element	FY88	FY89	Total
Nonrecurring Engineering	1,000	1,000	2,000
1st Article Testing		200	200
Technical Data	200	300	500
Total R&D Costs	1,200	1,500	2,700

Fig. 10-13. Predicted research and development costs.

Life Cycle Cost Prediction
Investment Costs ($ × 1000)

Cost Element	FY88	FY89	FY90	FY91	FY92	FY93	FY94	FY95	FY96	FY97	FY98	FY99	Total
Production			8000.00	18000.00	30000.00	44000.00	44000.00	44000.00	12000.00			200000.00	
Logistics support													
Provisioning		20.00	20.00										40.00
Spares/rep parts		200.00	300.00										500.00
Inv mgmt		4.00	6.00										10.00
Technical data		150.00	150.00										300.00
Training													
Operator		198.40	311.40	519.00	761.20	761.20	761.20	207.60					3520.00
Maintenance													
O Level		418.13	358.13	358.13	358.13								1492.50
I Level		289.20	229.20	229.20	229.20								976.80
D Level		128.76	68.76	68.76	68.76								335.04
Support equip													
O level		125.00	250.00	250.00									625.00
I level		80.00	160.00	160.00									400.00
D level		30.00	63.00	63.00									15.00
Tranportation		6.00	9.00										15.00
Totals (current FY $)	0.00	1408.49	9443.49	19175.09	31417.29	44761.20	44761.20	44207.60	12000.00	0.00	0.00	0.00	207174.34
Totals (future FY $)	0.00	1492.99	10610.70	22837.83	39663.60	59900.58	63494.62	66471.89	19126.18	0.00	0.00	0.00	283598.39

Fig. 10-14. Predicted investment costs.

plying the scheduled annual delivery quantity by the production unit cost. In actual practice, a more complex depiction of payment schedules and escalation may be used to refine the calculations. Initial logistics support costs are divided into costs for identification and acquisition of spares, preparation of technical data, training of operator and maintenance personnel, acquisition of support equipment, and initial transportation for spares. Most logistics support costs occur in FY89, the year preceding first system delivery so that the support package is in place when the first systems become operational. Training of personnel is spread over time to support the increased number of systems in operation. If all required operator and maintenance personnel were trained at the beginning of system delivery, a significant number of these individuals would be unavailable for assignment to operator or maintenance duties due to normal rotation and personnel turnover. Likewise, support equipment costs are spread over time as more systems become operational. Costs for training operator personnel during FY89 are calculated by: 1) multiplying the number of operators per system (1) times the number of systems to be delivered in FY90 (40) times the training course length (80 hours) times the operator labor cost per hour ($12); 2) multiplying the number of operators per system (1) times the number of systems to be delivered in FY90 (40) times the training support cost per student ($2,500); and, 3) adding the results of calculation 1) ($38,400), plus the results of calculation 2) ($100,000), plus the initial training course cost ($60,000), which results in a cost of $198,400 for operator training in FY89. Initial operator training for the following 6 years are calculated using the same process, with the exception of the cost of the initial training course, which is not included. Maintenance technician training calculation is done using basically the same process, except that it is spread over only 4 years in order to complete staffing of maintenance facilities.

Operation and Support Costs

Operation and support costs are the most complex to calculate because of the number of variables that must be considered and the interrelations between input parameters. The predicted operation and support costs for the example system are shown in FIG. 10-15. This prediction addresses costs for operation and maintenance. Operation costs are further divided into costs for personnel, training, and facilities. Support costs include maintenance personnel, spares and repair parts, support equipment maintenance, training, and facilities for each level of maintenance, costs for packaging and transportation of failed items, and cost for preparation of technical data on maintenance actions.

Operations Costs   Personnel costs for operation are calculated by multiplying the annual operating hours times the service to flight ratio times the number of operational systems times the labor cost for an operator. This results in an operations personnel cost in FY90 of ($2,000 \times 1.25 \times 20 \times \$12 =$) $600,000. Training requirements are included to replace operators who leave

Life-Cycle Cost Prediction
Operation and Support Costs ($ × 1000)

Cost Element	FY88	FY89	FY90	FY91	FY92	FY93	FY94	FY95	FY96	FY97	FY98	FY99	TOTAL
Operation													
Personnel			600.00	2100.00	6900.00	13500.00	17400.00	24000.00	28200.00	30000.00	30000.00	30000.00	182700.00
Training			6.92	335.62	598.58	916.90	961.88	1038.00	532.84	346.00	346.00	346.00	5428.74
Facilities			200.00	700.00	2300.00	4500.00	5800.00	8000.00	9400.00	10000.00	10000.00	10000.00	60900.00
Support													
Personnel													
0 Level			30.00	105.00	345.00	675.00	870.00	1200.00	1410.00	1500.00	1500.00	1500.00	9135.00
I Level			56.00	196.00	644.00	1260.00	1624.00	2240.00	2632.00	2800.00	2800.00	2800.00	17052.00
D Level			112.00	392.00	1288.00	2520.00	3248.00	4480.00	5264.00	5600.00	5600.00	5600.00	34104.00
Spares/Rep Parts													
0 Level			20.00	70.00	230.00	450.00	580.00	800.00	940.00	1000.00	1000.00	1000.00	6090.00
I Level			160.00	560.00	1840.00	3600.00	4640.00	6400.00	7520.00	8000.00	8000.00	8000.00	48720.00
D Level			200.00	700.00	2300.00	4500.00	5800.00	8000.00	9400.00	10000.00	10000.00	10000.00	60900.00
Inv Mgmt			7.60	26.60	87.40	171.00	220.40	304.00	357.20	8000.00	8000.00	8000.00	48720.00
SE Maint													
0 Level			62.50	62.50	62.50	62.50	62.50	62.50	62.50	62.50	62.50	62.50	625.00
I Level			40.00	40.00	40.00	40.00	40.00	40.00	40.00	40.00	40.00	40.00	400.00
D Level			15.00	15.00	15.00	15.00	15.00	15.00	15.00	15.00	15.00	15.00	150.00
PHS&T													
Packaging			4.00	14.00	46.00	90.00	116.00	160.00	188.00	200.00	200.00	200.00	1218.00
Transportation			20.00	70.00	230.00	450.00	580.00	800.00	940.00	1000.00	1000.00	1000.00	6090.00
Training													
0 Level			11.85	35.55	59.25	59.25	59.25	59.25	59.25	59.25	59.25	59.25	521.40
I Level			7.58	22.75	37.92	37.92	37.92	37.92	37.92	37.92	37.92	37.92	333.70
D Level			2.28	6.83	11.38	11.38	11.38	11.38	11.38	11.38	11.38	11.38	100.11
Facilities													
0 Level			3.75	3.75	3.75	3.75	3.75	3.75	3.75	3.75	3.75	3.75	37.50
I Level			4.80	4.80	4.80	4.80	4.80	4.80	4.80	4.80	4.80	4.80	48.00
D Level			1.20	1.20	1.20	1.20	1.20	1.20	1.20	1.20	1.20	1.20	12.00
Tech Data			20.00	70.00	230.00	450.00	580.00	800.00	940.00	1000.00	1000.00	1000.00	6090.00
Totals (Current FY $)	0.00	0.00	1585.48	5531.60	17274.78	33318.70	42656.08	58457.80	67959.84	72061.80	72061.80	72061.80	442969.64
Totals (Future FY $)	0.00	0.00	1781.44	6588.22	21809.01	44587.93	60508.46	87898.91	138317.65	121746.89	129051.70	136794.80	719085.02

Fig. 10-15. Predicted operation and support costs.

Life Cycle Cost Prediction
Summary ($ × 1000)

Cost Element	FY88	FY89	FY90	FY91	FY92	FY93	FY94	FY95	FY96	FY97	FY98	FY99	Total
R & D Costs	1200.00	1500.00	0.00	0.00	0.00	0.00	0.00	0.00	0.00	0.00	0.00	0.00	2700.00
Investment Costs	0.00	1408.49	9443.49	19175.09	31417.29	44761.20	44761.20	44207.60	12000.00	0.00	0.00	0.00	207174.34
Operation & Support	0.00	0.00	15.85.48	5531.60	17274.78	33318.70	42656.08	58457.80	67959.84	72061.80	72061.80	72061.80	442969.64
Totals (Current FY $)	1200.00	2908.49	11028.96	24706.68	48692.06	78079.90	87417.28	102665.40	79959.84	72061.80	72061.80	72061.80	652843.98
Totals (Future FY $)	1200.00	3082.99	12392.14	29426.05	61472.61	104488.51	124003.08	154370.80	127443.83	121746.89	129051.70	136794.80	1005473.41

Fig. 10-16. Predicted total life-cycle costs.

191

the service. Calculation of training costs is accomplished the same as for investment training, with the addition of the personnel turnover rate percentage being included in the formula.

Support Costs The cost of maintenance personnel is calculated in two steps; 1) multiply the annual operating hours times the service to flight ratio and divide the results by the predicted MTBF; and then 2) multiply the results of step 1) times the quantity of operational systems, the percent of failures repaired at the level of maintenance, the MTTR for that same level of maintenance, and the labor cost for a maintenance technician. Spares costs are calculated by multiplying the annual operating hours times the service to flight ratio and dividing the result by the predicted MTBF, which is then multiplied by the percent of failures at the maintenance level, which is finally multiplied by the production unit cost times the percent of system cost allocated for spares at the maintenance level.

Support equipment maintenance costs are a straight percentage of the acquisition cost of the support equipment for each year of the prediction. Training of replacement support personnel is accomplished the same as previously described for replacement operation personnel. Facilities costs are calculated by multiplying the number of maintenance sites times the allocated percent of unit cost times the production unit cost times the system allocation percentage. The calculated facilities cost at intermediate level in FY90 is (8 sites × 2 percent × $200,000 × 15 percent=) $4,800. The cost of technical data is calculated by multiplying the annual operating hours times the service to flight ratio times the number of operational systems, the result of which is divided by the predicted MTBF then multiplied by the cost of technical data per repair. The cost for technical data in FY90 is [(2,000 × 1.25 × 20)/500 × $200] = $20,000.

Prediction Analysis

The first step in analyzing the results of the prediction is to sum the calculated yearly costs as shown in FIG. 10-16. In addition to the prediction in current year dollars, the predicted annual escalation factor has been included to show the impact of inflation on the extended costs over the system life. It may be surprising to see that this relatively simple system, having a unit cost of only $180,000, can generate a life cycle cost during its first 10 years of operation of $650,000,000 in current year dollars and $1,000,000,000 in escalated dollars. Figure 10-17 shows a percentage breakdown of these costs. If the number of operational years is extended from 10 to 20 years, the resulting life cycle cost prediction would be $1,373,461,940 in current year dollars, as shown in FIG. 10-18, and an astounding $2,373,421,440 in escalated dollars, which highlights the importance of incorporating into the design features that increase the reliability, maintainability, and testability of the system.

Predicted Cost Breakdown (Current Year Dollars)		
R&D Costs	$2,700,000	0.4%
Investment Costs	$207,174,340	31.7%
Operation and Support Costs	$442,969,640	67.9%
Total Life-Cycle Cost	$652,843,980	100.0%

Fig. 10-17. Percent allocation of predicted costs.

Predicted Cost Breakdown 20 Years Operation (Current Year Dollars)		
R&D Costs	$2,700,000	0.2%
Investment Costs	$207,174,340	15.1%
Operation and Support Costs	$1,163,587,600	84.7%
Total Life-Cycle Cost	$1,373,461,940	100.0%

Fig. 10-18. Predicted costs for 20 years operation.

Prediction Sensitivity

Generation of the initial prediction establishes a baseline for performance of sensitivity analyses to identify and analyze alternatives for reducing total life-cycle cost. An example of this type of analysis would be consideration of incorporating a new technology feature into the design. Support a new feature was under consideration for incorporation that would increase the production unit cost by $10,000 to $190,000, but would also increase the predicted system MTBF from 500 to 750 hours. What would be the impact on life-cycle cost? Figure 10-19 shows that for the first 10 years of operation, the life-cycle cost would

Sensitivity Analysis			
	Baseline	With Change	% Change
R&D Costs	$2,700,000	$2,700,000	0.0%
Investment Costs	$207,174,340	$217,174,340	+ 4.8%
Operation and Support Costs	$442,969,640	$386,049,260	− 12.9%
Total Life-Cycle Cost	$652,843,980	$605,923,600	− 7.2%

Fig. 10-19. Prediction sensitivity analysis.

be decreased by 7.2 percent, and therefore should be incorporated if there are no overriding technical, schedule, or other reasons to the contrary. If the prediction is extended to 20 years of operation, the design change would result in a predicted savings of $140,388,840, which cannot be ignored. Similar sensitivity analyses should be performed for all design alternatives until a balance is achieved between performance, support, and cost.

11

Organizational Interfaces

For the LSA process to be successful in meeting the established goals of impacting the design and providing the most cost-effective support possible, interfaces between all affected and contributing organizations must be clearly defined and planned. The responsibility of each organization to provide inputs to others must be recognized and understood by all concerned. The coordination of efforts to reach the common goals of the LSA program is understandably one of the toughest challenges that a company must meet. This challenge is further complicated by the fact that each organization has its own priorities, which in many cases, especially for nonlogistics disciplines, are not support or supportability related. The major categories of interfaces that must be addressed can be divided into four different areas: integrated interfaces between logistics support disciplines, interfaces with engineering disciplines, interfaces with other internal company organizations that impact support, and interfaces between the company and the customer. Each of these interfaces must enhance the company's ability to meet the requirements and goals of the LSA program.

INTEGRATED LOGISTICS SUPPORT DISCIPLINES

Internal interfaces within the integrated logistics support disciplines are surely the most important interfaces for success of the LSA program. As described in previous chapters, the efforts of each discipline are so intertwined, that it is sometimes difficult to easily identify who is actually providing inputs and outputs, or vice versa. While it may seem that these interfaces occur naturally as a normal course of doing business, that is rarely the case. There must be a clear distinction as to who does what when and how. So many things must occur almost simultaneously to meet program requirements, and these actions

Organizational Interfaces

are so dependent on the actions of others, that management and control of interfaces is critical to the LSA program. The inputs and outputs of tasks performed by each discipline must be delineated, tracked, and monitored to ensure that the proper information is available, at the time when it is required, to support the subsequent actions of other groups. Figure 11-1 shows how information flows between logistics disciplines in a typical LSA program.

Maintenance Planning

The maintenance planning discipline, whether titled maintenance planning, maintenance engineering, or something similar, performs a function critical to the LSA process: identification of the maintenance tasks that will be required to support maintenance. The success of the LSA program depends on the accuracy and detail of the maintenance plan developed for the system being designed. However, identification of maintenance tasks is only a part of the LSA process. This information must be documented and provided to other logistics disciplines for further analysis. Typical inputs provided by maintenance planning to other logistics disciplines are shown in FIG. 11-2. As shown in this figure, the outputs of the maintenance planning effort are key inputs to virtually every other logistics discipline. One point that must be stressed is that the interface must be a flow of information, not periodic or intermittent data dumps, and

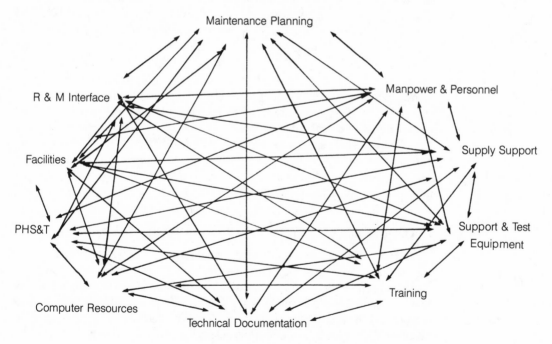

Fig. 11-1. Interfaces between logistics disciplines.

there must be a corresponding return of analysis results from the other disciplines.

Additionally, one of the hardest parts of effective interface is keeping track of changes either to the design or the maintenance requirements, or both. Because the maintenance planning outputs drive analyses of other disciplines, all changes must be provided in a manner that enables changes to other analyses to be readily identified and updated or changed as necessary to reflect the most current design configuration.

Support Equipment

Outputs from maintenance planning are used as inputs to the support equipment development process. As the maintenance requirements are identified, support equipment requirements are documented at the system level to ensure that the types and numbers of support equipment required for maintenance are available when the system becomes operational. Complete justifications for support equipment are developed based on this analysis. A two-way

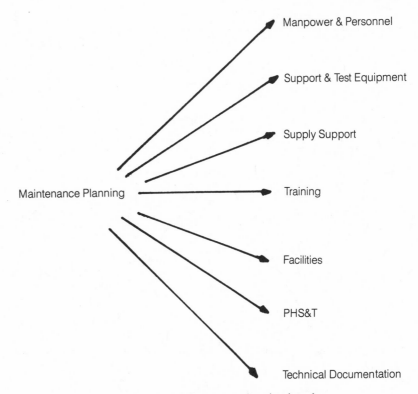

Fig. 11-2. Maintenance planning interfaces.

interface between maintenance planning and support equipment is necessary to limit the support equipment requirements to the minimum possible and still support maintenance.

The results of support equipment analyses are also used and reviewed by other logistics disciplines as shown in FIG. 11-3. Technical publications, in developing technical documentation, must include the use of support equipment, and sometimes the maintenance of support equipment. Training development must have information of what support equipment is to be used so that adequate training can be planned. Spares provisioning must have support equipment information for development of provisioning technical documentation. Any changes to support equipment requirements must be provided to all these disciplines to update overall support requirements.

Training Development

For the training program to be effective, training development must have the most accurate information available and the information must be provided in

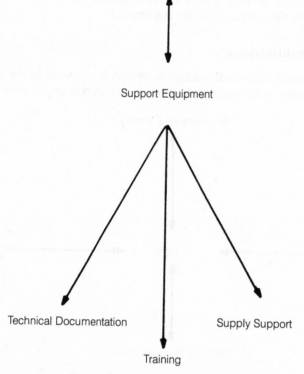

Fig. 11-3. Support equipment interfaces.

a timely manner that is supportive of the system operational schedule. The training courses developed must match the maintenance plan, technical documentation, spares, and support equipment exactly. There must be no differences or the training program will not be effective. As shown in FIG. 11-4, interfaces between the training development organization and other logistics disciplines provide the vehicle for ensuring the accuracy of the training program.

Spares Provisioning

Identification of the types and quantities of spares and repair parts that will be required to support maintenance is dependent on receipt of the most accurate information on system design and maintenance requirements. This information is obtained through close and continuous interface between the spares provisioning organization and the maintenance planning activity. The output spares requirements must then be provided to other logistics disciplines, so the overall support package for the system considers all the things needed for support. Figure 11-5 shows the interfaces between spares provisioning and other logistics disciplines. Information about spares requirements is derived from many sources and the total system spares requirements must be documented for use by both the company and the customer.

Technical Publications

The technical documentation that is ultimately delivered to the customer must be reflective of the actual system design and support requirements. It is of

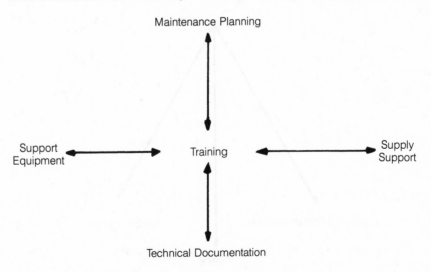

Fig. 11-4. Training development interfaces.

the utmost importance that all information that is available be provided in a timely manner to the technical publications organization for this purpose. One of the last actions before delivery is to compare the system and support requirements with the technical documentation. Any errors or omissions must be corrected before delivery. The documents are also used for the basis of the training program, so this doubles the importance of accuracy. To obtain the best and most accurate information, an interface must be maintained between the technical publications organization and all other logistics disciplines. Throughout the design process, the information generated by other analyses should be provided to technical publications for startup of the technical documentation. As the maintenance planning becomes finalized and support equipment requirements are being resolved, the technical publications organization should have access to virtually all the information needed to complete the technical documentation for the system. This includes operation and maintenance manuals and other documentation required to operate, maintain, or support the system. As shown in FIG. 11-6, there are several interfaces between technical publications and other logistics disciplines that must be controlled and monitored to ensure that necessary information is available for preparation of technical documentation for the system.

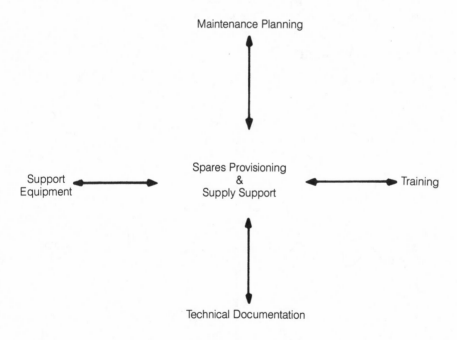

Fig. 11-5. Spares provisioning interfaces.

Other Logistics Elements

There are several other logistics elements that must be considered. These elements consist of significant logistics aspects of the system that must be addressed during design; however, a formal logistics discipline may not be established to handle the necessary efforts. The areas of manpower and personnel, computer resources, facilities, and packaging, handling, storage, and transportation form a significant part of the overall support requirements for a system, but there is rarely a formal logistics discipline to address any of these issues. It seems that these areas are viewed as a byproduct of some other logistics analysis, so there is no emphasis on maximizing support and minimizing cost. The logistics disciplines and organizations previously described in this chapter all provide inputs to these elements and use outputs from these elements. As shown in FIG. 11-7, there is a large volume of information provided by interfaces between these logistics elements and other logistics disciplines. For a logistics program to be complete, all these areas must be addressed in sufficient detail to produce the required support package for the system being designed.

ENGINEERING INTERFACES

The interfaces between logistics disciplines and engineering disciplines are much harder to establish and coordinate than internal logistics disciplines

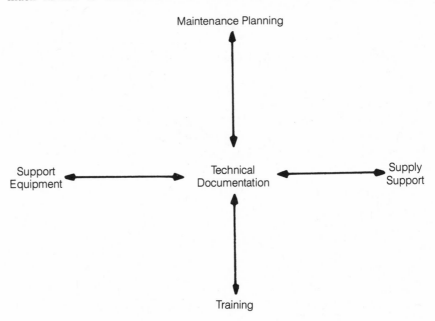

Fig. 11-6. Technical publications interfaces.

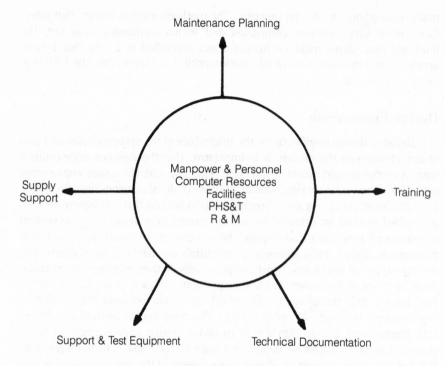

Maintenance Planning

Supply
Support

Manpower & Personnel
Computer Resources
Facilities
PHS&T
R & M

Training

Support & Test Equipment

Technical Documentation

Fig. 11-7. Other logistics element interfaces.

because engineering is oriented towards creating a design that meets performance requirements rather than support requirements. This basic difference in direction causes support issues to take a back seat to support, unless there is a clear understanding of how the final design must also be supportable and how information must be shared and processed in parallel throughout the design effort. Figure 11-8 shows the typical engineering disciplines that contribute to a design development program. Each of these engineering disciplines makes decisions that can significantly affect supportability. The key to success is an open and continual dialog and sharing of information, both formally and infor-

Design Engineering
Hardware Design
Software Design
System Integration
Reliability Engineering
Maintainability Engineering
Testability Engineering
Safety Engineering
Human Factors Engineering

Fig. 11-8. Engineering disciplines.

mally, throughout the design process. The methods used to ensure that interfaces work vary between companies and within companies; however, the interface procedures must be managed and controlled in a way that fosters access to and dissemination of information critical to support and the LSA process.

Design Engineering

Because design engineers are the originators of the system design and also of any changes to the design, it is imperative that the logistics organizations have a complete and working interface with any and all design engineering activities. Due to the varying number of types of design engineering disciplines that may be working on a given program, it is important that a company develop a standard method for establishing and monitoring interfaces. A typical system development program could require the assignment of electronic, electrical, mechanical, digital, radio frequency, structural, aeronautical, microelectronic, or other types of engineers. Most companies divide their engineering organizations by types of disciplines. A logistics problem surfaced by the LSA program may impact and, therefore, require effort for resolution from many different organizations within design engineering. The most logical method to address this requirement for an interface is to divide design engineering into three generic functions: hardware design, software design, and system integration. Each of these functions is an identifiable segment of the overall system design effort.

Hardware Design The physical characteristics of the design are the results of the efforts of hardware design engineers. The hardware design engineers are responsible for all aspects of the physical form, fit, and function of the hardware. A typical hardware design team could consist of any number of different types of engineering disciplines, including mechanical, electrical, electronic, structural, component, and aeronautical engineering. An interface between the LSA program and the hardware design engineering team is essential in two regards; first, the LSA process requires the latest and most accurate design information available, and, second, in order for logistics concerns to impact the design, there must be an established interface for communication and resolution of supportability issues.

Software Design In cases where a system contains software, or firmware, it may appear that little interface is necessary between the LSA program and software design engineers. However, this is not true. In most designs, the capability for the system to conduct self-test, fault detection, and reporting is accomplished through software or software initiated hardware actions. The basic capability to start the maintenance process is resident in the system software. Therefore, it is imperative that the maintenance decisions output by the LSA program reflect the test capability of the system. Requirements for testing to support maintenance must be communicated through continual interfaces between software design engineers and the LSA program. As the program matures, the LSA program can provide substantial input and feedback to software designers on the effectiveness or shortcomings of the software driven test capabilities of the system.

System Integration

The engineering function that is responsible for the overall system performance is called system integration, or system engineering. This organization is responsible, early in the program, for definition of the detailed system requirements, requirements for subsystems and lower level system parts, and internal and external interconnections. When each of the previously noted engineering disciplines has finished with its portion of the design, system integration is responsible for fitting all the pieces together to form a complete system. This does not happen all at once; it happens in phases as the design matures, which is why there must be a close interface between the LSA program and system integration. System integration is one place where logistics disciplines can have access to the total system overview to determine the logistics implications or impacts of design, performance, or supportability issues identified by the LSA process. These issues can only be addressed and resolved if an adequate interface is established and maintained throughout the development program.

Reliability

The interface between the LSA program and reliability engineering provides a significant amount of information critical to planning and developing the logistics support package for the system being designed. As stated in previous chapters, the reliability engineering program conducts several analyses that support the LSA effort, such as reliability predictions and failure modes, effects, and criticality analyses. These outputs of the reliability program are key inputs to the LSA process because they drive the amount of resources that will be required to support the system. There are other tasks that are equally important that should not be overlooked. Figure 11-9 lists the tasks that are performed as part of the reliability engineering program. Each of these tasks can impact the ability of a company to achieve LSA goals and therefore must be considered when developing interfaces between the reliability and LSA programs.

Reliability Program Plan (Task 101) The reliability program plan describes how the reliability program will meet the reliability requirements for the system design. It provides detailed information of how each task will be performed and the methods that will be used to achieve each reliability goal. A description of how the reliability program will interface with other programs, including the LSA program, should be contained in the plan. This description must coincide with the interface methodology of the LSA program plan in order for the two programs to be a coordinated effort. The interrelationships established by this plan should support the LSA effort throughout the development program. By ensuring that interfaces between reliability and LSA are clearly defined at the outset of the overall program, the ability of both organizations to meet program requirements is enhanced.

Monitor and Control of Subcontractors (Task 102) The interface between the contractor and subcontractors should be identical for every facet of the development program. The methodology set forth in the reliability program for monitoring subcontractors should be in line with the methods that will be used to monitor subcontractor LSA performance. This allows a standardized approach to sharing of information between both internal and external organizations in a cohesive manner. Clear delineation of who does what and when and how coordination of the overall program between the prime contractor and subcontractors will be handled, will help to ensure smooth interfaces throughout the program.

Program Task	Acquisition Phase			
	Concept	Dem/Val	FSD	Prod
100 Series				
101 Reliability program plan	X	X	X	X
102 Monitor/control of subcontractors	X	X	X	X
103 Program reviews	X	X	X	X
104 FRACAS		X	X	X
105 Failure review board		X	X	X
200 Series				
201 Reliability model	X	X	X	X
202 Reliability allocation	X	X	X	
203 Reliability prediction	X	X	X	X
204 FMECA	X	X	X	
205 Sneak circuit analysis			X	
206 Tolerance analysis		X	X	
207 Parts program	X	X	X	X
208 Reliability critical items	X	X	X	X
209 Effects of functional testing, maintenance, and PHS&T		X	X	
300 Series				
301 Environmental stress screening			X	X
302 Reliability development/growth testing		X	X	
303 Reliability qualification test			X	
304 Production reliability acceptance test				X

Fig. 11-9. Reliability program tasks.

Program Reviews (Task 103) Reliability issues are normally addressed during program status reviews, design reviews, or other management or technical meetings. Because these issues can have a profound effect on the LSA program and the logistics support requirements for the system, representatives from logistics disciplines should be included in the meetings or be provided with the results of any decisions. An exchange of information and dissemination of critical design changes or problems can be fostered through clearly defined interfaces resulting from these reviews and meetings. Participation by representatives of the LSA program in reliability reviews provides up-to-date information on the status of the design with regard to reliability.

Failure Reporting, Analysis, and Corrective Action System (FRACAS) (Task 104) The first actual usage information available on the system design is generated during contractor conducted tests. The FRACAS portion of the reliability program deals with reporting, analyzing, and development of corrective actions as a result of system failures during test. This information should give at least preliminary indications of requirements for logistics support when the system is placed into operation. Any FRACAS data should be available for review to identify trends for future system maintenance and to evaluate the design for ease of maintenance. Even though this failure data is very preliminary and subject to design changes to correct deficiencies, it is better than having no information as to how the system performs and what maintenance problems can be anticipated.

Failure Review Board (Task 105) The failure review board goes hand in hand with FRACAS. All recommended corrective actions must be approved by the failure review board before any changes can be implemented. The decisions of the failure review board should be provided to the LSA program to determine any impact on the logistics support package or for further definition of support problems. In some companies, a member of the logistics staff serves as a member, or observer, on the failure review board. This ensures that all pertinent design decisions are reviewed for logistics impacts and that failure related information is disseminated to all concerned with the LSA organization.

Reliability Modeling (Task 201) In the initial stages of a design or development program, the reliability organization creates a mathematical model of the conceptual system design. This model represents the configuration of the system, how each segment of the module will be interfaced in the total system, and how the reliability of the design will be predicted. The model should be used by the LSA program as an aid in developing analyses for maintenance-tradeoffs and other early studies. Using the model also establishes a relationship between the reliability organization and the LSA program that can continue throughout the program.

Reliability Allocations (Task 202) Early in the design program, reliability engineers develop an allocation of the overall system failure rate to the lowest level possible. Reliability allocations are used as guides for design engineers in the actual design of the system; the theory being that if each module or segment of the design meets its allocated failure rate, the total system will meet the specification requirement at the top level. These allocated failure rates should serve as a basis for development of early predictions of logistics resource requirements by the LSA program. By estimating the resources based on the allocated failure rates, logistics engineers have the ability to identify the drivers for maintenance and support costs early enough in the design process to recommend areas where design changes are necessary to reduce life-cycle cost of the system. These early estimates also provide a basis for tradeoff analyses and evaluation of the design as changes occur.

Reliability Predictions (Task 203) The detailed system reliability predictions, described in Chapter 8, are a key input to the determination of the amount of resources required to support the system. Because the reliability of the system can be a significant driver for life-cycle costs, it is imperative that a continual flow of the most current information between reliability and the LSA program be maintained. Even minor changes in reliability can have a major impact on the logistics support cost, and sometimes the maintenance concept, for the system.

Failure Modes, Effects, and Criticality Analysis (FMECA) (Task 204) The FMECA is a very important input to the LSA process that requires timely coordination and interface between reliability and the LSA program. As discussed in Chapter 9, the FMECA drives identification of the maintenance tasks and detailed maintenance task analysis for the system. The FMECA is an integral portion of the LSAR. The importance of the interface between reliability and the LSA program to accurately track the FMECA cannot be overstressed. Failure to coordinate this analysis can invalidate the LSA effort.

Sneak Circuit Analysis (Task 205) A sneak circuit analysis may be performed by reliability engineers to identify latent failure modes in the system. This analysis is normally performed late in the design process and design errors uncovered by the analysis can have a significant impact because of changes required to fix problems. If changes to the design are required as a result of the sneak circuit analysis, the LSA program must be included in the process of identification of all change impacts to the logistics support requirements.

Electronic Parts and Circuits Tolerance Analysis (Task 206) The purpose of electronic parts and circuits to determine tolerances under worst case conditions is to determine the effect, if any, of extreme operating conditions on these items. As with the sneak circuit analysis, any results of the tolerance analysis that cause a design change must be evaluated to determine any impact on the logistics support resource requirements of the system.

Parts Program (Task 207) Selection and review of parts that are used in a system design can be a critical item when meeting the required MTBF. Components engineers working within the reliability organization review each part to ensure that it is the highest reliability level possible to meet the specification requirements. Often, this requires generation of specifications or source control drawings for parts. This process is normally required by contract as a parts control program in accordance with MIL-STD 965, Parts Control Program. The output of this effort is a program parts selection list (PPSL) that is used by design engineers as a source for selecting parts to be used in the design. Parts that do not meet established requirements are classified as nonstandard parts and must be approved by the customer before use. The PPSL and nonstandard parts information become an input into the provisioning process, which is a subset of the LSA program. Much of the parts related information can be transferred from the parts control program to the LSAR, which saves time in research and enhances the accuracy of the provisioning data generated as a deliverable to the customer. This information is also used as an input for preparation of technical manuals. Using the output of the parts program as the common input to both provisioning and technical manual preparation should ensure that the outputs of these two processes are identical.

Reliability Critical Items (Task 208)   The purpose of this task is to give added emphasis to items in the system design that are the drivers for reliability. Candidates for further analysis can be potential single-point failures, drivers for overall system level reliability, or drivers for mission reliability. Information from this analysis, especially where reliability is increased or decreased, should be provided to the LSA program to determine any impact on the logistics support resources or concepts.

Effects of Functional Testing, Storage, Handling, Packaging, Transportation, and Maintenance (Task 209)   One of the often overlooked aspects of system reliability is the effect that functional testing, storage, handling, packaging, transportation and maintenance may have on the system or spares. The reason that these events are overlooked is that they are outside of the operational performance requirements stated by the product specification. Systems do not normally go from the manufacturing line to an operational environment without undergoing some type of packaging, handling, and storage. During storage, especially long-term storage, functional testing and maintenance may be required to ensure that the system or spare items are in an operational condition. The purpose of this analysis is to identify design areas where reliability can be effected by any of these events. Any problems identified can have a direct effect on the amount of pipeline resources that will be required to support the system. For example, if the analysis shows that 25 percent of a critical spare is susceptible to failures during storage due to periodic testing or maintenance, then additional spares will be required to maintain an adequate amount of items to support maintenance of operational system. Information from this analysis must be provided to the LSA program so that adequate planning for spares requirements can be accomplished.

Reliability Testing   Throughout the full-scale development and production phases of a program, reliability engineering conducts testing to improve design reliability and verify that reliability specification requirements are met. MIL-STD 785 contains four reliability tests. Environmental stress screening (Task 301) subjects each level of the design, from piece part up to total system level, to accelerated conditions of temperature and vibration to identify weak points in either the parts or the design. Reliability development/growth testing (Task 302) is the process of operating the equipment under conditions that are as close to actual as possible to cause system failures. The failures are analyzed to determine any required design changes to increase reliability. Reliability qualification testing (Task 303) is conducted to demonstrate that the final design meets the product specification requirements for reliability. Production reliability acceptance testing (Task 304) is normally performed on samples from each production lot of the system to verify that subsequent copies of the design maintain the required reliability levels. The purpose of each of these tests is to evaluate the reliability of the design and identify ways in which the design can be improved to increase reliability. The result of each testing process should be provided to the logistics organization as inputs for refining support resource requirements. When testing reveals that the actual reliability of the system design is lower than anticipated, additional resources may be required to support the system throughout its useful life. Figure 11-9 shows when these reliability testing tasks are normally performed.

Maintainability

The LSA program and the maintainability program must work in tandem to develop the final maintenance capability for the system being designed. The maintainability program is chartered to guide the design effort to ensure that the design contains all the attributes necessary to meet maintainability requirements, whereas, the LSA program is charged with taking the design and developing the detailed maintenance requirements. A successful maintainability program should, in theory, reduce the scope of LSA generated design changes for maintenance. Because the thrust of the maintainability program is centered around theoretical studies and analyses, it is up to the LSA program to follow through and develop actual maintenance requirements for the system. Much of the data generated by the maintainability engineers is used as a direct input to several LSA analyses and the LSAR database. A lack of sufficient interface between the maintainability and LSA programs will result in incomplete or redundant maintenance planning and support for the system. Therefore, continual interface between these two organizations is essential throughout the design program. The maintainability program consists of a series of tasks contained in MIL-STD 470 as shown in FIG. 11-10. Many of these tasks are very similar in purpose to those described previously for the reliability program.

Maintainability Program Plan (Task 101)   The program plan for the maintainability effort is very similar to the reliability program plan. This plan describes in detail how each maintainability program requirement will be achieved. It is important that the plan be in concert with the LSA plan, so that the efforts of both organizations are complementary. Specific interfaces between maintainability and the LSA program include coordination of task inputs and outputs, formal and informal methods of communications, methods for sharing information or observing task performance, and participation in meetings where both organizations have a vested interest. Organization, communications, and interfaces between the LSA program and the maintainability effort, which enhance sharing of information and other design related items, increase the abilities of both to meet program requirements.

Monitor and Control of Subcontractors (Task 102) The maintainability program continually monitors and directs the activities of subcontractors on all maintainability related issues. The ongoing dialog between prime contractor and subcontractor provides current status and information on the ability of the subcontractor to meet maintainability, and subsequently maintenance, requirements. Any information passing between prime and subcontractor that relates to maintenance should be provided to the LSA program for information, review, and action as appropriate. Often, the decisions made in the early stages of a program by maintainability engineers drastically affect the downstream maintenance capability for the system. By including the LSA program as a routine participant in these exchanges, surprises can be avoided that would cause problems in developing the detailed system maintenance requirements.

Program Reviews (Task 103) Maintainability program reviews are normally conducted as a part of a system level program review that addresses all aspects of the development program. If separate reviews are conducted for only maintainability, representatives of the LSA program should be either participating attendees or, at a minimum, observers. The program review provides

Program Task	Acquisition Phase			
	Concept	Dem/Val	FSD	Prod
100 Series				
101 Maintainability program plan		X	X	X
102 Monitor/control of subcontractors		X	X	X
103 Program reviews	X	X	X	X
104 Data collection		X	X	X
200 Series				
201 Maintainability model	X	X	X	X
202 Maintainability allocations	X	X	X	X
203 Maintainability predictions		X	X	
204 FMECA		X	X	
205 Maintainability analysis	X	X	X	
206 Design criteria		X	X	
207 Inputs to maintenance plan and LSA		X	X	
300 Series				
301 Maintainability demonstration			X	

Fig. 11-10. Maintainability program tasks.

a forum for discussion of maintainability and maintenance related issues that will ultimately affect the LSA program.

Data Collection, Analysis, and Corrective Action System (Task 104)　Maintainability engineers collect and analyze a tremendous amount of design and maintenance related data while completing program tasks. The purpose of Task 104 is to formalize the data collection process so that the information can be reviewed and retained for comparison or other uses. Much of this information is directly applicable to the LSA effort. This data can provide valuable inputs to the LSA program and reduce program costs. There should be a planned sharing of this information to ensure two points. First, that the detailed maintenance requirements for the system developed by the LSA program are a continuation of the effort initiated by the maintainability program. And, second, so that any duplication of efforts can be eliminated by the LSA program not having to collect and reanalyze the same data.

Maintainability Modeling (Task 201)　Early in the design program, a mathematical model is developed that is used to show the relationship between each portion of the system down to the lowest maintenance significant item level. This model is used as the basis for calculating maintainability figures for the system such as mean time to repair. As the design matures, the model is updated to reflect the latest design configuration. The model allows tradeoff analyses and comparisons to be completed to select the best alternatives for meeting maintainability requirements. The maintainability model should be a key input to the LSA program for standardizing similar types of analyses so that the system baseline for both the maintainability and LSA programs is the same. This will avoid confusion and conflicting analysis results and design change recommendations developed by these organizations.

Maintainability Allocations (Task 202)　The product specification for the system being designed normally contains maintainability parameters such as mean time to repair or mean time between maintenance. Initially in the program, maintainability engineers allocate these parameters down to the lowest maintenance level. The allocations are then used as goals for meeting system level requirements. In theory, if each portion of the system meets its allocated maintainability numbers, the product specification requirements will be met at the system level. The allocations form some of the first inputs for the LSA process and the LSAR and can be used in developing initial maintenance requirements for the system.

Maintainability Predictions (Task 203)　As the design evolves, maintainability engineers develop predictions of the actual maintainability of the system. The predictions involve analyzing the design and estimating the time that will be required to repair a failure of each portion of the system. The maintainability prediciton should meet or exceed the allocated maintainability parameters developed previously. The predictions are a direct input to the LSA process and the LSAR. It is crucial that the analyses performed for developing these predictions be made available to the LSA program as inputs for performing the upfront analysis tasks so that there is a commonality of direction and elimination of duplicate efforts.

Failure Modes and Effects Analysis (FMEA) (Task 204) Maintainability engineering provides the criticality inputs for the failure modes and effects analysis that produces the completed failure modes, effects, and criticality analysis. This information is developed through analysis of the system design to identify those failure modes that pose the most significant critical situations to either system, operator, or maintainer. Using criticality as a guide, further analyses can be directed towards methods for reducing either the failure potentials or controlling the situations created upon failure occurrence. This information, as part of the FMECA, is a direct input to both the LSA process and the LSAR.

Maintainability Analysis (Task 205) Maintainability engineers analyze the design as it matures to identify and recommend actions necessary to improve system maintainability. The thrust of this analysis process is based on portions of the system where the predicted maintainability values do not meet the allocated values. Any changes developed and incorporated must be provided to the LSA program for determination of maintenance impact. This analysis process is the most direct method for improvement of the capability for performance of maintenance because design decisions made early in the program normally provide the best improvements for maintenance with the least cost impact to the design process. A clear interface between the LSA program and the maintainability program is essential to maximize the output of this task.

Maintainability Design Criteria (Task 206) Maintainability engineers prepare a set of design criteria to be used as guidelines to be used by design engineers as the system is developed. The purpose of the criteria is to standardize the maintainability aspects of the system and to provide a checklist the design engineers can use to maximize the ability of the final system design to be maintained. Figure 11-11 provides examples of typical items addressed in a maintainability design criteria. Using criteria such as these, design engineers know at the start of the design process what attributes should be incorporated into the design to ensure that maintainability requirements are met. This crite-

---

- Assemblies and repair parts having the same part numbers will be functionally and physically identical.
- Access to maintenance-significant items will be provided through entries that do not require removal of other components.
- Scheduled maintenance, alignments, and calibration requirements will be avoided.
- Special tools or test equipment will not be required to perform maintenance at organizational- or intermediate-maintenance levels.
- Captive, quick-release fasteners will be used to secure maintenance access panels or covers.
- All screws and bolts will be of standard dimensions to reduce tool requirements.

Fig. 11-11. Maintainability design criteria.

ria can also be useful to the LSA program because in presenting the general capabilities for maintenance that should be designed into the system.

Preparation of Inputs to the Detailed Maintenance Plan and Logistics Support Analysis (Task 207)   The significance of the need for a close and continual interface between the LSA program and the maintainability program is reinforced by the existence of this task. Having a task specifically dedicated to the requirement for the formal planning and transfer of information from the maintainability program to the LSA program shows just how important the availability and coordination of sharing of maintenance information is to the achievement of the overall program goals. The successful execution of this task and the transfer of information starts with adequate planning and documentation in both the maintainability program plan and the LSA plan. These documents must be in concert on how the coordination and transfer of information will be handled, the responsibility for review and updating, and management authority for both the maintainability and LSA programs.

Maintainability Demonstration (Task 301)   The proof of the effectiveness of the maintainability program is determined through maintainability testing and evaluation. The maintainability demonstration is necessary to verify that the maintainability design criteria have been incorporated into the system design, resulting in the achievement maintainability goals. The process for conducting the demonstration is relatively simple. It is conducted using the actual system late in the full-scale development phase of the program. Also required are the technical manuals, required tools, and the other support equipment necessary to accomplish maintenance. The object of the demonstration is to take an operational system, induce failures into it, and use only the technical manuals and support equipment that will be available to maintenance personnel when the system is fielded to find and fix the failure.

This demonstration, obviously, is not only to show the maintainability of the system, but also that the entire logistics support package for the system is accurate and effective. The maintainability demonstration can and should be used as a significant input to MIL-STD 1388-1A LSA Task 501, Supportability Test, Evaluation, and Verification, because it addresses the adequacy of the results of the LSA program to accomplish maintenance.

Testability

One of the most crucial points to be considered for expedient accomplishment of maintenance is the ability to quickly and easily detect and isolate failures. If the failure is difficult to find, it takes a long time to begin actually fixing the system. The purpose of the testability program is to work with design engineers to make the system testable. The results of the testability program have a significant impact on the logistics support resources required to support maintenance and the ultimate life-cycle cost of the system. A continual interface between the LSA program and the testability program is necessary to ensure that the testing requirements for the system are developed using existing test equipment and maintenance procedures whenever possible and that all unique requirements for new test equipment, personnel skills, facilities, or procedures are addressed early in the program to assess the impact on logistics support resources. The testability program is conducted using tasks similar to those for the reliability and maintainability program. In fact, the program is intimately linked to the maintainability program, because maintainability parameters include time required to perform fault detection and isolation. Often the time required for testing drives maintainability figures. Figure 11-12 illustrates the testability program tasks contained in MIL-STD 2165, Testability Program for Electronic Systems and Equipments.

Testability Program Planning (Task 101) As with the reliability and maintainability programs, the testability program is guided by a program plan that specifically addresses how each program task will be accomplished. In addition to guiding the program, the plan establishes the interfaces between testability and other organizations, including reliability, maintainability, design engineering, and the LSA program. These interfaces are significant because the ability to test the design is reported and used in other analyses that impact the system availability and supportability.

Testability Reviews (Task 102) Testability should be an issue addressed at every design and program review. Although separate reviews are not normally conducted specifically for this program, it should be a distinct segment of every review. The key point to be addressed is how testing is being implemented, the impact on other portions of the design program, and sharing of critical test information between organizations.

Task		Con	D&V	FSED	Prod	Oper
101	Testability program planning		X	X		
102	Testability reviews	X	X	X		
103	Data collection/analysis planning			X	X	X
201	Testability requirements	X	X	X		
202	Preliminary design and analysis			X		
203	Detailed design and analysis			X		
301	Testability demonstration			X		

CON - Concept Phase
D&V - Demonstration and Validation Phase
FSED - Full Scale Engineering Development Phase
PROD - Production Phase
OPER - Operation Phase

Fig. 11-12. Testability program tasks.

Testability Data Collection and Analysis Planning (Task 103)
Testability engineers, in order to accomplish program tasks, must collect and analyze a significant amount of design data. This data is similar in most cases to that collected by maintainability engineers. Because the results of the testability analyses must coincide with and complement the results of the maintainability program, the collection and analysis of data must be coordinated. This same data is applicable to analyses performed later by logistics engineers for support issues. Establishing and following a standard methodology for collection, analysis, and dissemination of data ensures that everyone involved with the program is in concert.

Testability Requirements (Task 201) Incorporation of design features that enhance the ability to test a system is the key to maximizing testability. If the design features are included in the initial design, rather than as an afterthought, costs of changes to increase testability can be avoided. Testability engineers develop design criteria, much like those developed by maintainability engineers, to guide design engineers. Figure 11-13 provides examples of typical testability design criteria. While some of these criteria seem like common sense, they are often overlooked and cause problems that must be corrected at additional costs late in the program if not included in the initial design.

Testability Preliminary Design and Analysis (Task 202) The purpose of the preliminary design and analysis is to review the early conceptual design to determine the inherent system testability and to identify ways to increase testability. The testability design criteria is used to a large extent as a guide for accomplishing this task. A comparison of the testability and testing concept of evolving design with the maintenance concept allows potential logistics support problems and cost drivers to be identified early. A close interface between the testability program and the LSA program is essential to ensure that planned testing of the system supports the planned maintenance concept. When a disconnect between test capabilities and maintenance concept occurs, immediate resolution is mandatory.

Testability Design Criteria

- The failure modes effects and criticality analysis performed by reliability engineers must be the basis for all testability planning.
- Functions must be partitioned so that each can be tested independently.
- Complex circuitry should be designed to allow isolation testing of portions of the circuit.
- Minimize the number of different part types used in the design.
- Locate test points to allow functional testing of each discrete active function.
- Built-in test (BIT) design should allow both on-equipment and off-equipment testing of the system.
- BIT design should support the maintenance concept for the system.

Fig. 11-13. Testability design criteria.

Testability Detail Design and Analysis (Task 203) A balance between testing methods can go a long way towards minimizing life-cycle cost of the system. Built-in test capabilities of the system at the organizational level can reduce the time required to detect and isolate faults; however, BIT can be expensive and require additional circuitry and dedicated built-in test equipment (BITE) to be included in the system design. The other alternative for testing at organizational level is manual fault isolation and troubleshooting, which is man-power intensive and normally requires a significantly longer time to detect and isolate faults. At intermediate level a similar tradeoff must be conducted between the use of automatic test equipment (ATE) and manual procedures. ATE is expensive, but can greatly reduce test time and increase repair capabilities. Achieving a balance between use of BIT, BITE, ATE, and manual testing is a tough assignment, but if done correctly, it can maximize system maintainability and supportability, while requiring the least logistics support resources. The results of this task are direct inputs to many LSA tasks and the LSAR.

Testability Inputs to Maintainability Demonstration (Task 301) As stated previously, the purpose of the maintainability demonstration is to prove that the logistics support package is adequate to maintain the system design. The ability to accurately and quickly test the system to detect and isolate failures is a key to accomplishing this goal and must be demonstrated. Testability engineers must work with maintainability engineers and logistics engineers in preparing the demonstration to ensure that the inherent ability of the design to be tested is completely demonstrated. Faults induced into the system for maintainability demonstration purposes that cannot be detected or isolated cause not only failure of the demonstration, but also indicate that the testability of the system is inadequate.

System Safety

A system design must be free of hazards to operator and maintenance personnel and also not contain materials hazardous to personnel or the environment. While this is not always possible, due to the inherent characteristics of a system, every effort must be taken to control or reduce hazards to an acceptable level. The system safety program is charged with the responsibility of ensuring that the final design configuration of a system is as hazard-free as possible. To accomplish this, safety engineers are involved with the total program from start to finish. MIL-STD 882, System Safety Program Requirements, contains the tasks that are performed by safety engineers. Each of these tasks, shown in FIG. 11-14, has either a direct or indirect impact on the LSA program; however, those tasks with which logistics engineers are most concerned are the system safety program plan (Task 101), the preliminary hazard list (Task 201), the preliminary hazard analysis (Task 202), and the operating and support hazard analysis (Task 205).

System Safety Program Plan (Task 101) The importance of program plans has been thoroughly discussed previously. System safety also prepares a program plan that guides the activities of safety engineers and describes how other organizations interface with the safety program. The system safety program plan should address how the interface will be handled between safety and the LSA program. Because safety is one of the major concerns with any system, a key issue from a logistics standpoint that must be included in the plan is how hazards associated with operation or maintenance of the system will be identified and resolved. This includes responsibilities for reporting, coordination, and resolution.

Preliminary Hazard List (Task 201)   A list of all hazards is maintained by safety engineering. The list is first generated from the concept of the design and then maintained throughout the program to ensure that every hazard is resolved, either through design change or appropriate procedures. The tabular listing can be extremely useful in aiding logistics engineers in developing operation or maintenance tasks. Hazards identified by logistics engineers through the LSA process must be included on this list.

	Task	Concept	DEMVAL	FSD	Prod
	100 Series Tasks				
100	System safety program	G	G	G	G
101	System safety program plan	G	G	G	G
102	Integration of subcontractors	S	S	S	S
103	Program reviews	S	S	S	S
104	System safety working group	G	G	G	G
105	Hazard tracking	S	S	S	S
106	Test and evaluation safety	G	G	G	G
107	Progress summary	G	G	G	G
108	Key personnel qualifications	S	S	S	S
	200 Series Tasks				
201	Preliminary hazard list	G	S	S	N/A
202	Preliminary hazard analysis	G	G	G	GC
203	Subsystem hazard analysis	N/A	G	G	GC
204	System hazard analysis	N/A	G	G	GC
205	Operation hazard analysis	S	G	G	GC
206	Health hazard assessment	G	G	G	GC
207	Safety verification	S	G	G	S
208	Training	N/A	S	S	S
209	Safety assessment	S	S	S	S
210	Safety compliance assessment	S	S	S	S
211	Safety review of ECPs/waivers	N/A	G	G	G
212	Software hazard analysis	S	G	G	GC
213	GFE/GFP system safety analysis	S	G	G	G

Applicability Codes
S   - Selectively applicable
G   - Generally applicable
GC - Generally applicable to design changes only
N/A - Not applicable

Fig. 11-14. Safety program tasks.

Preliminary Hazard Analysis (Task 202)   Safety engineers analyze each hazard recorded on the preliminary hazard list to eliminate or control the hazard. Any operation or maintenance hazard should be analyzed with the results being recorded appropriately in the analysis, which should be done collectively by both safety and logistics engineers.

Operating and Support Hazard Analysis (Task 205)   Each operation or maintenance task must be reviewed to determine if a potential hazard to either personnel or equipment exists when the task is performed. In most cases, the review can be done rather quickly because most tasks normally do not create a hazard. When the review indicates that a hazard may exist, several actions are mandatory. The potential hazard must be recorded on the hazard list until resolved, an analysis of the hazard must be performed, and the resolution must be implemented. When a potential hazard cannot be eliminated, it must be recorded in both the operating and support hazard analysis results and on the appropriate LSAR data records. The hazard is recorded in the LSAR database on the LSAR Data Record C by annotating the safety requirement block and in the text of the maintenance task description on the LSAR Data Record D as either a warning or as a caution. A warning identifies a potential hazard to personnel, and a caution identifies a potential hazard to the equipment. Ultimately, all unresolved hazards must be included in the operation and maintenance technical manuals for the system. To ensure that this series of events occurs, close interface must be maintained between the system safety program and the LSA program.

Human Engineering

With few exceptions, all systems require human interface to perform intended functions. The man-to-machine interface is addressed by the human engineering program. Each operation and maintenance task is analyzed by human engineering to ensure that the task can be performed with minimum

---

- Physical man-to-machine interface (physical, aural, visual)
- Physical man-to-man interface (physical, aural, visual)
- Physical comfort of operator/maintenance personnel
- Equipment-handling requirements (weight, cube)
- Temperature, humidity, etc., to be encountered
- Inclement conditions (rain, snow, mud) anticipated
- Climate (arctic, desert)
- Equipment environment (vibration, noise)
- Useable space availability
- Effects of special clothing (gloves, NBC, coat)
- Safety and hazard protection
- Mission-related requirements (tactical environment)

Fig. 11-15. Human engineering program.

---

negative impact to either the system or the human. MIL-STD 1472, Human Engineering Design Criteria for Military Systems, Equipment and Facilities, guides human engineering in analyzing each operation and maintenance task. Many of the concerns of the human engineering program are shown in FIG. 11-15. Where dimensions of the human body are necessary to determine if a task can physically be accomplished, DOD-HDBK 743, Anthropometry of U.S. Military Personnel, provides the maximum and minimum dimensions of the aggregate military population. Sometimes, it is necessary to actually perform operation and maintenance tasks to determine if they are physically acceptable. This performance can be done as part of the maintenance task verification process accomplished by logistics engineers to reduce effort and ensure that all parties agree on how tasks are to be performed. Results of the human engineering program are reflected in several LSA program outputs, including the technical manuals and training program. Obviously, close interface between human engineering and the logistics disciplines must be maintained throughout the design program.

Other Internal Interfaces

In addition to interfaces within the ILS disciplines and between ILS and engineering disciplines, other internal company interfaces provide significant inputs to the LSA program. Some interface requirements are very obvious, while others are more subtle, but just as important. The most common organizations that must interface with the LSA program are configuration management, quality assurance, and manufacturing. Because every company is organized differently with different titles for types of organizations, these generic titles represent the functions that must interface continually with the LSA program.

CONFIGURATION MANAGEMENT

System design is a dynamic process that creates a constantly changing situation where the LSA program must be flexible enough to incorporate or change support requirements based on the most accurate information available. The interface between the LSA program and the configuration management organization provides the visibility necessary to maintain the consistency between the LSA effort and the system design. Configuration management is a discipline that applies technical and administrative direction and surveillance to identify and document function and physical characteristics of a configuration item, control changes to those characteristics, and record and report change processing and implementation status.

The configuration management organization is responsible for maintaining records of the evolution of a system design. MIL-STD 483A, Configuration Management Practices for Systems, Equipment, Munitions, and Computer

Organizational Interfaces

Programs, contains a detailed explanation of a configuration management program. The purpose of the program is to control the configuration of a system being designed throughout the design process. This is an important function because many organizations require information on the most current design in order to perform their assigned tasks. Logistics engineers must have the most configuration for analysis to determine if the design meets specified supportability requirements. This can only be accomplished if the most current data on the design are available. If the logistics organizations have outdated design information, their efforts will be wasted and the actual status of the design with regard to meeting support requirements will be unknown. A maintenance task analysis performed on obsolete design data will also be useless. Inaccurate information can cause a needless expenditure effort and result in ineffective product development. That is why the formal configuration management process is normally contractually required on all government programs. This forces the contractor to maintain configuration control.

Baseline Management

The concept of baseline management is one of the most important aspects of configuration management. A baseline is normally established at key intervals in a design development program as a tool for freezing the design configuration at a given point in time as a formal control point for identification and control of subsequent changes in performance or design. The practice of baselining a system design allows each recommended change to be evaluated before it is approved and incorporated. This method, when strictly enforced, is the foundation for configuration control. The generally accepted system baselines are functional, allocated, and product. Each baseline has a definite purpose and normally is established at key intervals in the design process. Figure 11-16 shows the relationship between these baselines and program development phases.

Functional Baseline A functional baseline is normally established immediately after the system requirements review in the early stages of the design process. The purpose of the functional baseline is to identify the top level hardware and software configurations that have been developed to meet

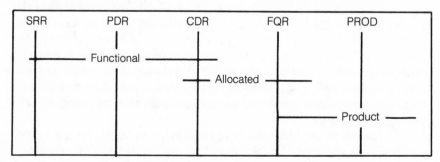

Fig. 11-16. Configuration baselines by program phase.

specification requirements. The functional baseline quantifies the functions that are to be designed and developed during the design process. Detailed design activity uses the functional baseline as a guide for development of the hardware and software required for the system. Any changes to the functional baseline normally constitute a major departure from the initial design concept.

Allocated Baseline The detailed design that is developed from the functional baseline is documented as the allocated baseline. This baseline is normally established just after completion of the critical design review. The allocated baseline contains identification of all the parts and assemblies necessary to meet specification requirements. Changes to the allocated baseline are strictly controlled by the change process discussed later in this chapter. The purpose of the allocated baseline is to record the status of the system design as approved at the critical design review and to provide a basis for reviewing the impact of all recommended design changes with regard to impact on the total system. The resulting documented configuration is form, fit, and functionally within specified system requirements. This baseline is maintained throughout the final design stages of the program until the system has completed testing and is ready to go into production.

Production Baseline The production baseline is the final "build-to" configuration of the system. It identifies the design of the system that will be produced using standard manufacturing processes and procedures. The production baseline is established after all qualification testing and first article testing have been accomplished on the allocated baseline configuration. This baseline is the configuration that is provided to the government as the final design of the system in the form of, at a minimum, level 2 and normally level 3 drawings. Level 2 drawings are of sufficient detail to allow limited production, whereas level 3 drawings contain complete production requirements for the system. All changes to the production baseline must be approved by the government before the change can be implemented. Contained in the production baseline documentation are all the engineering drawings, test procedures, and manufacturing processes necessary to transition the system design into full production.

Configuration Items

The individual functional items that comprise a system are also controlled to maintain accountability of the configuration of each item through the design process. At the initial stages of the design, the critical items are identified as configuration items. In most cases, the configuration items are the major functional assemblies and subassemblies and software modules of the system. By controlling the configuration of these items, an audit trail of the development of the design can be maintained, which allows recommended design changes or revisions to be analyzed as to the change effect on other portions of the system before approval and implementation. Configuration items are categorized as either hardware configuration items or computer software configuration items.

The reason for this division is that the developmental processes for hardware and software are different and require unique control processes.

Hardware Configuration Item   A hardware configuration item (HWCI) is any item whose design configuration is significant in accomplishing a required function of the system. HWCIs normally include hardware units, assemblies, and subassemblies down to, and including circuit card assemblies. Piece parts such as capacitors, resistors, and mechanical hardware are not classified as HWCIs. The key to controlling the configuration of a HWCI is to review all proposed changes to determine if the change will affect the form, fit, or function of the item. Detailed documentation of each HWCI is mandatory. An HWCI can also include imbedded firmware that is required to perform a given function.

Computer Software Configuration Item   Any software contained in a system and the identifiable major modules of a software package are identified as a computer software configuration item (CSCI). Because the development and control of software is normally accomplished using different processes and procedures from those of hardware items, software configuration control may be accomplished by an organization specifically chartered for that purpose. DOD-STD 2167, Defense System Software Development, contains detailed procedures for maintaining control of software during development and testing.

Interface Control

When a system being designed is to be integrated with other independently developed systems or subsystems, it is imperative that interface requirements of the systems to be combined are completely identified and documented both physically and functionally. This is accomplished through the use of interface control documentation. The most common interface control documents are the interface control specification (ICS) and the interface control document (ICD). The prime contractor, responsible for integrating all systems being developed when there are two or more large segments of a system being designed by two different companies, is normally responsible for preparing and maintaining these documents. Interface control is an important consideration of configuration control in order to determine if changes made to one system being developed will affect one or more of the other systems with which it is to be integrated.

Change Control

The development and implementation of a formal change control process is the crux of configuration management. There is a systematic method for achieving control of changes that must be followed in order to attain the goal of having an overall configuration control. The control method is basic and logical. It consists of initial identification of the item configurations to be controlled, a standard procedure for recording, processing, review, and approval or disapproval of recommended design changes, and tracking and documenting the implementation of adopted changes.

Configuration Identification The basis for the change control process is establishing and maintaining a system baseline as previously described in this chapter. Identification of the functional and physical characteristics of the system through baselining forms a point of departure for controlling all changes. The configuration baseline must be sufficient to adequately control changes throughout the design process. As a normal practice, the configuration management organization publishes and maintains a list of configuration items that can be used for reference by all participating organizations. This listing may also be a contractual requirement. All recommended design changes are documented for configuration items.

Change Process The change control process, though minor differences exist between companies, is basically the same in all organizations. Figure 11-17 illustrates the flow of recommended changes from inception to incorporation. Recommended design changes, commonly called engineering change requests (ECR), can be initiated by anyone in the company and can be due to varying reasons, from basic change of components to modifications for increasing reliability or increasing producibility. There are two classifications of changes: a Class I change affects the form, fit, or function of the configuration item; a Class II change addresses all other cases such as changes of piece part components, when form, fit or function are not changed, or to correct documentation errors. Once initiated, the ECR is tracked through the change process by configuration management.

The configuration control board (CCB), also called a change control board in some organizations, is responsible for review and approval or disapproval of all ECRs. Board membership, as shown in FIG. 11-18, consists of cognizant representatives from all discipline areas and can include design engineering, relia-

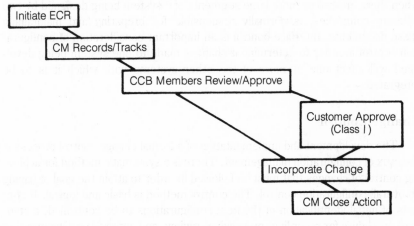

Fig. 11-17. Design change flow.

liability, quality assurance, integrated logistics support, manufacturing, purchasing, contracts, program management, configuration management, and any other organization deemed appropriate. This is where the initial information on impending changes is made available to the LSA program. At this time, each recommended change must be evaluated to determine if there is any impact to the LSA program or the final logistics support package.

The CCB has final company authority for review and approval of ECRs. Each recommended change is reviewed for impact on the design performance to specification, cost, and schedule impact of the change if implemented, and impact the change may have on other areas, such as the interface control document or contractual requirements. If the baseline being changed has been accepted by the government, then government approval of the change may also be required. For product baseline, the change may require preparation and submittal of a formal request for the change in the form of an engineering change proposal (ECP). When approved, the change is forwarded to configuration management for implementation.

Configuration Audits

During the latter stages of the design process, the final system configuration is audited by the government to determine the adequacy of the design and design documentation. These audits are a functional configuration audit and a physical configuration audit. Successful completion of these audits is mandatory before a production baseline can be established and the program can proceed into the production phase.

Functional Configuration Audit   The purpose of the functional configuration audit (FCA) is to verify that the design meets all functional requirements of the product specification. The FCA is conducted by a team of government representatives who compare the system design with the design specification to determine that all functional design requirements have been met and are included in the design. Test and analysis data may be used to verify that the system design has achieved the performance, reliability, maintainability, and testability requirements specified in the allocated configuration.

Program Management
Configuration Management
Design Engineering
Mechanical Engineering
Reliability Engineering
Logistics Engineering
Safety
Quality Assurance
Manufacturing
Contracts

Fig. 11-18. Configuration control board membership.

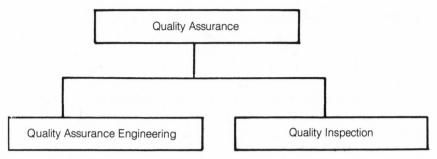

Fig. 11-19. Quality assurance organization.

Physical Configuration Audit   The physical configuration audit (PCA) is used to establish the product baseline for initial production and acceptance of the system design. The PCA team verifies that the documentation prepared for the system accurately reflects the physical design of the system. The audit also ensures that the acceptance testing requirements prescribed by the documentation are adequate for acceptance of production units. Production cannot begin until the contractor has successfully passed the PCA. All recommended design changes that are generated after PCA must be approved by the government before incorporation.

Quality Assurance   Interface between the LSA program and the quality assurance organization is not normally considered when planning how logistics information will be gathered and coordinated in a development program; however, quality assurance can provide some significant inputs to the LSA process. Quality assurance is charged with the responsibility of continually reviewing the entire program to ensure that all aspects conform to the requirements of the procurement contract and the product development specification. The quality assurance organization is usually divided into two separate groups, as shown in FIG. 11-19, each having distinct responsibilities. Quality assurance engineering is responsible for reviewing the overall program for compliance with procurement requirements. Figure 11-20 illustrates the typical actions of the quality assurance engineering group. An interface between the LSA program and qual-

- Specification review
- Specification compliance monitoring
- Engineering drawing review and approval
- Part specification review and approval
- Part procurement document review
- Material review board
- Failure review board
- Configuration control board
- Procedure and process review
- Test procedure review and approval
- Quality conformance review

Fig. 11-20. Quality assurance engineering tasks.

ity assurance engineering provides current information on the status of compliance with program requirements. Whenever a problem arises with compliance, such as parts that are unacceptable for use, out of specification performance, or errors in procedures or drawings, an impact to the LSA program can occur. An effective interface with the LSA program will provide notification of such problems and also alert logistics engineers to impending changes or requirements for impact analysis. Having current information can result in timely inputs to changes, rather than having to find out about the change after the fact, when any inputs to the change process will be impossible.

The quality inspection group is responsible for overseeing the actual manufacturing process from beginning to end. Typical quality inspection functions are shown in FIG. 11-21. The results of this ''over the shoulder'' look at the building of the system provides information of how the system is put together, problems encountered in assembly and testing, visibility with regard to accuracy of engineering documentation, and adequacy of manufacturing and testing instructions. Any problems encountered, especially in testing, can provide inputs to the maintenance requirements for the system.

Manufacturing   The actual building of the system can provide invaluable information to the LSA program for input to development of the detailed maintenance requirements. There are two aspects to this theory. First, maintenance can be viewed as a reversal of the assembly process. Disassembly should be accomplished by reversing the assembly process. Using the assembly procedures as a base, logistics should be able to plan the disassembly by starting with the last assembly process and working backwards. To deviate from this pattern would mean that a different process rather than the most effective for assembly is being used. Second, manufacturing performs tests to verify functional performance at each step of the assembly process. Any procedures used in manufacture to test, especially those used to detect and isolate failures, should be used as inputs for planning how maintenance testing will be performed. Often, the test equipment and test procedures used during production are identical to that which will be used in the field to perform testing. This allows fault detection and isolation procedures to be validated very early in the program on actual production systems. Any information concerning maintenance procedures that can

---

- Manufacturing in-process inspection
- Test performance monitoring
- Rework instructions
- Parts review
- Final assembly and test monitoring
- Performance test monitoring
- Quality test monitoring
- Qualification and acceptance test monitoring

Fig. 11-21. Quality inspection tasks.

be obtained from the manufacturing process reduces the amount of effort that will be required to develop the final maintenance program for the system.

Producibility One of the common problems that plagues companies is transitioning from an engineering design to a design that can be economically reproduced using standard manufacturing processes and procedures. There can be a significant difference between a design that meets all performance requirements and a design that can be produced easily. The producibility organization is responsible for taking the engineering design and translating the design to a manufacturing design. The best example of this phenomenon is to compare an engineering development model that is built during the design phase and comparing it with a production model of the same product. The engineering model is normally built by highly skilled technicians to demonstrate the functional performance of the design. An engineering model is costly to complete in terms of both materials and labor. Materials for an engineering model are bought in small quantities, which increases the unit cost. Labor required to build an engineering model is expensive due to use of manual processes and procedures.

Transitioning from design to production can require what appears to be a complete redesign of the system. Figure 11-22 illustrates typical producibility concerns for this transition. The key to increasing producibility is to have a design that can be manufactured, assembled, and tested by production personnel using standard manufacturing equipment, processes, and procedures. When the preparation for the transition starts, a close interface must be maintained between the producibility and LSA organizations. Design changes to enhance

---

- Are standard components used that are readily available from more than one qualified source?
- Is any new, unproven manufacturing technology required for production?
- Are envelope clearances and package densities adequate for assembly and testing?
- Are special tooling, jigs, or fixtures required for production?
- What new assembly and test training are required for manufacturing personnel?
- Can standard automatic insertion equipment be used for electronic assembly?
- Is hand soldering required?
- Will the assembly process allow in-process testing before final assembly?
- What incoming inspection is required to yield reliable components?
- Will in-process and final test and inspection significantly shorten the product life expectancy?
- Are tolerances contained in the specification adequate to support full production?
- Is hardware and software design integrated at a level that allows testing before final assembly?
- Are sufficient test points for production testing included in the design?
- Is BIT to be used as a part of production testing?
- Have production inspection, test, and evaluation been included in the design concept?
- Are existing configuration management procedures sufficient to control design change during production?

Fig. 11-22. Producibility concerns.

producibility can have a major impact on the detailed logistics support planning that has been developed based on the engineering model. While the basic functional performance of the design will normally not change, the physical characteristics may change drastically. Changes in size, weight, assembly and component layout, wiring, parts, materials, internal interfaces, and assembly and test procedures can occur in order to increase the producibility of the design. Any design changes required to increase producibility must be input into the LSA process so that the logistics support database can be updated to reflect the most current system design.

Customer Effective interface between the customer and the LSA program on both a formal and informal basis is crucial to ensure that all program requirements are completed. As stated in previous chapters, the customer is a key source for significant inputs to several LSA program tasks. The actual exchange of information may occur through formal contractual transmittal or as a result of informal meetings. In either case, the flow of information must be monitored and controlled to ensure the inputs are received in a timely and usable manner. Initial customer supplied information is provided in the system procurement specification. Explanations or clarifications of the procurement specification that impact performance, program cost, or schedule are usually processed through the company's contract administration organization to ensure that impact to the contract is documented. This type of interchange is normally time-consuming, because the organization requiring the information must go through an intermediary to obtain inputs.

Whenever possible, the exchange of information is handled on an informal basis through guidance conferences or meetings with customer representatives. Informal meetings may be conducted on a semiformal basis, with minutes being prepared to document the results of the meeting. Some meetings are handled on a periodic basis with standing meeting groups. Typical examples of these standing informal groups are the joint technical working group (JTWG) and the integrated logistics support management team (ILSMT). By working through these informal groups, the company can discuss pertinent issues with the customer and reach resolution of problems or obtain information in an expeditious manner.

Joint Technical Working Group The purpose of the JTWG is to provide a forum for discussion of technical issues that arise through the course of the design and development of the system. Particular emphasis may be placed on interface requirements between the system being designed and other systems, either in existence or being designed by other companies. The JTWG may be attended by other companies whose products may interface with the system being designed. Any issue of a technical nature may be addressed at these meetings. The JTWG may meet at regularly scheduled intervals, such as monthly or quarterly, depending on the need to discuss issues or resolve problems. The LSA program should be represented at all JTWG meetings to have inputs on the impact of the technical issues being discussed.

Integrated Logistics Support Management Team The purpose of the ILSMT is to provide a method of establishing and maintaining a continuing interface between customer and company logistics organizations. The ILSMT, which is normally chaired by the customer, is convened to discuss the progress of the overall logistics portion of the program. The ILSMT should be looked upon as an outgrowth of the guidance conference concept where information is routinely exchanged and program status and issues are discussed. Any subject or issue concerning the LSA program should be discussed at this meeting. The ILSMT normally meets on a scheduled basis with a predetermined agenda set in advance with inputs from both the customer and the company. The ILSMT meeting may be held in conjunction with other meetings or reviews such as an LSA review, design reviews, etc. Representatives from every logistics discipline in both the customer and company organizations should attend each ILSMT.

12

LSA Program Management

Management of a Logistics Support Analysis program is a difficult assignment. The reasons for this statement are many and varied. The major problem associated with LSA management is that the number of individual efforts to be coordinated and the number of different performing organizations responsible for key portions of the overall LSA program can be staggering. As highlighted in previous chapters of the text, virtually every part of the organization involved with the design and support of the item being developed plays a part in the LSA process. Crossing organizational boundaries and coordination of parallel and series efforts that are interrelated and form a critical part of the LSA process can be a monumental undertaking. For an LSA program to be effective, the planning and coordination for management of the program must start at day one and continue throughout the program. Figure 12-1 shows the key major program milestones for LSA program management. These key milestones include pre-proposal activities, proposal preparation and submittal, contract award, program initiation, program control and tracking, and program closeout. Each of these milestones represents significant events in successful completion of an LSA program. Program success depends on the effectiveness and thoroughness of planning, implementation, and management applied to reaching and completing each milestone.

PRE-PROPOSAL ACTIVITIES

There are several things that should be done to prepare a company for an LSA program. These items, listed in FIG. 12-2, include development of company policies and procedures pertaining to how an LSA program is to be implemented, basic LSA training for key managerial and worker-level employees,

Pre-Proposal Activities
Proposal Preparation
Contract Award
Program Initiation
Program Control and Tracking
Program Closeout

Fig. 12-1. Major LSA Program Milestones.

long-range planning for acquisition of the personnel and equipment needed to support an LSA program, and market research on potential customer LSA requirements. These can and should be accomplished and in place before proceeding with an LSA program. Without a firm basis for how a company will address an LSA program, any attempt to complete such a task usually ends in a less than desirable result.

Company Policies and Procedures

A sound LSA policy supported with workable implementing procedures provides the foundation for a successful LSA program. Few companies have standing policies and procedures pertaining to LSA. Most companies jump into an LSA program with little overall company guidance on organizational responsibilities, coordination, or accountabilities for the program. Where companies have done previous LSA tasks, the normal operating mode is to informally proceed and let events direct the course of the program. When this has occurred, the LSA program usually ends up costing much more than anticipated, with little or no real impact on the final product design.

Figure 12-3 provides the basic points that should be covered in a standing company LSA policy. The policy is a concise statement of the manner in which the company will address and accomplish key LSA requirements. The procedures developed for implementing an LSA program depend on a company's unique requirements, organization, business direction, and potential LSA programs. The areas identified in FIG. 12-4 are the typical minimum procedures necessary to implement an LSA policy. These documents are vital to both company overall business and application to specific programs. Without definitive company guidelines, the success of any LSA program will be in jeopardy.

- Develop standard company LSA policies
- Develop standard company LSA procedures
- Provide managerial and worker level LSA training
- Long-range LSA capabilities planning
- LSA requirements market research

Fig. 12-2. Pre-Proposal Activities.

> The Logistics Support Analysis process, as defined in MIL-STD 1388-1A, will form the basis for preparation, analysis, and dissemination of all support and support related information for all products designed and produced by LMA, Inc. As LSA program will be conducted for all development contracts. A program manager will be assigned to oversee each LSA program. All program plans prepared for a contract will identify responsibilities for management and control of the use and dissemination of data and other analysis results using the LSA process to the fullest extent possible. Unless directed otherwise, the ILS functional manager will exercise direct control of and be accountable for the LSA program.

Fig. 12-3. LSA Policy.

Training

The cornerstone of an LSA program is adequate training at both the managerial and working levels. All too often, companies rely on past experience or on-the-job training to meet LSA program requirements, a practice which is unacceptable. The first point where a lack of training is disastrous is in pre-proposal activities. A company cannot develop adequate standing LSA policies and procedures if the LSA process and program requirements are not completely understood. Preparation of proposals for LSA efforts creates a significant risk when the preparers do not know the LSA process and do not understand the ramifications of what they are proposing. All too often, companies submit proposals for programs that: do not address critical issues, show a lack of understanding of the LSA process, and grossly over or underestimate the resources required to complete the program. When any of these occur, the company risks either losing a proposal or winning a contract that it cannot perform.

The second point where training is critical is in accomplishing required LSA tasks and associated efforts. A lack of training at the working level precipitates wasted effort and resources. When untrained employees are assigned tasks to be accomplished for the LSA program, the predictable results, with almost complete certainty, will be inaccurate, incomplete, and unusable. This creates cost overruns, schedule delays, and wasted resources. A company must provide adequate LSA training. Figure 12-5 is a matrix of LSA training that should be accomplished on a continuing basis. Managerial level training is necessary to develop company LSA policies and procedures, prepare comprehensive, accu-

LSA Implementation Guide
Standing LSA Program Plan
Standard Analysis Methods
Logistics Integration Procedures
Internal Program Coordination Guide

Fig. 12-4. Typical LSA Procedures.

Position	Familiarization	LSA Tasks	LSAR
Upper Management	X		
Engineering Management	X	X	
Logistics Management	X	X	X
Other Management	X		
Logistics Engineers	X	X	X

Fig. 12-5. LSA Training Requirements.

rate proposals, and manage LSA programs. Worker level training is necessary to ensure timely and accurate completion of detailed LSA program tasks and requirements.

Long-range Planning

Successful LSA programs don't just happen; they require detailed long-range planning. The planning must start well in advance of any program and must address in detail how a company will accomplish any program. The most obvious things that long-range planning should be concerned with are the resources needed to acquire and complete an LSA program. Program acquisition is dependent on preparation and submittal of a winning proposal. Proposals will be discussed later in this chapter, but it should be pointed out that proper planning is necessary in order to have adequate resources available to prepare the proposal when required. The other side of long-range planning is to have the resources necessary to conduct and complete an LSA program available from start to finish. A common mistake is for a company to wait until a contract is awarded and then try and figure out what resources are required and where the resources will come from, which are the makings of a losing program. To be effective, an LSA program must be afforded the resources needed to complete all tasks on time and within budget. These resources must include personnel, facilities, and equipment. Different phases of an LSA program require differing types of resources. Early phases of LSA require senior personnel who can provide needed technical decisions concerning support and supportability issues during design development. Full-scale development is manpower intensive in completing maintenance task analysis and supporting analyses; a significant increase in the numbers and types of personnel will occur during this program phase.

Training of personnel, as stated previously, is a key to a successful program in any phase and must be planned well in advance of the need for these individuals. Adequate facilities and equipment must also be available. The lack of proper tools to do the job, such as computer hardware and software, models, or

- Adequacy of company LSA policies and procedures
- Availability of personnel needed to prepare LSA portion of proposals
- Adequate training of personnel preparing proposals
- Availability of personnel required to perform LSA tasks
- Adequate training of personnel required to perform LSA tasks
- Availability of facilities needed to support an LSA program
- Availability and adequacy of computer hardware and software needed to support an LSA program
- Availability and adequacy of models and other tools needed to support an LSA program

Fig. 12-6. Long-range Planning Topics.

research materials, can hamper any program. All of these material resources require a significant amount of lead time in review, evaluation, analysis, and funding to have them available when needed. Figure 12-6 provides a list of long-range planning topics that any company concerned with LSA should continually address. Long-range planning must be timely and should be completed and the results implemented well in advance of the start of any program.

Market Research

Successful companies have an aggressive marketing activity that continually looks and plans for future business opportunities. This organization is normally product-oriented, with focus on those areas that have a potential for continuing or new business. As an adjunct to this search, the company should also look toward the LSA requirements of the marketplace and the potential customers who may require an LSA program as part of any purchase contract. LSA requirements vary between customers, each having their own particular interpretation and delivery needs. Figure 12-7 lists areas where LSA market research can prove to be extremely beneficial. Knowing potential customers

- Who are the company's potential customers?
- What are those potential customers doing now in the area of LSA?
- What new programs are being planned?
- How will LSA be used on those new programs?
- What is the competition doing in the area of LSA?
- What new applications and techniques in LSA are being developed?
- How can LSA be used more effectively to meet customer requirements?

Fig. 12-7. LSA Market Research.

and anticipating future LSA requirements allows a company to effectively accomplish long-range planning. It also increases the probability of producing winning proposals. Most important, advance information on the needs and detailed requirements that a customer has in the area of LSA and related issues, allows a company to be prepared to accomplish the tasks of an LSA program much better than "starting cold" after contract award. A small amount of upfront research, planning, and customer coordination will significantly increase the ability of a company to fulfill a customer's requirements.

PROPOSAL ACTIVITIES

Effective management of Logistics Support Analysis programs must begin during the preparation of proposals for future business. A proposal is a document prepared by a company that contains a description of the efforts, price, and schedule that the company is willing to accept to complete a potential customer's contract. The contract could be for any or all the actions required for design, development, testing, manufacture, and service of a given item or items. Program management must play a key role in developing the overall proposal, because the proposal sets forth everything that is to be done during the actual program, including LSA. The proposal preparation process for most companies is a time of too much work and too little time and resources. That is why the pre-proposal activities stated previously are so important to provide the basic capabilities and guidelines for actual preparation. Proposal activities can be divided into four basic areas as shown in FIG. 12-8: requirements identification, proposal preparation, responding to the potential customer inquiries, and negotiation of a contract. Each area requires specific actions where program management must be involved.

Requirements Identification

In most instances, companies prepare a proposal in response to a potential customer's formal solicitation for goods or services. Solicitations are normally entitled as a request for quotation (RFQ) or request for proposal (RFP). An RFQ normally applies to a definitive item where little or no development is required, such as items that have been built previously and the customer plans to purchase more of the same item. An RFP usually includes development of something new, or some undefined amount of effort, such as development of a

- Requirements Identification
- Proposal Preparation
- Customer Inquiries
- Negotiations

Fig. 12-8. Proposal Activities.

- Product Specification
- Statement of Work
- Contract Data Requirements List

Fig. 12-9. Proposal Requirements Identification Sources.

new aircraft or tank. For the purposes of this discussion, RFP will be used to signify either an RFQ or RFP since the process for preparing a proposal is the same for either type of solicitation. Sometimes prior to issuing an RFP, a request for information (RFI) may be distributed to get inputs from those interested in pursuing the business opportunity. In a few rare cases, a company may prepare an unsolicited proposal for submittal to a potential customer; however, the basic process for proposal preparation is the same for both solicited or unsolicited proposals, except that unsolicited proposals tend to be less structured in nature. In either case, the first step that must be taken in proposal preparation is an identification of the detailed customer requirements to be addressed in the proposal.

The primary source for requirements identification is customer supplied documents. These documents, shown in FIG. 12-9, are a product specification, statement of work (SOW), and contract data requirements list (CDRL), which are included as an integral part of the RFP. Each of these documents has a specific purpose and provides portions of the customer's requirements that must be combined to obtain a total requirements package.

Product Specification

The product specification provides a complete and detailed description of the product that the customer desires to be produced. Product specifications normally follow the basic outline provided in FIG. 12-10. Contained in the specification are all the requirements that the final product design must meet, both physically and functionally, to be acceptable to the customer. The following paragraphs address the contents of each section of a typical product specification.

Section 1 - Scope The scope section of the product specification is normally a brief overview statement that describes the product that the specifica-

Section 1 — Scope
Section 2 — Applicable Documents
Section 3 — Requirements
Section 4 — Quality Assurance
Section 5 — Preparation for Delivery
Section 6 — Notes

Fig. 12-10. Product specification outline.

tion is for and what the product is supposed to do. An example of a scope section is in FIG. 12-11. As noted in this illustration, the scope contains enough information to provide the reader with an understanding of the intent of the product and what the customer intends to address in the specification. From the point of putting together an LSA program, this section gives an overall direction of what the LSA program is supposed to plan for, design a support package around, and use as a final goal in sustaining operations.

Section 2 - Applicable Documents The applicable documents section is a listing of all the documents that are referenced or implied in the specification. These documents apply to the performance, design, development, testing, or delivery of the product. The list is normally several pages and typically contains the types of documents shown in FIG. 12-12. An important point to remember is that the issue, or revision, of each of the listed documents in effect on the date of any contract awarded apply to specification. This can become a significant point, because documents are constantly being changed and updated. It is not uncommon for a referenced document to be changed during the course of a contract. Such changes can impact the work being performed and cause both cost and schedule changes. When this occurs, the company must identify the change and take appropriate action to deal with any changes through contractual methods, or identify the fact that the change will not be incorporated into the ongoing effort.

Section 3 - Requirements The requirements section is normally the most extensive portion of the product specification. It provides, in great detail, the performance, design, and development specifics for the product. Figure 12-13 shows that this section addresses virtually every aspect of the product. While the information in this section is all-important to the design process, the areas that are of a significant nature to the LSA program include: reliability, maintainability, environmental conditions, transportability, safety, human engineering, logistics, and personnel and training. These areas greatly influence and guide logistics and supportability considerations throughout the design process. The reliability and maintainability subsections contain specific requirements for mean time between failure, mean time to repair, and built-in test.

The maintainability subsection also contains the number of maintenance levels and the maintenance concept envisioned by the customer. The environ-

---

1.0   Scope

This specification establishes the performance, design, development, and test requirements for the XXX system. The XXX system, also called the item or the equipment, consists of a Subsystem A, a Subsystem B, and a Subsystem C. The system will incorporate hardware and software to perform analog and digital functions of scanning, tracking, and identification of emitters operating in predetermined frequency bands.

Fig. 12-11. Product Specification, Section 1—Scope (example).

mental conditions subsection deals with the conditions where the product will be used, and the safety and human engineering subsections address how the design will affect the man-to-machine interface. The transportability subsection deals with physical movement constraints for the product in its intended environment. Normally the logistics and personnel and training subsections contain generic type references to other sections of the specification that affect supportability. An LSA program manager must be fully conversant in these specification areas in order to understand if and how the design and the LSA program are meeting customer requirements for the product.

Section 4 - Quality Assurance Contained in the quality assurance section are the customer requirements for testing the product to ensure that it meets the specification requirements, as shown in FIG. 12-14. Each test represents a milestone in product development and delivery. While all the tests are significant to meeting the customer's requirements, the tests that have the tendency to have the most impact on the LSA program are those tests in the areas of reliability and maintainability. The purpose of reliability testing is to prove that the product will function as designed. Because many of the logistics support requirements are based on the reliability of the design, any deficiencies noted in this testing will probably adversely affect the ability of the logistics support package to sustain the product when it becomes operational. Maintainability testing proves that the product can be supported by the logistics support package through either built-in test or demonstration testing. Failure to pass these

---

2.0 Applicable Documents
2.1 Government Documents
2.1.1 Government Specifications
    Military Specifications
    Other Government Specifications
2.1.2 Government Standards
    Federal Standards
    Military Standards
    Other Government Standards
2.1.3 Government Handbooks
    Military Handbooks
    Other Government Handbooks
2.2 Nongovernment Documents
    ANSI Standards
    IEEE Standards
    SAE Standards
    Other Industry Standards

Fig. 12-12. Product Specification, Section 2—Applicable Documents.

3.0 Requirements
3.1 Item Definition
3.1.1 Item Diagram
3.1.2 Interface Definition
3.1.2.1 Mechanical Interfaces
3.1.2.2 Electrical Interfaces
3.1.2.3 Power Interfaces
3.1.2.4 Cooling Interfaces
3.2 Characteristics
3.2.1 Performance Characteristics
3.2.2 Physical Characteristics
3.2.3 Reliability
3.2.4 Maintainability
3.2.5 Environmental Conditions
3.2.6 Transportability
3.3 Design and Construction
3.3.1 Materials, Processes and Parts
3.3.2 Thermal Design Requirements
3.3.3 Electrostatic Discharge
3.3.4 Marking
3.3.5 Workmanship
3.3.6 Interchangeability
3.3.7 Safety
3.3.8 Human Engineering
3.4 Logistics
3.5 Personnel and Training
3.6 Documentation

Fig. 12-13. Product Specification, Section 3—Requirements.

tests will cause the customer to demand that the product design or the support package be changed to meet specification requirements.

Section 5 - Preparation for Delivery Instructions for the preparation and physical delivery of the product for shipment are in Section 5, which contains packaging requirements, transportation, and destination, which are usu-

4.0 Quality Assurance
4.1 General
4.2 Quality Conformance
4.2.1 Acceptance Testing
4.2.2 Qualification Testing
4.3 Reliability Testing
4.3.1 Development Testing
4.3.2 Production Testing
4.4 Maintainability Testing
4.4.1 Self-test Acceptance Testing
4.4.2 Maintainability Demonstration Testing
4.5 Production Testing

Fig. 12-14. Product Specification, Section 4—Quality Assurance.

ally a restatement of contractual delivery terms. This section is normally brief, because it deals only with the preparation and physical movement of the product from the company to the customer.

Section 6 - Notes Nontechnical clarifications or other types of general information can be included in the last section of the product specification as notes. Typical types of information in this section include lists of abbreviations and acronyms used in the specification. Any other information that the customer feels appropriate can be in the notes section; however, the lists stated above are the usual limit to this section.

Statement of Work

The statement of work is a customer prepared description of the types of efforts required to do whatever is desired to be done with or to the item described by the product specification. In contrast to the structured and detailed product specification, the SOW may be limited to the major types of efforts the customer desires, with very little information as to how the work is to be done. The purpose of the SOW is to provide the company with the framework for responding to the customer with the proposed effort for the contract. A typical SOW will address the topics shown in FIG. 12-15, which is an outline that is commonly used by customers. Contained within the SOW may be very few words that describe the actual LSA effort that will be required to satisfy the support and supportability issues related to the item being designed. Figure 12-16 provides examples of SOW LSA requirements. As shown in these examples, the choice of method of implementing the LSA program is left to the company. This is where the LSA program management nightmare begins. Poorly-defined LSA requirements, especially the necessary contributions of organizations outside the logistics disciplines, can create real problems for programs and program management. If the real requirements are not completely identified by the company at the initial stages of starting to prepare a proposal, the program has little hope of meeting requirements. As shown by the examples in FIG. 12-16, the LSA program is virtually left to the imagination or ingenuity of the reader. Underlying and ill-defined LSA responsibilities for all organizations must be fully identified and highlighted.

Engineering Tasks
Manufacturing Tasks
Program Management
Reliability Engineering
Maintainability Engineering
Configuration Management
Data Management
Quality Assurance
Integrated Logistics Support

Fig. 12-15. Statement of work outline.

> 3.3.4 *Logistic Support Analysis (LSA) Program* - The contractor shall develop an LSA program in accordance with MIL-STD-1388-1A/2A. The LSA program will cover the basic Weapon Replaceable Assemblies, support equipment, support equipment test program sets, and related support equipment in support of these equipments.

Fig. 12-16. Statement of work excerpts.

Contract Data Requirements List

The third requirements section of the request for proposal is a list of the data that must be prepared and delivered to document the design or supporting analyses and tests to be performed by the company. The basic requirements for preparation and submittal of standard data items are published by the government as data item descriptions (DID). Each DID provides a standardized reference for a particular data item and should be used as a guide for preparation. Some DIDs are very specific in content and format, while others provide only a basic intent for the final document. The standard DID, consisting of ten sections, is prepared using DD Form 1664. An example of a DID for LSAR data is provided in FIG. 12-17. (Figure 12-18 explains the more significant portions of the DID format.) While the DID provides a description of a data item that the customer requires, the actual contractual requirement for the data item is contained in the contract data requirements list prepared on DD Form 1423. The CDRL is the link between the customer's specific requirements for data and the data item description. Figure 12-19 is an example of a CDRL. Up to four different data items can be recorded on a single DD Form 1423. The CDRL is divided into sixteen information blocks, which are described in FIG. 12-20. Tabulation of all data items to be submitted and the associated delivery dates for each data item will identify the total data requirements of the customer. The tabulation can then be used to construct a data preparation and delivery schedule to identify the resources that will be needed to meet the requirements of the CDRL.

Program Schedule

A key to complete identification of customer requirements is not only what is to be done, but when the work must be completed. The basic schedule for a program is made up of specific major milestones that occur at the beginning, during, and at the end of the program. Some milestones are mandatory events that must occur at a specific point in time and others are somewhat flexible, depending on program requirements. In some cases, a milestone must be achieved before the program can continue on toward the next milestone. A list of milestones common to most programs is in FIG. 12-21. Each of these milestones represents a significant point in a program.

DATA ITEM DESCRIPTION	Form Approved OMB No. 0704-0188 Exp. Date: Jun 30, 1986

1. TITLE	2. IDENTIFICATION NUMBER
Logistic Support Analysis Record (LSAR) Data	DI-ILSS-80114

3. DESCRIPTION/PURPOSE

3.1 This Data Item Description (DID) identifies deliverable LSAR data and describes the hardcopy media for their delivery. These data identify logistic support resource requirements in a correlated and integrated fashion and provide a basis for support system development activities and subsequent procurement actions and decisions.

3.2 LSAR data are used as source data in the preparation of equipment (continued on Page 2)

4. APPROVAL DATE (YYMMDD) 860221	5. OFFICE OF PRIMARY RESPONSIBILITY (OPR) TM	6a. DTIC REQUIRED	6b. GIDEP REQUIRED

7. APPLICATION / INTERRELATIONSHIP

7.1 This DID contains the format and content preparation instructions for LSAR data required by 205.2, 301.2 and 401.2 of MIL-STD-1388-1A, and appendices A and F of MIL-STD-1388-2A.

7.2 This DID is applicable to the acquisition of military systems and equipment.

7.3 DI-ILSS-80115, DI-ILSS-80116 and DI-ILSS-80117 are related to, and may be used in lieu of this DID to obtain the three automated LSAR Master files.

(continued on Page 2)

8. APPROVAL LIMITATION	9a. APPLICABLE FORMS	9b. AMSC NUMBER A3780

10. PREPARATION INSTRUCTIONS

10.1 Source Document. The applicable issue of the documents cited herein, including their approval date and dates of any applicable amendments and revisions, shall be as reflected in the contract.

10.2 Data Record Preparation. LSAR data element definitions, data field lengths, and formats for recording and reporting LSAR data shall be in accordance with appendix A of MIL-STD-1388-2A. Data requirements shall be as specified on DD Form 1949-1, LSAR Data Selection Sheet, contained in the Statement of Work. Supplemental forms, worksheets, block diagrams, and other data that are specified in the logistic support analysis plan or other plan as forming part of the LSAR data shall be deliverable to the extent specified in the Contract Data Requirements List (CDRL), DD Form 1423.

10.3 Data Delivery Media. LSAR data shall be deliverable by one or a combination of the following media, as specified by the requiring authority on DD Form 1423.

   a. Hardcopy (original, reproduced copies or computer generated copies).

   b. Microcopy (microfiche/microfilm).

10.4 Data Records. The following LSAR data records, as described in MIL-STD-1388-2A, are deliverable data under this DID as specified by the requiring authority on DD Form 1423.

   a. Data Record A, Operations and Maintenance Requirements (paragraph 20, appendix A of MIL-STD-1388-2A).

   b. Data Record B, Item Reliability and Maintainability (R&M) Characteristics (paragraph 30, appendix A of MIL-STD-1388-2A).

   c. Data Record B1, Failure Mode and Effects Analysis (paragraph 40, appendix A of

(continued on Page 2)

DD Form 1664, FEB 85	Previous edition is obsolete.	PAGE __1__ OF __2__ PAGES

Fig. 12-17. Data item description (example).

DI-ILSS-80114

3. DESCRIPTION/PURPOSE (continued)

publications; maintenance procedures; manpower and personnel requirements; training requirements; tool, support, test, measurement and
diagnostic equipment requirements; and other Integrated Logistic Support
element documentation.

7. APPLICATION/INTERRELATIONSHIP (continued)

7.4 This DID supersedes DI-L-7145A.

10. PREPARATION INSTRUCTIONS (continued)

MIL-STD-1388-2A).

d. Data Record B2, Criticality and Maintainability Analysis
(paragraph 50, appendix A of MIL-STD-1388-2A).

e. Data Record C, Operations and Maintenance Task Summary
(paragraph 60, appendix A of MIL-STD-1388-2A).

f. Data Record D, Operations and Maintenance Task Analysis
(paragraph 70, appendix A of MIL-STD-1388-2A).

g. Data Record D1, Personnel and Support Requirements (paragraph
80, appendix A of MIL-STD-1388-2A).

h. Data Record E, Support Equipment and Training Material
Description and Justification (paragraph 90, appendix A of
MIL-STD-1388-2A).

i. Data Record E1, Support Equipment and Training Material
Description and Justification continued (paragraph 95, appendix A
of MIL-STD-1388-2A).

j. Data Record E2, Unit Under Test and Automatic Test Program
(paragraph 100, appendix A of MIL-STD-1388-2A).

k. Data Record F, Facility Description and Justification
(paragraph 110, appendix A of MIL-STD-1388-2A).

l. Data Record G, Skill Evaluation and Justification (paragraph
120, appendix A of MIL-STD-1388-2A).

m. Data Record H, Support Items Identification (paragraph 130,
appendix A of MIL-STD-1388-2A).

n. Data Record H1, Support Items Identification (Application
Related) (paragraph 140, appendix A of MIL-STD-1388-2A).

o. Data Record J, Transportability Engineering Characteristics
(paragraph 150, appendix A of MIL-STD-1388-2A).

☆U.S. GOVERNMENT PRINTING OFFICE: 1988 — 605-035/80056

1. Title - name of the DID
2. Identification Number - a unique DID number formatted as DI-AAA-NNNN or DI-AAAA-NNNNN (A = alphabetic and N = numbers)
3. Description/Purpose - a brief explanation of the data item and use of the data
4. thru 6. - Administrative information
7. Application/Interrelationship - relates the DID requirements to other documents and data items
8. thru 9. -Administrative information
10. Preparation Instructions - detailed instructions on the actual requirements for format, content, preparation and delivery media

Fig. 12-18. Standard data item description format.

Contract Award   The first and one of the two most obvious program milestones is contract award. This date establishes the starting point for all contractual efforts. Many of the interim deliveries of both products and documentation are keyed to this date. As shown previously, the CDRL commonly requires delivery of many data items a stated number of days or months after contract award. The product delivery schedule is also normally stated in months after contract award. The reason for using this milestone is that the contracting process does not lend itself to predicting exactly when a contract will actually be awarded; so, rather than using specific delivery dates for many things in the contract that will probably have to be changed upon actual award, it is much easier and more efficient to simply use contract award as the single point of reference.

System Requirements Review   Normally within the first month after contract award, the company meets with the customer in a system requirements review (SRR). The purpose of the SRR is to ensure that the customer and the company are in agreement with the overall functional and performance requirements for both hardware and software of the system to be developed. Logistics aspects of the system are also discussed at this review to identify any problems that should be addressed in the requiring documents or to iron out any problems that have been identified. A logistics guidance conference that addresses LSA, provisioning, technical manuals, training, and other logistics efforts can also be held concurrently with the SRR. A successful SRR results in all concerned starting the program in agreement on overall concepts and requirements for the contract.

Initial Design Review   An initial design review (IDR) may be conducted a few months subsequent to the SRR on lengthy programs to provide the customer with an initial status on how the company is proceeding to implement the decisions reached at the SRR. At the IDR, the company demonstrates to the customer how the design is progressing to meet functional and performance requirements.

Preliminary Design Review   A preliminary design review (PDR) is conducted when the design has progressed to the point where an allocated sys-

CONTRACT DATA REQUIREMENTS LIST

CATEGORY ___ ILS ___

SYSTEM ITEM ___ BXB360-1 ___
CONTRACTOR ___ LMA ___

ATCH NR ___ TO EXHIBIT ___ D ___

TO CONTRACT PR ___

SEQUENCE NUMBER	TITLE OR DESCRIPTION OF DATA / CONTRACT REFERENCE	TECHNICAL OFFICE	FREQUENCY / AS OF DATE	DATE OF 1ST SUBMISSION / DATE OF SUBSEQUENT SUBM/EVENT ID	DISTRIBUTION AND ADDRESSEES
D001	Integrated Logistics Support Plan (ILSP) SOW 4.5	DD A	ONE/R	30DAC	AAFCXX 1/0 TOTAL 1/0
D002	Documentation, Logistic Support Analysis (LSA) SOW 4.5	DD A	ONE/R	12MAC	AAFCXX 2/0 TOTAL 2/0
D003	Logistic Support Analysis Record (LSAR) Data DI-ILSS-80114 SOW 4.5	DD A	QRTLY	6MAC	AAFCXX 1/0 TOTAL 1/0
	REMARKS: TO BE REVIEWED AT QUARTERLY LSAR REVIEWS. HARD-COPY ACCEPTABLE. FINAL DELIVERY BY MAGNETIC TAPE IN MIL-STD-1388-2A FORM AT 30 DAYS PRIOR TO CONTRACT COMPLETION.				
D004	Provisioning and Other Pre-procurement Screening Data SOW 4.5	DD A	ONE/R	SEE BLOCK 16,	DLSC 1/0 TOTAL 1/0
	REMARKS: TO BE SUBMITTED TO DLSC 60 DAYS PRIOR TO EACH PROVISIONING CONFERENCE.				

PREPARED ___ DATE 10/0/96

APPROVED BY ___ DATE 10/3/86

DD FORM 1423, 1 JAN 75   S/N 0102 LF 014-2300   REPLACES EDITION OF 1 JUN 68, WHICH IS USABLE.   PAGE ___ OF ___ PAGES

Fig. 12-19. CDRL (example).

Block 1, Sequence Number - Contract line item number links the data item to a unique contractual requirement

Block 2, Title - Title of the data item

Block 3, Subtitle - May be used when the actual data item to be submitted requires further definition

Block 4, Authority - Identifies the data item description (DID) that applies to the data item to be prepared

Block 5, Contract Reference - Links the data item to a specific statement of work paragraph

Block 6, Technical Office - Identifies the customer organization that has cognizance of the data item

Block 7, DD250 Req - States whether a DD form 250 (code DD) is required to be submitted for payment or if a letter of transmittal (code LT) is required to accompany the submittal

Block 8, APP Code - States if the data item is to be submitted for approval, review, or information only

Block 9, Input to IAC - Identifies data items controlled by automated processing by the customer

Block 10, Frequency - The frequency that the data item must be submitted, i.e., ONE/R = one time submittal with revisions as necessary, QRTLY = quarterly submittals, etc.

Block 11, As of Date - Normally used for recurring reports such as a monthly report that is as of the 15th of the month

Block 12, Date of 1st Submission - When the data item is to be submitted. Normally keyed to events such as xx number of days after contract award (3MAC = 3 months after contract award) or xx number of days prior to an event (30 DPT = 30 days prior to test)

Block 13, Date of Subsequent Submittals - May be used to schedule submittals after 1st submittal, most commonly used when the 1st submittal is for a preliminary report and the subsequent report is a final report

Block 14, Distribution and Addressees - Identifies to whom the data item is to be submitted and the number of regular and reproducible copies to be submitted to each addressee. Recipients are normally identified by using government office symbols. These office symbols are explained in the information text portion of the RFP

Block 15, Total - Sums the total number of regular and reproducible copies to be provided with each submittal

Block 16, Remarks - Contains other pertinent information about the data item. When the customer deviates from the standard DID requirements or has other changes information that affects the preparation or delivery of the data item, that information is entered in this bock.

Fig. 12-20. CDRL information.

Contract Award
System Requirements Review
Initial Design Review
Preliminary Design Review
Critical Design Review
First Article Test
Qualification Test
Functional Configuration Audit
Physical Configuration Audit
Maintainability Demonstration
Production Readiness Review
Product Delivery
Contract Completion

Fig. 12-21. Typical Program Milestones.

tem baseline can be established. The purpose of the PDR is for the company to demonstrate how the system design will meet each functional requirement of the product specification. At the PDR, such issues as reliability, maintainability, testability, and preliminary logistics considerations are also addressed. The PDR is normally a key contractual milestone. If the company cannot completely define how each functional requirement will be met, the customer can direct changes or further definition, and successful completion of the PDR may be required before the program can continue.

Critical Design Review The purpose of the critical design review (CDR) is for the company to completely demonstrate to the customer how each functional, physical, and performance requirement for the design will be met. Each segment of the design, down to the lowest hardware and software level, is discussed in detail. A complete documentation package for the system may be required. All aspects of the contract are addressed at CDR. Customer approval of all portions of the CDR is normally required before the program can proceed. The system design presented at CDR becomes the system functional baseline. Any changes to this baseline must normally be approved by the customer.

First Article Test Formal testing of the first system built is called first article test. The purpose of first article test is to demonstrate that the system, as designed, meets all functional and physical performance requirements. The first article is normally a system that is built with extreme care to ensure that each manufacturing and assembly process is done correctly. First article testing is witnessed by customer representatives and conducted and documented per a preapproved test procedure. Successful completion of first article test is a major program milestone and almost always a mandatory contractual requirement.

Qualification Testing The purpose of qualification testing is to prove that the final design meets functional and physical performance requirements in the intended use environment of the system. The system tested must have been produced using the standard manufacturing processes and procedures that will be used during production of all deliverable systems. Qualification testing is conducted using customer approved test procedures and verifies that the system fulfills all customer requirements. Before any production systems can be delivered, the company must successfully complete qualification testing.

Functional Configuration Audit After qualification testing is completed, the customer performs an administrative audit of all test results to confirm that the system design meets all functional requirements. The FCA verifies that the design functional configuration of a system that has passed qualification testing is in compliance with the product specification. This audit addresses both hardware and software. The audit is conducted per an approved audit plan, and the results are formally documented and approved by the customer.

Physical Configuration Audit The purpose of a PCA is to verify that the final design of the unit that passed qualification testing matches the company prepared engineering design documentation package. The audit consists of a physical teardown of a system with the correlation of each assembly and piece part to the drawing package. The customer normally either conducts or witnesses the PCA. Any differences between the documentation package and the actual configuration of the system must be corrected before the audit is complete. The approved PCA documentation package becomes the production baseline for the system. Any design changes to the production baseline must be approved by the customer before implementation.

Maintainability Demonstration The ability of the system, as designed, to be supported using the company developed logistics support package is evaluated by a maintainability demonstration. The demonstration can be conducted by either the company, the customer, or a combination of both per a customer-approved demonstration procedure. The demonstration is conducted by introducing predetermined faults into an operating system and evaluating the ability of built-in test capabilities or manual troubleshooting to find the fault. After the fault is identified, only the company prepared technical documentation and approved support and test equipment must be used to repair the system. Normally, the company prepares a list of faults from which the customer selects a predetermined number. To successfully complete the maintainability demonstration, all faults must be corrected within the maintainability parameters contained in the product specification. If the design proves to be such that maintainability parameters cannot be met due to design problems or incomplete or inadequate logistics considerations, the customer can direct that changes be incorporated before the program proceeds.

Production Readiness Review A production readiness review (PRR) may be conducted to verify that the company has in place all the controls, processes, and procedures necessary to start production of the system. Normally, the PRR addresses the administrative side of production, i.e., documentation, training, etc., and the availability of the facilities, equipment, and personnel necessary to physically manufacture the system. The PRR may also address the ability of subcontractors and vendors to produce applicable portions of the qualified system. When a PRR is contractually required, successful completion is normally a mandatory requirement before production begins.

Product Delivery   Actual delivery of production systems is one of the most important contract milestones. Delivery schedules are contractually mandated and any changes or reasons for not meeting a delivery schedule are considered major program occurrences. Every event that leads up to product delivery contributes to the ability of the company to deliver on time. Inability to meet delivery schedules can negatively impact the company's profitability for current and future contracts, because historical delivery performance is a significant evaluation factor for contract awards.

Contract Completion   Completion of all contractual requirements is, of course, the last milestone for any program; however, delivery of the last production system does not constitute contract completion. After final delivery, several administrative actions and documentation deliveries may be required to complete the contract. This includes final billings, cleanup and archival of design documentation, and closeout of internal accounts. Actual contract completion may not occur until weeks or even months after final system delivery. If a contract includes warranty, contractor support, or field service provisions, completion may not occur for several years after delivery is completed.

PROPOSAL PREPARATION

Preparation of a proposal is a time-consuming and extremely high-pressure activity. It seems that there is never sufficient time to do all the things that appear necessary to produce a proposal that addresses every aspect of the work to be done. To maximize a company's proposal process there must be a concerted effort to use all available resources as efficiently as possible within the time allotted for a response to the customer's request. In addition to providing the formal RFP, the customer also provides each prospective respondent with other information that is critical to preparation of a winning proposal. This information must be used to the company's advantage during proposal preparation. Using this information, the company must produce a proposal that is responsive to the customer's requirements and schedule at a competitive price.

Customer Information

In addition to the product specification, statement of work, and contract data requirements list, a customer will normally also provide, with an RFP, other information that relates to actual proposal preparation. This information, shown in FIG. 12-22, is to aid each bidder in preparing a proposal that is uniform to allow equitable evaluation and provides the company with an opportunity to gain more information through a controller dialog with the customer.

Preparation Instructions   The customer provided preparation instructions normally deal with administrative detailed as to how the proposal is to be

Preparation Instructions
Evaluation Criteria
Questions and Clarifications
Bidder Conference

Fig. 12-22. Customer Proposal Preparation Information.

organized, formatted, and submitted. The typical areas addressed in preparation instructions are shown in FIG. 12-23. Proposals have at least two and many times five or more volumes, each dedicated to a specific topic or topics. A limited proposal may have only two volumes, technical and cost, where a significant program can require volumes for technical, management, integrated logistics support, past performance and related experience, and cost. Note that cost is always a separate volume. The technical volume addresses how the technical requirements of the product specification are to be met. The management volume presents the company's management organization, approach, and philosophy to be used on the program.

Integrated logistics support may be discussed in a separate volume, depending on the emphasis placed on this area. When a separate ILS volume is required, the LSA program should be a major part of the volume and it must also be tied to the technical volume through identification of the interrelated efforts outside the ILS arena that will be implemented to support the total program. Past performance and related experience deal with the company's abilities that have been demonstrated on previous programs and how this expertise and capabilities will be applied to the proposed program. The cost volume contains detailed cost and pricing information on the labor and materials required for the effort that is being proposed. In many cases, the customer will provide a basic outline for each volume. The outline identifies all the topics that the customer feels must be addressed in order to show that a company understands and has the capabilities to perform the proposed efforts. Some outlines are brief, where others are extremely detailed. These outlines should be followed to the letter. The number of possible pages of paper submitted in response to an RFP can be unbelievable. A few years ago, it was not uncommon for a company to submit proposals that could be measured in feet rather than inches. To curb this practice, customers have started placing a limit on the number of pages that can be in each volume of a proposal. Page limitations must be adhered to or a proposal can be rejected. The number of copies of each volume

Number and Title of Proposal Volumes
Volume Outlines and Content
Page Limitations
Number of Copies of Each Volume
Type Size and Printing
Proposal Binding

Fig. 12-23. Proposal Preparation Instructions.

to be submitted vary by RFP and the evaluation scheme to be used by the customer. Copy instructions must also be adhered to when submitting responses.

Figure 12-24 is an example of the preparation instructions for an ILS volume of a proposal. Note that these instructions contain a brief topic outline, page limitations, and number of copies of the volume to be submitted. Other administrative information contained in the proposal preparation instructions may include the type size to be used in printing the proposal, limits on the number

---

Volume 4, ILS Proposal - The ILS proposal must demonstrate the offeror's ability to satisfy ILS requirements during the periods of design, development, and transition to Navy support. The proposal shall be one (1) volume, bound separately, and shall not exceed fifty (50) pages including Table of Contents with reference to topic, applicable paragraphs and page numbers of the proposal. Convincing details on understanding of the requirements and ability to meet these requirements is required.

The ILS proposal shall contain Sections as follows:

(1) Table of Contents
(2) Introduction
(3) ILS Planning and Management - This section shall contain as a minimum convincing details on the following:

    a. an understanding of the requirements to manage Integrated Logistics Support and to monitor, analyze and correct ILS deficiencies.
    b. an understanding of integrated logistics support program requirements for Aeronautical systems and equipment.
    c. an understanding of the life-cycle cost for ILS.
    d. Integrated Logistics Support Plan.
    e. Operational Logistics Support Plan.
    f. Logistic Support Analysis Plan.
    g. Compatibility with Existing ILS program.

(4) Logistics Support Analysis (LSA) - This section shall include as a minimum, convincing details on the following:

    a. Logistics Support Analysis
    b. Maintenance Engineering - planning and analysis
    c. Work Unit Codes

(5) Support Equipment and ILS for Support Equipment - This section shall include as a minimum convincing details on the following:

    a. an understanding of Support concept
    b. an understanding of Support Equipment ILS
    c. an understanding of Test Program Set (TPS) development
    d. an understanding of Support Equipment Requirements Document (SERD).

(6) Supply Support - This section shall include as a minimum convincing details on the following:

    a. an understanding of the requirements for supply support
    b. interim supply support
    c. provisioning requirements
    d. spare and spare parts delivery process
    e. packaging, handling, storage and transportation of spares and spare parts.

Fig. 12-24. ILS Proposal Volume Preparation Instructions (example).

and size of foldout pages for illustrations, how pages are to be numbered, and acceptable methods for binding proposals. A common statement contained in preparation instructions is that overly elaborate or decorative proposals are not to be submitted.

Evaluation Criteria The customer will normally provide prospective companies with the criteria by which all proposals will be evaluated. This information gives the company an insight as to which areas of the proposal the evaluators will view as most important and where the most emphasis should be placed when preparing the proposal. It is obvious that, in most instances, the lowest proposed price normally wins. However, to be considered for contract award, a company must be technically qualified and must demonstrate the ability to perform all required tasks within the allotted schedule. Therefore, the evaluation criteria should be used as a guide to ensure that a proposal is responsive to all customer requirements contained in the RFP. Figure 12-25 illustrates the evaluation criteria for the ILS volume shown in FIG. 12-24.

Questions and Clarifications After reviewing an RFP, there are always questions about what the customer is requesting. The normal proposal process allows companies to ask the customer for clarification of issues or other questions that may have arisen during the review of the RFP. The proposal instructions contain the approved method for submittal of questions and requests for clarifications. However, certain rules must be followed. The customer will usually accept written questions and requests for clarification for a period between release of the RFP and the due date for proposals. Responses are normally provided in a timely manner so that any changes can be incorpo-

---

Integrated Logistics Support Capability - (as evidenced by the content of the Integrated Logistic Support Proposal) - Evaluation of Integrated Logistics Support Capability will be based upon the following elements, listed in descending order of importance (Elements 1 and 2 are considered to be of equal importance and together constitute the major portion of the ILS evaluation; Elements 3 and 4 are also of equal importance but not as significant as elements 1 and 2; Elements 5, 6 and 7 are also of equal importance but not as significant as elements 3 and 4. Elements 8, 9, 10, 11 and 12 are also of equal importance and together are of least importance for evaluation purposes):

Element   1. ILS Planning and Management
           2. Logistics Support Analysis
           3. Support Equipment and ILS for SE
           4. Supply Support
           5. Personnel, Training and Training Material
           6. Publications
           7. Facilities
           8. Pre-Operational Support
           9. ILS Evaluation
          10. Compatibility with Existing ILS program
          11. Configuration Management
          12. Depot and Intermediate Maintenance

Fig. 12-25. ILS Volume Evaluation Criteria.

rated into the proposal. A copy of all questions and requests for clarification and the customer responses are distributed to all companies that received the RFP. This is to ensure that each company has a fair and equal chance in award of a contract.

Bidder Conference The customer usually conducts a bidder conference. All companies that are considering submitting a proposal are invited to attend this conference. The purpose of the conference is to provide a forum for direct customer to company interface to discuss issues and areas of concern. The customer may require that written questions and concerns be submitted for discussion at the conference. Minutes of the conference are normally provided for all recipients of the RFP. An important sidelight of the conference is that it allows a company to determine the other companies who will be competing for the contract.

Preparation Methodology

Preparation of the company's response to an RFP should be done in a systematic and methodical process to ensure that all aspects of the potential contract are addressed. An accepted methodology for preparing a proposal consists of the steps shown in FIG. 12-26. Using the product specification, statement of work, and contract data requirement list as a baseline in conjunction with the customer supplied information concerning the requirements for the preparation of the proposal, a company can follow this methodology to prepare a responsive and realistic proposal.

Work Breakdown Structure The first thing that must be done to start developing a proposal is to determine all the tasks to accomplish the customer requirements that were identified as previously described. A work breakdown structure (WBS) has proven to be a very effective method for ensuring that every task is properly identified. Development of a complete WBS can be a time-consuming and complicated task due to the necessary level of detail and the coordination of obtaining and correlating the inputs of all the organizations and functions that will contribute to the overall program. It is recommended that the team approach be used to ensure that interrelated tasks are completely addressed. The best way to describe a WBS is that it is a diagram of all tasks, starting at the top level with each major task divided into subtasks, then sub-

- Prepare detailed work breakdown structure
- Prepare detailed program schedule
- Write responsive proposal text
- Estimate contract cost
- Determine proposal price
- Proposal review
- Submit proposal

Fig. 12-26. Proposal Preparation Steps.

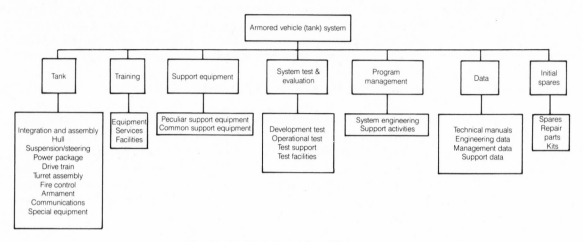

Fig. 12-27. Work Breakdown Structure.

tasks are further divided into subtasks until every task, down to the lowest level has been identified. The goal is to break down the program wherever possible to an identifiable and manageable amount of effort. A rule of thumb is to reduce each task to a duration of about 40 hours, one manweek, of effort. A major program may have hundreds or thousands of lowest level tasks.

When completed, the WBS provides complete identification and duration of every task that must be done, the interrelationship, precedence, and dependency of each task, and the organization or function responsible for completing each task. MIL-STD 881A, Work Breakdown Structures for Defense Materiel Items, provides general guidance on preparation of a WBS. The guidance contained in this standard must be tailored to fit each specific application; however, the concepts for a WBS are applicable to any program. Figure 12-27 shows the top three levels of a typical WBS. Note that in this figure it is easy to distinguish the generic application of a WBS to virtually any program. Figure 12-28 is a lower

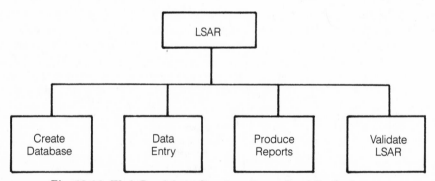

Fig. 12-28. Work Breakdown Structure (Lower Level Portion).

level portion of a WBS that identifies the tasks that must be done to prepare the LSAR for a specific assembly of the system being designed. This portion of the WBS should be repeated for each assembly, which, when summed, would provide the total effort necessary to research, prepare, and maintain the LSAR for the system. The WBS provides a medium for communicating the total effort for a program. When properly used, the WBS serves as a primary tool for not only preparing a proposal, but also for continuous management of the program from cradle to grave.

Program Schedule   The next step in preparing a proposal is to develop a detailed program schedule. This schedule is different from the customer supplied program schedule discussed previously in this chapter in that it identifies all the tasks that the company will accomplish to meet the customer's desired schedule. The basis for constructing the schedule is the program WBS. By using the WBS, which identifies all the tasks to be done as input, the company program schedule should be inclusive of all program tasks. The WBS tells what must be done and the schedule tells when tasks must be started and completed to meet the customer schedule. The final schedule must support the customer's schedule. There are two ways to approach putting the schedule together. One way is to select the first WBS task to be started and build a schedule sequentially until every WBS task has been completed. The other method is to start with the completion of the last WBS task and work backwards through the entire WBS until each task has been started. The key to either method is knowing the duration of each task and the interrelationship and dependencies of each task. Either method works and provides a road map through the program.

The first method tends to result in a longer total program duration, because it builds on task starts and uses outputs to other tasks as starting points for program continuation. The second method usually results in a tighter overall elapsed program time, because it looks at when a previous task must end in order to give following tasks the required inputs. Both methods have pluses and minuses; however the second method is normally used because it usually results in the minimum length of time that will be required to complete the program. Because schedule is normally a key evaluation criteria, it is imperative that, regardless of which method is used, the final program schedule is as responsive as possible to customer requirements. Developing a schedule from a complete and accurate WBS is the only way that a company can be assured that every task is properly identified and scheduled. Figure 12-29 provides excerpts from a typical company prepared program schedule. Note that the schedule excerpt gives complete identification of each task, responsible organization for task completion, task start and completion, and task relationships.

Proposal Writing   Proposal writing is an art. A proposal is written to convey to the customer the capability of the company to perform the effort required by the RFP. There is no set style or method for writing proposals, but it is of the utmost importance that the final proposal adequately address each

Events	Weeks																																																			
	1	2	3	4	5	6	7	8	9	10	11	12	13	14	15	16	17	18	19	20	21	22	23	24	25	26	27	28	29	30	31	32	33	34	35	36	37	38	39	40	41	42	43	44	45	46	47	48	49	50	51	52
Contract Award	△																																																			
Preliminary Design Review								△																																												
Critical Design Review																				△																																
Functional Configuration Audit																																			△																	
Physical Configuration Audit																																								△												
Qualification Test																																														△						
Equipment Delivery																																																			△	
Program Reviews					△					△				△					△					△						△					△									△						△		
LSA Guidance Conference				△																																																
LSA				○————————————————————————————————————▷																																														
LSAR												○——————————————————————————————————▷																																							
LSAR Reviews																△						△				△									△			△														
Provisioning Conference																																					△														
Technical Manual Preparation																											○——————————————————————————————————————▷																				
Spares Delivery																																															△					
Contract Completion																																															△					△

Legend
△ Milestone
○ Activity Start
— Activity End

Fig. 12-29. Detailed Program Schedule.

point contained in the RFP. Proposals should be readable, as brief as possible, and factual. Often, proposals merely repeat the words contained in the RFP, and this is unacceptable. The proposal text must show that the company has a complete understanding of the scope and requirements of the tasks to be done. The proposal writer must tie all of the various requirements contained in separate parts of the RFP into one central thought. For example, an RFP will normally have requirements for a single task distributed in several different segments of the RFP.

A typical statement of work identifies a requirement for LSAR data, but contractual delivery requirements for the LSAR data are contained in the CDRL, and a detailed description of the data to be submitted is provided in the DID for LSAR data. The proposal writer must tie all three of these requirements into a single response in the proposal to demonstrate a complete understanding of the total requirement for preparation and submittal of LSAR data. An example of an unacceptable and an acceptable proposal response to the requirement for LSAR data is provided in FIG. 12-30. A similar response must be prepared for every task in the WBS.

Cost Estimating Contractors must not only be able to perform the work required by the RFP; they must be able to complete the contract for a reasonable profit. Cost estimating of proposals is as important as writing. In many cases, the bottom line price is the determining factor as to which contractor will receive a contract. When a contractor submits a price to the government, it must be fully justified, and the cost for performing each task must be identifiable. Proposal cost estimating is accomplished systematically by first determining the labor and materials required to perform each task identified in the work breakdown structure. After the labor and materials are identified the total proposal cost estimate is computed using a standard method based on the following:

Unacceptable Response
LSAR data will be submitted as required by the Statement of Work. The data will be the results of the required LSA effort.

Acceptable Response
LSAR data will be prepared as required by paragraph 4.5 of the Statement of Work. The data will be produced as an output of Task 401 of MIL-STD 1388-1A and will be recorded using LSAR data records contained inMIL-STD 1388-2A. Data elements for applicable LSAR data records will be provided as required by DD Form 1949-1 contained in Appendix A of the Statement of Work. The data will be managed through the use of a single computerized database currently installed in the ILS activity facility. Through the use of this computerized system, all logistics personnel will have access to the information as it is generated for used in developing support resource requirements for the new equipment design. The LSAR database will be delivered, as required by DI-ILSS-80114, using magnetic tape media. LSAR summary reports will be provided in hardcopy media.

Fig. 12-30. Example Proposal Response.

- Direct labor - Labor that is required to specifically accomplish tasks that are required by the SOW. Examples of persons who normally perform direct labor are design engineers, logistics engineers, assembly line personnel, direct supervision personnel, and technicians. Direct labor is always quantified in terms of the number of hours required to perform a task.

- Overhead - Expenses that are incurred as part of the overall effort to complete a contract that cannot be attributed to a single task. Overhead expenses normally fall into three categories: indirect labor, employee benefits, and resources. Examples of indirect labor include secretaries, shipping clerks, and computer operators. These individuals are required to support the contract and their daily activities are necessary to complete the contract, but their efforts cannot normally be linked to a specific task. Employee benefits normally include health and life insurance, vacation and sick pay, pension plans, and any other benefits that the company provides to employees. Resources can include any expense that is required to support the contract. Examples of this expense include rent, utilities, office supplies, and equipment. Overhead is expressed as a percentage of direct labor and is determined based on historical expenditures. A company's overhead rate must be approved by the government. Overhead rates vary between companies. A company that does not require a large investment in equipment or facilities may have an overhead rate of 75 percent, where a heavy manufacturer may have a rate as high as 250 percent.

- Material - The cost of materials required to build or produce an item of equipment or accomplish tasks that result in deliverable items must be specifically identified. Examples of material costs are raw steel, resistors, nuts and bolts, or any other items that can be traced through the manufacturing process. Actual quotes from the sources of materials or reasonable historical data are used when preparing a proposal price.

- Other Direct Costs (ODC) - Expenses that are required to fulfill the contract, but are not categorized above. ODC can include contract labor, consultants, and travel expenses if directly connected with the contract. Actual anticipated costs must be used.

- General and Administrative Expenses (G&A) - Expenses that are incurred by the company as a part of doing business, but cannot be attributed directly to any contract. Examples of G&A include salaries for upper management, contracts and marketing personnel, and legal expenses, and expenses for facilities that are not directly related to any contract. G&A is also expressed as a percentage based on historical data and must be approved by the government.

- Fee or Profit - The amount of money that a company expects to earn by completing the proposed effort. Fees are expressed as a percentage and normally range between 7 percent and 15 percent, depending on the type of effort being performed.

The standard method for estimating the cost for a proposal is illustrated at FIG. 12-31. In this example, the direct labor hours have been estimated for a portion of a typical LSA task. All other program tasks would be estimated in the same manner. The best way for estimating the number of hours required to accomplish a task is to use historical information from completion of similar tasks. After the direct labor hours have been estimated, the number is multiplied by the labor rate for each type of labor required. Labor rates are maintained by contractors and reflect the median wage for different categories of personnel. In the example, the labor rates are for a senior logistics engineer, a logistics engineer, and a clerk. The direct labor dollars are then multiplied by the overhead rate to determine the anticipated cost for employees and other resources to support the contract. The next step is to add the cost of materials and ODC. This figure is then multiplied by the G&A rate. The resulting figure is the projected cost for the company to complete the contract. Although each company has its own rates, the method for using the rates to price a proposal is the same. These figures, especially direct labor estimates, have a dual significance. They form the basis for the proposal cost, and the estimated direct labor should later be used as a starting point for budget allocations when the contract is awarded.

Proposal Price   There is a significant difference between the cost and price of a proposal. The proposal cost is the dollar value of the direct and indirect labor and materials that will be required to complete the program as defined by the WBS and schedule. The proposal price is the dollar value that the company is willing to accept to meet the contract requirements. The big difference between cost and price is the profit, or sometimes loss, that the company expects at the completion of the contract. This is a management decision. In order to make this decision, management must first know how much it will cost to complete the contract requirements, which is why accurate costing is imperative. The decision as to the amount of profit, or loss, that the company expects to accrue is dictated by overall company business goals. A company may elect to accept a loss on a contract if the long-term benefits, such as follow-on production or strengthening of market position, outweigh the short-term losses for a single contract. The final proposal price is therefore solely a management decision. The program manager must be cognizant of the decision and use the proposed program costs as a guide to meeting the management profit or loss decision. If a company routinely looks for a 10-percent profit on contracts, the proposal price can easily be determined by adding this percentage to the total estimated costs, as shown in FIG. 12-31.

Step 1. Compute direct labor

Task: Prepare LSAR data

Labor Grade	Hours Required	Labor Rate	Total
Senior logistician	800	$22.00	$17,600.00
Logistician	2100	16.00	33,600.00
Data Entry	200	9.50	1,900.00
Total direct labor cost			$53,100.00

Step 2. Compute overhead costs

(Direct labor cost × Overhead rate)
$53,100.00 × 75 percent =   39,825.00

Total direct labor and overhead costs $92,925.00

Step 3. Compute material and other direct costs

Material costs = none
Other direct costs
   Computer charge (400 hrs @ $55/hr) =   22,000.00
   LSAR software   20,000.00

Total costs $134,925.00

Step 4. Compute G&A expenses

(Total costs × G&A rate)
$134,925.00 × 15 percent =   20,238.75

Total cost plus G&A   155,163.75

Step 5. Compute fee

(Total cost plus G&A × Fee rate)
$155,163.75 × 15 percent = $23,274.56

Total proposal price $178,438.31

Fig. 12-31. Proposal Cost Estimating.

Proposal Review   A proposal must go through a series of various types of reviews before submittal to the customer. The review process must be planned and controlled to be effective and efficient or the problems caused through miscommunications and lack of direction will outweigh any benefits received from the review. The purpose of the review should be to verify that the proposal addresses the customer requirements, that all statements contained in the proposal are accurate and consistent, and that the overall proposal is in compliance with the RFP. The review should be divided into three distinct areas: general administrative conformance, written text, and cost. No single person should do the total review. Companies normally have a set procedure for proposal review centered around a review team, sometimes called a red team or tiger team. The team consists of individuals who are extremely knowledgeable in the proposed product and the technical requirements of the RFP. A company may use an outside organization or selected consultants to augment an internal company review team. The members of the review team must not have been a part of the team that prepared the proposal in order to have a completely objective review.

The review process should allow time for incorporation of comments and changes. Figure 12-32 shows how the review process fits into the overall proposal process. Administrative review of the format should be based on the preparation instructions contained in the RFP. This activity should be relatively simple to accomplish; however, because it is so obvious, it is often overlooked. Failure to comply with the basic preparation instructions can be cause for disqualification; therefore, every effort must be made to ensure that the basic formatting requirements are followed explicitly. Review of the written text is extremely significant, because it must convey the company's ability to perform and produce to the customer's requirements. The text must be in sufficient detail to cover all aspects of the proposed effort and it must be consistent in theme and provide logical analyses of the work to be done.

As pointed out earlier in this chapter, requirements for a given task may be split into several different areas of segments of the RFP. The written text must consolidate requirements into a single response. Review of cost estimates must be accomplished in view of the written text response to the RFP. There must be a correlation between the effort described in the text and corresponding cost estimate. This is an area where much care should be given to ensure that the two segments of the proposal match or the customer may be given an image of the company not understanding the scope or detailed requirements of the RFP. The overall review process should be structured to provide specific usable inputs back to the proposal preparation team. Preprinted review forms can aid in conveying needed changes or areas of concern, and the forms give management the ability to focus on specific proposal problems or areas where the company should bolster its proposal preparation capabilities.

Proposal Submittal Submittal of the proposal to the customer should be a relatively simple process, but, inevitably, problems usually occur just when least expected. Availability of the resources necessary for actual publication and duplication of the proposal documents has proven to be the make or break point for many companies fighting a deadline for submittal. Every RFP contains explicit instructions on the physical submittal of proposals. The instructions will identify the time and place for submittal. If the instructions state that the proposal is due at 3:00 p.m. on a certain day, then that is the latest acceptable time, not 3:01 p.m. Over the years many companies, even the giants in the industry, have lost out on an opportunity, simply because the proposal arrived too late.

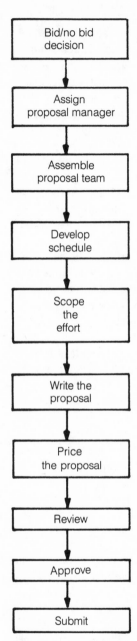

Fig. 12-32. *Proposal Preparation Process.*

Another item that can be overlooked is the number of copies of each proposal volume that are required to be submitted. It is not uncommon for a different number of copies of each volume must be submitted. Little details such as these can have major impacts on whether or not a company's proposal is accepted by the customer.

Post-Submittal Activities After the proposal is submitted, the proposal process is not finished if the company expects to receive a contract. There are normally three significant occurrences before a contract is awarded: another round of clarifying or revising the proposal, an audit performed by the customer, and contract negotiations. Initially, the customer may review all proposals received to determine the companies who have submitted the most acceptable proposals. Based on this first evaluation, the customer may issue a request for best and final offer (BAFO) from selected companies. The BAFO may restate or revise the scope of work to be done, delivery quantities, or program schedule. The company may be required to answer questions concerning their proposal, revise proposed tasks, or address changes to the statement of work, product specification, or contract data requirements list. The BAFO cycle may be as lengthy and time-consuming as the original proposal effort; however, it must be done if the company wishes to continue to pursue the business opportunity.

From the final offers submitted, the customer normally selects the top two or three for continuing the proposal effort. These final contenders may be audited to verify rates, proposed effort, or overall understanding of the RFP requirements through a process called fact-finding. The period of fact-finding is normally limited in duration to the minimum time required to gain the information necessary to select the eventual contract recipient. The proposal process draws to a close with negotiations between the customer and the company tentatively selected for contract award. Contract negotiations, when complete, result in contract award to the company that best meets the customer requirements. Negotiations are not a trivial process, because the customer and the company must reach agreement on every aspect of the work to be performed, program schedule, and price, and then a written contract is signed.

PROGRAM INITIATION

Initiation of the program after contract award should be an extension of the proposal process. The planning and effort expended on completing the proposal should be used to form the basis for getting the program started off on the right foot. There are several basic areas that are logical follow-ons from proposal to actual contract performance. These areas include the program plan, work breakdown structure, and detailed program schedule prepared as part of the proposal. Each of these should be used to the fullest extent possible to implement the program.

Program Plans

Logistics disciplines are routinely tasked, as part of the CDRL, to prepare planning documents such as an Integrated Logistics Support Plan and a Logistics Support Analysis Plan. Submittal of draft copies of these documents may have been required as part of the proposal. The preparation and use of these documents prove to be invaluable in managing the LSA effort. As previously described in Chapter 7, the LSA plan provides detailed concepts and implementing instructions for how the LSA program is to be conducted. The LSA plan must be one of the first things that is done upon contract award. Any program plan should be treated as a dynamic document that is continually reviewed and updated throughout the program to provide the best possible continuity and direction for completing program tasks.

Work Breakdown Structure

The work breakdown structure prepared for the proposal must be used as the foundation for planning contract performance. Because the proposal WBS reflects the company's concept for the effort and tasks to be performed, and it matched the cost estimate for completing the program, the WBS is the only logical place to begin managing the program. The first thing that must be done is to compare the WBS with the negotiated contract. It is not uncommon for significant changes to the program to be made as a part of the contract negotiation process. These changes must be incorporated into the WBS to ensure that the proper tasks are planned and eventually performed. This is an area, incorporation of negotiated changes, where many companies run into problems that are not realized until schedules are missed or unnecessary effort is expended.

Where necessary, the WBS should be refined and expanded based on better program information obtained from the customer during fact-finding, negotiations, and after contract award. A properly prepared WBS identifies every task to be done, the duration of the task, and the type of resources in both materials and labor required to complete the tasks. The WBS has proven to be an invaluable tool for the LSA program manager in identifying and coordinating the dispersed efforts contributed by logistics and nonlogistics organizations within the company that are necessary to complete the LSA program tasks. Using this structured management tool, the individual task inputs and outputs can be organized and coordinated to allow a smooth flow of information throughout the program.

Program Schedule

The effort stated for review and updating the WBS must also be done for the proposal program schedule. Any modifications due to negotiated changes must be incorporated into the schedule to reflect the final contract performance and delivery requirements. Often, a company, after contract award, will start a new program schedule from scratch. This is a waste of time and resources and will probably not be as accurate or supportable as the updated original proposal schedule. The combination of the program schedule with the WBS provides invaluable information for the program manager for program initiation and management throughout the program. One of the single most important points to managing an LSA program is to continually monitor and control LSA task inputs and outputs. The most common problems in controlling tasks inputs occur when the inputs are being generated as outputs of a non-LSA effort. As shown in previous chapters, a majority of the initial inputs to the LSA program are outputs as the result of efforts of other than the logistics organization. Coordination of the timely availability of this information is where the LSA program manager makes or breaks a program.

Additionally, the WBS and schedule provide detailed information on resources needed to complete the program. An in-depth analysis of the combination of these two documents can result in the identification of all the resources needed to complete the program, the types of resources required, and when the resources are required. A time-phased tabulation of the labor requirements provides the information necessary for planning personnel staffing, facilities requirements, and other resources needed over the course of the contract.

Program Budgeting

Most companies require a program budget to be prepared, approved, and released before much effort can be expended toward contract performance. The budgeting process can be a long, drawn out process, if not ridiculous at times. Many companies start building budgets from the ground up and pay little attention to what was contained in the proposal. This may be due to the fact that the proposal was not fully supported by a detailed WBS and schedule. These two documents should be all that are required to prepare a complete budget for the entire program. Because each element of the WBS identifies the type and amount of labor required to perform the task, and the schedule dictates when each task is to start and stop, the budgeting process should be as easy as tabulating the WBS tasks per the schedule to create a labor staffing matrix that provides the budget requirements to the granularity level of the WBS. By using the WBS and schedule, everything that must be done to complete the contract is addressed both in type and quantity and over time. In theory, the resulting budget should reflect the resources necessary to complete all contract requirements.

Program Organization

The organization established by a company for a program must maximize the coordination and efficiency between disciplines and allow the best possible visibility for management. This organizational concept is applicable both internally and externally. The organization must be formal and it must be rigidly followed. There must be a clear definition of the responsibilities and accountabilities of each segment of the organization and clear lines of management, review, and reporting must be established. This is especially true in the case of LSA programs because of the need to cross traditional organizational lines to achieve the optimum program results.

Internal Organization   No two companies are organized exactly the same. The reason for this difference is that organizations have evolved over the years based on the business base of the company and performance on previous contracts. Even the names of similar organizations having virtually the same responsibilities in two companies may be different. That is why it is important to clearly identify the responsibilities and accountabilities of each part of the organization. Figure 12-33 illustrates a typical company organization and the problems that an organization can cause an LSA program manager. The functions that perform and provide a significant portion of the upfront inputs to the LSA process are clearly divided from the traditional ILS organization. Lines of communication and decision-making that affect the LSA program are spread over at least three levels of management. In a large company, this can cause disaster if not adequately addressed and coordinated.

The ILS organization itself can be significantly different, depending on the acquisition phase of the contract. An organizational structure that divides the ILS disciplines functionally would look like the diagram at FIG. 12-34; however, this type of organization rarely exists. More typically, the ILS organization is in a constantly changing mode with the flexibility of meeting the requirements of a particular contract. Figure 12-35 shows what an ILS organization could look like in the concept phase. Note that the divisions of the organization are keyed to the major ILS tasks required for that acquisition phase. Figures 12-36 and 12-37 show ILS organizations in the full-scale development and post-production phases, respectively. Comparing FIGS. 12-35, 12-36, and 12-37 shows that the basic functions of ILS can be addressed in many different types of organizations. It should be pointed out that none of these organizational structures have a block labeled LSA. That is because every discipline, division, and function is intimately involved with the LSA process. That is why the role of the LSA program manager can be so challenging. It is imperative that the ILS organization and the overall company organization, whatever it is, fully support the LSA process.

Program Tracking

The progress and status of the program must be tracked, analyzed and reported continuously from start to finish. A program that is initiated properly with the necessary controls and monitoring tools can be tracked on a near-routine basis. The key is starting the program correctly. There are several tools that have proven their worth in tracking programs. These tools include program milestones, task definers, program timeline status, and earned value.

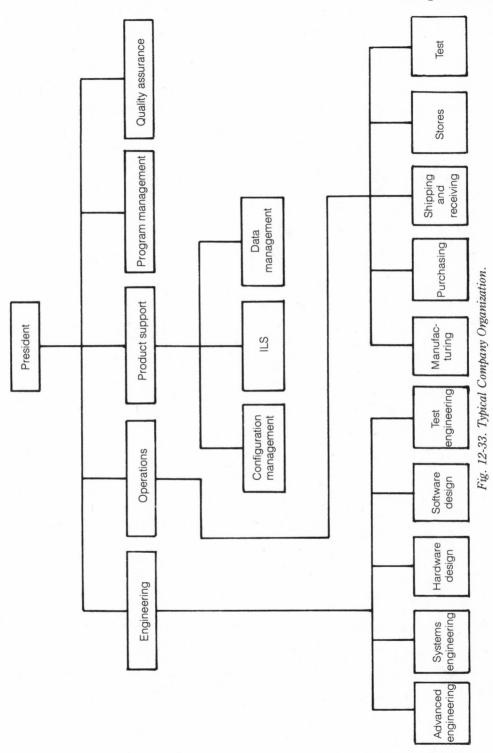

Fig. 12-33. Typical Company Organization.

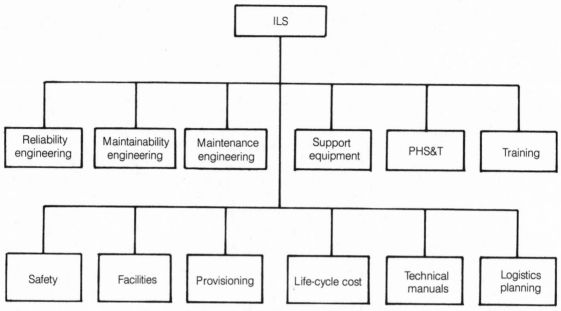

Fig. 12-34. *Organization of ILS Disciplines by Function.*

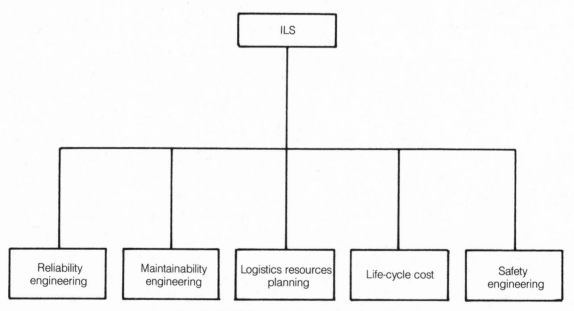

Fig. 12-35. *ILS organization (concept phase).*

Program Milestones

The use of milestones is one of the most common methods for tracking a program. These milestones are major program events, most of which have already been discussed previously in this text and are illustrated in FIG. 12-21. Achievement of these milestones signify that the program has progressed to an identifiable point. The underlying assumption is that all the tasks required to reach the milestone have also been completed. This may or may not be true. Only a detailed way of monitoring task completion can reveal the answer to this question. Management by achievement of program milestones is acceptable for top level managers who are concerned with the overall long-term progress of

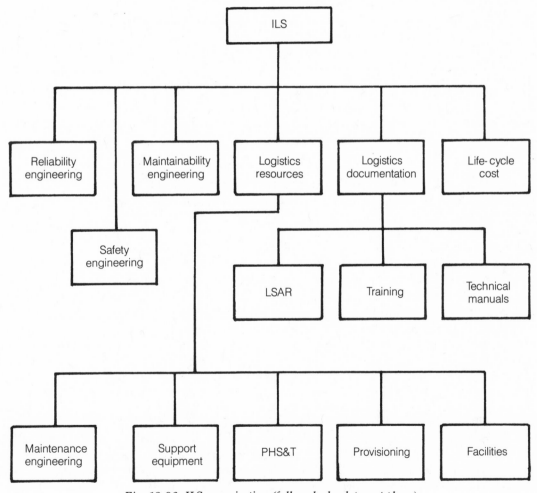

Fig. 12-36. ILS organization (full-scale development phase).

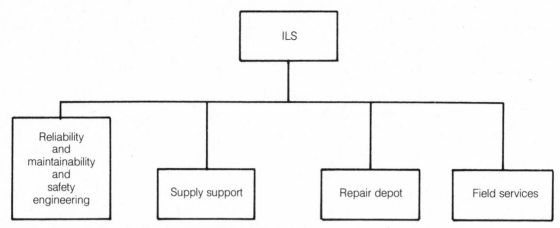

Fig. 12-37.   ILS Organization (post-production phase).

the program, but this type of management for the LSA program manager will lead to failure if the tasks required to meet the milestone are not continually monitored.

Task Definer

A proven program management tool that sets the stage for complete status and visibility is the task definer. As previously stated, the program work breakdown structure should be made up of tasks defined down to the lowest level possible. It is desirable that tasks be divided and subdivided until the bottom tasks are no more than 1 week in duration whenever possible. Working from the top down, task definers can be prepared for every block in the WBS. For example, the program manager writes task definers for each second level task, second level task managers write task definers for third level tasks, and on down until definers have been written for every task in the WBS. An example of a typical task definer is shown in FIG. 12-38. As illustrated in this example, the task definer provides complete identification of the task to be completed, references for completing the task, interrelationships with other tasks, identification of the persons responsible for managing and completing the task, and the schedule and budget for the task. Each task definer must be negotiated and approved before any effort can be expended. When every task definer is in place, the total responsibility and accountability for meeting program requirements will have been identified. This may appear to be an administrative nightmare, and agreeably it is no easy effort to complete, but the long-term benefits from the upfront planning and investment will far outweigh any short-term negatives. The task definers provide management at every level, especially the program manager, with the ability, visibility, and information needed to track the entire program.

PROGRAM TASK DEFINER	
WBS	Task Title

Task Description

References

Start Date_____

Completion Date_____

Budget

Task Inputs Required/From

Tasks Outputs/To

Assigned by	Accepted by

Fig. 12-38. Task Definer.

Program Timeline Status

The program manager must always know the current status of the program at any point in time. The task definers described previously provide the vehicle for complete status monitoring. Upward task status reporting, from the lowest levels to the top, will give the program manager the current program status. The key to this process is the level of detail of task definers and the reporting mechanism used to collect information. The most effective way to collect information is through a computerized database containing the scheduled start and completion dates of each task. Task status is then reported as not started, completed, or percent complete. This information is then compared to the schedule for the tasks. For example, if a certain task was to be completed on a specific date and the task has not been completed or maybe not even started yet, then the program manager is provided the visibility to identify the cause of the schedule slip and take any corrective action necessary to get back on schedule. In the case of the LSA program manager, this is doubly important because of the dependency of subsequent tasks to receive inputs. Without detailed information, this is not possible. Many companies have gotten into schedule trouble and not known it until it was too late to take any corrective action at all short of major crisis management actions.

Budget and Earned Value

An all too frequent concept is that the budget is expended, so the work must be completed. In most cases, this is not true, because budgets are based on estimates for task completion and estimates are just that, estimates. The task definer process allows budgets to be controlled at the lowest level possible to avoid significant unnoticed overruns. The combination of budget and schedule allows complete tracking of expenditures and does give management at every level an accurate picture of the funding status of the program; however, it does not tell the correlation between expenditures and progress.

The most common tool for correlating expenditures and progress is earned value reporting. Earned value equates to the dollar value of the completed contract to the company. At contract completion, the company should realize 100 percent of the earned value. Earned value does not correlate to the amount of expenditures on a contract. For example, if a task has a budget of 40 hours, the value of the task is 40 hours times the appropriate direct labor rate plus overhead, G&A, and fee.

When the task is completed, the company can consider the value of the task as earned. But here is the tricky part. If the task actually took only 30 hours to complete, the company still considers the value of the task earned to be 40 hours. Conversely, if it took 50 hours to complete the task, the company can only consider the completed task earned value to be 40 hours. When cumulative earned value matches the budget, the performance on the contract can be considered on track.

Any discrepancies between earned value and budget should be cause for further investigation to determine where overruns are occurring. Typically, earned value lags behind budget and actual expenditures may exceed the budget during the early stages of a program. Figure 12-39 illustrates the relationship between budget, expenditures, and earned value. In theory, if all tasks are completed exactly on schedule and on budget, the cumulative figures for all three should meet at a single point at the end of the contract. The earned value process provides management with an indication of how well performance is meeting the end goal of returning the target profit for the program. A secondary indicator for future use is the accuracy of the company's estimating process versus actual contract performance.

Program Closeout

The closeout of a program consists of the actions necessary to complete all deliveries, audit and close accounts, and archive all program records. Each of

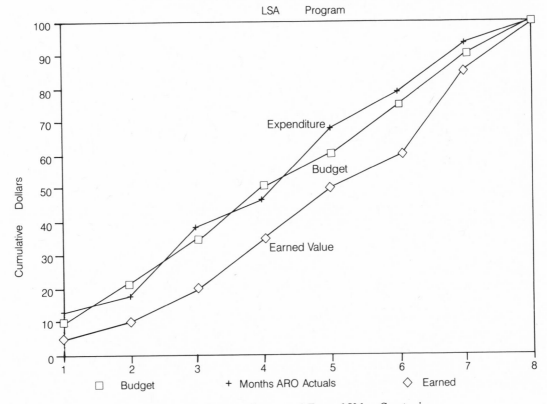

Fig. 12-39. Budget, Expenditure, and Earned Value Comparison.

these actions is necessary to ensure that all aspects of the program are completed both for the customer and for the company. Final delivery of contractually required items should be the easiest of the actions, because it is a mandatory part of the program. Sometimes there are residual items that must be addressed on an exception basis. For example, hardware deliveries may have been short selected portions or other items. The customer may allow partial deliveries in order to support other ongoing interrelated actions. These partial deliveries must be completed before the contract is closed. When a contract has a warranty provision, the company may not be able to completely close the program until the warranty period has expired.

Internal accounts must be audited, sometimes by both the company and the customer, before the accounting books are closed. This process can drag out for an extended period of time if all charges have not been correctly substantiated or if there are outstanding expenditures or agreements with subcontractors that must be resolved. Finally, the actual overhead and G&A rates may have to be audited to verify that the customer has not been overcharged. The last action, archival of program records, is an area where most companies do not expend sufficient time and materials. It seems that companies continually reinvent the wheel on every program, rather than using past programs as a starting point for the future. Especially in the logistics areas where a significant amount of data is generated, much of the information is generically usable on future programs.

In a relatively short period of time, due to personnel turnover and changing requirements, records become misplaced, lost, or even discarded. Every company should have a formal procedure for maintaining historical records on all past and current programs. The procedures should include cataloging, control, storage and access of all archives. This information will prove invaluable on future programs. Program closeout, which affects completion of the current contract and can have an impact on the ability of the company to perform on future contracts, must not be overlooked as an important program milestone.

A

LSA Summary Reports

A brief description and example of each LSA summary report produced by the Logistics Support Analysis Record (LSAR) Automatic Data Processing (ADP) System is provided in this appendix. All reports, except those identified as management reports, are selected using the LSA selection card process described in MIL-STD 1388-2A. Management reports are produced when the ADP System is initiated, when additional information is added to the database, or as supplementary information produced in the generation of one or more of the selected summary reports.

- LSA-001 Direct Annual Maintenance Manhours by Skill Specialty Code and Level of Maintenance
  Lists the annual manhour requirements of a skill specialty code (SSC), broken out by the level of maintenance at which the manhours are required. The report can be produced for either a specific SSC or all SSCs.

- LSA-002 Personnel and Skill Summary
  Lists tasks and associated manhours, by SSC, expended on each maintenance task, and the annual manhours per task based on the number of systems supported.

- LSA-003 Maintenance Summary
  Report displays a comparison between the specified system maintenance parameters documented on the LSA Data Record A and the achieved status developed through the detailed analyses documented on the LSA Data Records C and D.

Appendix A   LSA Summary Reports

- LSA-004   Maintenance Allocation Summary
  Provides a summary of the maintenance task allocations by maintenance function and level of maintenance. Can be selected in either draft or proof. Proof meets the requirements for a maintenance allocation chart (MAC). Also provides for selection of a companion LSA-020 report that lists the tools and test equipment required to perform each task.

- LSA-005   Support Item Utilization
  Report will list maintenance tasks that utilize selected support items. The report is sequenced by item category code and displays maintenance tasks associated with a given support item sequenced by maintenance level and LSACN.

- LSA-006   Critical Maintenance Task Summary
  Lists maintenance tasks which meet or exceed a user established critical value for task frequency, elapsed time, manhours, or annual manhours. The report can be limited to either scheduled or unscheduled maintenance tasks. Output is sequenced in descending critical value.

- LSA-007   Support Equipment Requirements by Skill Specialty Code and Level of Maintenance
  Listing of the support equipment required to perform maintenance tasks. Equipment is identified by skill specialty of the person performing maintenance and the level of maintenance. Output can be sequenced either by SSC and then level or by maintenance of level of maintenance and then SSC.

- LSA-008   Support Item Validation
  Report summarizes the support items and personnel required to perform maintenance at each level.

- LSA-009   Support Item List
  Lists all repair parts, tools, and test equipment necessary to support the items for which the report is requested. Items to appear on the report are selected by item category code (ICC).

- LSA-010   Parts Standardization Summary
  Lists reference numbers and selected parts information that can be used as a basis for the parts control and the replenishment parts breakout programs.

- LSA-011   Requirements for Special Training Device
  Lists the maintenance tasks that require training material to prepare maintenance personnel to perform the task. The report is keyed to tasks containing a "Y" in LSA Data Record C, card C06, block 8b.

- LSA-012   Requirements for Facility
  Identifies maintenance tasks that require new or modified facilities. The report is keyed to tasks containing a valid entry in LSA Data Record C, card C06, block 8a.

- LSA-013   Support Equipment Grouping Number Utilization
  Lists, by maintenance level and support equipment grouping identification number, the maintenance tasks which use the support equipment group. Report is used to provide the requirements, quantity, and justification for the acquisition of support equipment.

- LSA-014   Training Task List
  Report provides a consolidated listing of all maintenance tasks sequenced by SSC. Provides information for development of SSC training program.

- LSA-015   Sequential Task Description
  Report provides a sequential description of all maintenance tasks documented in the LSAR. Output can be used in preparing draft maintenance publications.

- LSA-016   Preliminary Maintenance Allocation Summary
  Report provides a preliminary description of task allocations by maintenance function and level.

- LSA-017   Preliminary Maintenance Allocation Summary - Tool Page
  Companion report to the LSA-016. Provides a listing of tools required to perform the tasks listed on the LSA-016 report.

- LSA-019   Maintenance Task Analysis Validation
  Report lists the support items and SSC requirements for maintenance tasks at any or all levels of maintenance. Designed to be used during any phase of system acquisition.

- LSA-020   Tool and Test Equipment Requirements
  Companion report to the LSA-004. Identifies and cross-references the tools and test equipment required for maintenance tasks listed on a corresponding LSA-004 report.

- LSA-021   Task Referencing List
  Report identifies maintenance tasks that reference other maintenance tasks in the sequential task descriptions within the LSAR.

- LSA-022   Referenced Task List
  Report identifies maintenance tasks that are referenced by other maintenance tasks in the sequential task descriptions within the LSAR. Can be used as a companion to the LSA-021 report.

- LSA-023   Maintenance Plan, Summary
  A four-part report. Part I provides maintenance concept and the minimum acceptable value and best operating capability parameters for the system. Part II provides the required, allocated, predicted, and measured reliability and maintainability parameters. Part III provides preventive and corrective maintenance tasks identified for the system. Part IV lists all support items required to perform each maintenance task.

- LSA-024   Maintenance Plan
  A three-part summary report identifying the maintenance and support equipment requirements for a portion or all of a system.

- LSA-025   Packaging Requirements Data
  Report provides the basic data requirements for preservation and packaging of common, selective, and special group items.

- LSA-026   Packaging Development Data
  Report provides information concerning basic packaging and preservation related characteristics of an item or items contained in a system.

- LSA-027   Failure, Maintenance Rate Summary
  Report provides the basic data for comparison of failure rate, task frequency, and maintenance replacement rates I and II for specific items or the system reflected in the LSAR.

- LSA-028   Reference Number/Additional Reference Number Cross-Reference List
  Report serves as a cross-reference between reference numbers and additional referenced numbers listed on the LSA Data Record H.

- LSA-029   Repair Parts List
  Report is a listing of the repair parts required to support system maintenance. Contains the data to meet the requirements of section II of MIL-STD 335 for a Repair Parts and Special Tools List (RPSTL). Can be run in either draft or proof. Proof is acceptable quality for official printing and distribution.

- LSA-030   Special Tools List
  Report is a listing of special tools required to support system maintenance. Contains the data to meet the requirements of section III of MIL-STD 335 for a Repair Parts and Special Tools List (RPSTL). Can be run in either draft or proof. Proof is acceptable quality for official printing and distribution. Companion report to the LSA-029.

- LSA-031   Part Number/National Stock Number/Reference Designation Cross Reference Index
  Companion report to the LSA-029 and LSA-030 reports. Cross-references part number, national stock number, and reference designator

listed on the LSA-029 and LSA-030 reports to illustration figure and item numbers. Can be run in either draft or proof. Proof is acceptable quality for official printing and distribution.

- LSA-032   DLSC Submittals
Report provides a hardcopy cross-reference of submitter control number to item reference numbers to aid in correlation of DLSC results.

- LSA-034   Stockage List Type-Four Report
Report produces a parts list as part of a type-four stock list manual. Output reports, when combined with separately developed illustrations, are used to produce a camera-ready parts manual.

- LSA-036   Provisioning Requirements
Report produces the following provisioning lists in accordance with the requirements of MIL-STD 1561:
    Provisioning Parts List
    Short-Form Provisioning Parts List
    Long Lead Time Items List
    Repairable Items List
    Interim Support Items List
    Tools and Test Equipment List
    Common and Bulk Items List
    Design Change Notice
    Post Conference List
    System Configuration Provisioning List

- LSA-040   Components of End Item List
Report produces components of end items list to be used in an operator's technical manual in accordance with the requirements of MIL-M-63036.

- LSA-041   Basic Issue Items List
Report produces a basic issue items list to be used in an operator's technical manual in accordance with the requirements of MIL-M-63036.

- LSA-042   Additional Authorization List
Report produces an additional authorization list to be used in an operator's technical manual in accordance with the requirements of MIL-M-63036.

- LSA-043   Expendable/Durable Supplies and Materials List
Report produces an expendable/durable supplies and materials list to be used in an operator's technical manual in accordance with the requirements of MIL-M-63036.

- LSA-045   Stockage List Type-Three Report
Report produces a listing of supply system and using unit responsible

items, principal end items, and collateral equipment as part of a type-three stockage list manual. Output report can be used to produce camera-ready manual pages.

- LSA-050   Reliability-Centered Maintenance Summary
  Report summarizes the results of the reliability-centered maintenance analysis performed on the failure modes of the repairable items identified in the LSAR.

- LSA-051   Reliability Summary - Redesign
  Report summarizes the results of the LSA process relative to failure modes and causes, logistics considerations, and redesign recommendations.

- LSA-052   Criticality Analysis Summary
  Report provides listings, in descending order, of each failure mode's computed criticality number of assigned failure probability level with individual safety hazard severity code categories.

- LSA-053   Maintainability Summary - Level of Repair
  Report provides the projected maintenance workload resulting from the failure modes, effects, and criticality analyses documented on the LSA Data Records B, B1, and B2.

- LSA-054   Failure Mode Analysis Summary
  Report highlights system failure modes that are most critical based on failure effect probability, failure mode ratio, and safety hazard severity code.

- LSA-055   Failure Mode Detection Summary
  Report provides information on operator and maintenance personnel tasks performed to diagnose and correct system failures. Output can be used as an aid in preparation of technical manuals.

- LSA-060   LCN Master File
  Report is an image listing of all or a selected range of records contained in the LCN master file.

- LSA-061   Parts Master File
  Report is an image listing of all or a selected range of records contained in the parts master file.

- LSA-070   Support Equipment Recommendation Data (SERD)
  A five-part report describing the requirements for a specific item of support equipment. Output is acceptable for meeting contractual submittal of SERD.

- LSA-072   Test Measurement and Diagnostic Equipment (TMDE) Requirements Summary Report

Report provides a summary of TMDE requirements and technical descriptions to verify the applicability of an item of TMDE for supporting maintenance.

- LSA-074   Support Equipment Tool List
  Report provides a listing of powered and nonpowered hand tools required to support maintenance. Applicable maintenance level for each item is identified.

- LSA-075   LSAR MANPRINT Report
  Report provides the baseline data for performance of hardware-manpower requirements analysis. Output data includes FMECA data, task summary information, and new or modified skill requirements.

- LSA-077   Depot Maintenance Interservice Data Summary
  A three-part summary report containing data concerning depot maintenance requirements. Part I lists all depot repairable items and associated maintenance tasks. Part II lists required support equipment and new or modified facility requirements. Part III lists depot support equipment and associated test program sets.

- LSA-080   Bill of Materials
  A two-part report. Part I is a complete bill of materials for all or selected ranges of a system. Items are shown relative to next higher assemblies where they are used. Part II is an automatically generated error listing. The report provides the ability to compare the parts master file with corresponding engineering assembly drawing to verify database completeness.

- LSA-100   Chronolog
  Management report created each time the ADP system is initiated that lists each program operation.

- LSA-101   Transaction Edit Results - Selection Cards
  Management report created each time the ADP system is initiated that reflects the results of edits performed on each report selection card.

- LSA-102   Transaction Edit Results - LCN Master
  Management report created each time records are added to the LCN Master File. Report reflects the results of edits performed on each new LCN master file record.

- LSA-103   Transaction Edit Results - Parts Master
  Management report created each time records are added to the Parts Master File. Report reflects the results of edits performed on each new parts master file record.

Appendix A LSA Summary Reports

- LSA-104 Transaction Edit Results - Task Narrative Master
Management report created each time records are added to the Task
Narrative Master File. Report reflects the results of edits performed on
each new task narrative master file record.

- LSA-105 Key Field Change Transactions
Management report that highlights all changes to key data fields that
occur when the ADP system is initiated with additions, updates, or
changes.

- LSA-106 Reference Number Discrepancy List
Report is an error listing that identifies part numbers in the LCN master
file, listed on an LSA Data Record D1, that do not appear in the parts
master file on an LSA Data Record H or H1.

- LSA-107 LCN-Task Identification Code Cross-Reference
Report provides a cross-reference between LSACN maintenance task
codes and the corresponding computer assigned task identification code.

- LSA-108 Critical Data Changes
Management report that automatically identifies any changes to the following critical data elements:
    Annual operating requirements
    Mean time between failures
    Mean time to repair
    Task frequency
    Mean elapsed time
    SSC evaluation
    Administrative and logistics delay time
    Federal Supply Code for Manufacturers
    Source, maintenance and recoverability code
    Maintenance replacement rate I
    Essentiality code
    Skill specialty code
    Technical manual code

- LSA-109 Unidentified Transactions
Management report that reflects transactions input into the ADP system
that cannot be identified as part of any process, master file, or report
selection card.

- LSA-150 Provisioning Error List
Management report produced automatically when the LSA-036 report is
run. Identifies data errors or omissions based on pre-established edit criteria for both the LSA Data Records H and H1.

- LSA-151   Provisioning Parts List Index
  A summary report cross reference of provisioning list item sequence number (PLISN) to LSACN and reference number for a specific provisioning list. The output is an aid to identification and location of items on a provisioning list.

- LSA-152   PLISN Assignment/Reassignment
  Listing of the results of the utility program that automatically assigns or reassigns provisioning list item sequence numbers (PLISN) to a specific provisioning list.

- LSA-154   Provisioning Parts Breakout Summary
  Report provides information on critical pricing and parts breakout program data, including parts application data.

- LSA-155   Recommended Spare Parts List for Spares Acquisition Integrated with Production
  List of spare parts data required for planning spares acquisition in conjunction with production of the system.

```
LSA-001  RCC A   CYCLE 0010            LOGISTIC SUPPORT ANALYSIS RECORD                         89/03/22  PAGE  1
                   DIRECT ANNUAL MAINTENANCE MAN-HOURS BY SKILL SPECIALITY AND LEVEL OF MAINTENANCE
EIAC        ITEM NAME           START LCN     ALC     STOP LCN            UDC        SERV DES    SSC
END         REFRIGERATION UNIT   0                                       DCZ        ARMY        ALL
NUMBER OF SYSTEMS SUPPORTED BY MAINTENANCE LEVEL:
                                                OPERATOR/CREW              (C)   1
                                    ORGANIZATION/ON EQUIP                 (O)  20
                    INTERMEDIATE: DS/AFLOAT/3RD ECH/OFF EQUIP             (F)   0
                         INTERMEDIATE: GS/ASHORE/4TH ECH                  (H)  40
                    INTERMEDIATE: ASHORE AND AFLOAT(NAVY)                 (G)   0
                         SPECIALIZED REPAIR ACTIVITY                      (L)   0
                              DEPOT/SHIPYARDS                             (D)  20
```

SSC	OPERATOR/ CREW	ORGANIZATIONAL/ ON EQUIP	INTERMEDIATE: DS/AFL/3RD ECH/OFF EQP	INTERMEDIATE: GS/ASHORE	INTERMEDIATE: ASHOR+AFL (NAVY)	SPECIALIZED REPAIR ACT	DEPOT/ SHIPYARDS
ZZZZZ	.00	.00	.00	.00	.00	.00	.00
52C10	.00	.00	.00	.00	.00	.00	.00
52C20	.00	17.22	.00	.00	.00	.00	.40
76J10	.23	1.48	.00	.00	.00	.00	.00

```
TOTAL NUMBER OF MAINTENANCE TASK:                      15
NUMBER OF TASK WITH PREDICTED MAN-HOURS:                8    53.3%
NUMBER OF TASK WITH MEASURED MAN-HOURS:                 7    46.6%
BASIC LCNS SELECTED:                                    4
ALTERNATE LCNS SELECTED:                                4
DUPE LCNS WITH FIRST RECORD ONLY IN THIS REPORT:        0
```

Fig. A-1. LSA-001—Direct Annual Maintenance Man-Hours by Skill Specialty Code and Level of Maintenance.

```
LSA-002   RCC A   CYCLE 0010           LOGISTIC SUPPORT ANALYSIS RECORD                    89/03/22   PAGE  1
                                         PERSONNEL AND SKILL SUMMARY

EIAC      ITEM NAME            START LCN    ALC    STOP LCN          UDC                    SSC    SSE    DISP OPT
END       REFRIGERATION UNIT   0                                    DCY                    ALL    A
NUMBER OF SYSTEMS SUPPORTED BY MAINTENANCE LEVEL:
                                          OPERATOR/CREW           (C)   1
                                  ORGANIZATION/ON EQUIP           (O)  20
          INTERMEDIATE: DS/AFLOAT/3RD ECH/OFF EQUIP               (F)  40
                  INTERMEDIATE: GS/ASHORE/4TH ECH                 (H)   1
                  INTERMEDIATE: ASHORE AND AFLOAT (NAVY)          (G)   1
                           SPECIALIZED REPAIR ACTIVITY            (L)   1
                                   DEPOT/SHIPYARDS                (D)  20
```

SSC	LCN / ITEM NAME	ALC TASK CD	TASK IDENTIFICATION	TASK FREQ	MB	SSE	SSC	NO TRG EQP	M-H PER SSC	SERV DES ARMY	ANL M-H/ ITEM	TOTAL ANL M-H	WUC/TM	FGC
52C10	0 REFRIGERATION UNIT	HGOAAAA	REPLACE REFRIGERATION UNIT	4.054	0	A	01	Y	.17(M)		.69	13.78	00	
	002 WIRE HARNESS ASSY	ABOCAAA	ORGANIZATIONAL INSP OF WIRES/CABLES	.300	0	A	01	Y	.10(P)		.03	.60	02	
	005 COMPRESSOR ASSY	HGFAAAA	REPLACE COMPRESSOR ASSY.	2.000	0	A	01	N	.05(P)		.10	4.00	05	
	006 ENGINE ASSY	HGOXAAA	REPLACE ENGINE ASSY	3.337	0	A	01	Y	.03(M)		.10	2.00	06	
52C20	0 REFRIGERATION UNIT	HGOAAAA	REPLACE REFRIGERATION UNIT	4.054	0	A	01	Y	.46(M)		1.86	37.30	00	
	0 REFRIGERATION UNIT	JGOAAAA	MINOR REPAIR ACTION	5.405	0	A	01	Y	.33(P)		1.78	35.67	00	
	0 REFRIGERATION UNIT	NGOAAAA	FAULT LOCATION - UNIT INOPERABLE	3.007	0	A	01	Y	.23(M)		.69	13.83	00	
	0 REFRIGERATION UNIT	NGOAAAB	FAULT LOCATION-INSUFFICIENT COOLING	2.801	0	A	01	N	.25(M)		.70	14.01	00	
	0 REFRIGERATION UNIT	NGOAAAC	FAULT LOCATION - NOISY OPERATION	5.105	0	A	01	N	.25(P)		1.28	25.53	00	
	00102 DOOR SIDE LEFT	HGOABAA	REPLACE DOOR	.572	0		01	Y	.18(P)		.10	2.06	0102	
	005 COMPRESSOR ASSY	HGOAAAA	REMOVE AND REPLACE AT DEPOT LVL	.200	0	A	01	N	.10(M)		.02	.40	05	
	005 COMPRESSOR ASSY	HGFAAAA	REPLACE COMPRESSOR ASSY.	2.000	0	A	01	N	.70(P)		1.40	56.00	05	
	005 COMPRESSOR ASSY	NGFAGAA	FAULT LOCATION - COMPRESSOR ASSY	1.800	0	A	01	N	.17(M)		.31	12.24	05	
	00501 VALVE PLATE ASSY	AGFAGAA	INSPECT VALVE PLATE ASSY.	1.244	0	A	01	Y	.10(M)		.12	4.98	0501	
	00501 VALVE PLATE ASSY	JGFAGAA	REPAIR VALVE PLATE ASSY.		0	A	01	N	.25(M)				0501	
	00501 VALVE PLATE ASSY	RGFAGAA	REMOVE VALVE PLATE ASSY	1.104	0	A	01	N	.12(M)		.13	5.30	0501	
	006 ENGINE ASSY	BGFAGAA	TEST ENGINE ASSY AFTER REPAIR	3.337	0	A	01	Y	.77(P)		2.57	102.78	06	
	006 ENGINE ASSY	HGOXAAA	REPLACE ENGINE ASSY	3.337	0	A	01	Y	1.51(M)		5.04	100.78	06	
	006 ENGINE ASSY	NGOAABB	FAULT LOCATION - ENGINE ASSY	3.309	0	A	01	Y	.78(M)		2.58	51.62	06	

Fig. A-2. LSA-002—Personnel and Skill Summary.

Appendix A   LSA Summary Reports

```
LSA-003   RCC B   CYCLE 0010          LOGISTIC SUPPORT ANALYSIS RECORD              89/03/22   PAGE  1
                                           MAINTENANCE SUMMARY

EIAC                          START LCN    ALC    STOP LCN    UOC    SERV DES    AOR         MB
END   REFRIGERATION UNIT          0                          DCY    ARMY        007200      0
ITEM NAME   CREW
```

MAINTENANCE LEVEL   CREW

	DAILY INSP		PREOP INSP		POSTOP INSP		PERIODIC INSP		MSSN PROF CHG		UNSCH MAINT	
	ELAP	M-H	ELAP	M-H	ELAP	M-H	ELAP	M-H	ELAP	M-H	ELAP	M-H
REQUIRED	.25	.25	.25	.25	.15	.15	.51	.51	1.00	1.15	1.00	1.00
STATUS	.00	.00	.13	.13	.00	.00	.00	.00	.00	.00	.33	.33

	TURNAROUND		MAX TIME TO REPAIR	PCT	ANNUAL M-H PER END ITEM			M-H PER OPER HOUR		
	ELAP	M-H			SCHED	UNSCHED	TOTAL	SCHED	UNSCHED	TOTAL
REQUIRED	3.00	2.80	1.00	95	75.0	300.0	375.0	.02	.05	.07
STATUS	.00	.00		100	54.0	4.2	58.2	.01	.00	.01

MAINTENANCE LEVEL   ORG

	DAILY INSP		PREOP INSP		POSTOP INSP		PERIODIC INSP		MSSN PROF CHG		UNSCH MAINT	
	ELAP	M-H	ELAP	M-H	ELAP	M-H	ELAP	M-H	ELAP	M-H	ELAP	M-H
REQUIRED	.25	.25	.25	.25	.15	.15	.50	.50	.05	.05	.75	.75
STATUS	.00	.00	.00	.00	.00	.00	.10	.10	.00	.00	.51	.52

	TURNAROUND		MAX TIME TO REPAIR	PCT	ANNUAL M-H PER END ITEM			M-H PER OPER HOUR		
	ELAP	M-H			SCHED	UNSCHED	TOTAL	SCHED	UNSCHED	TOTAL
REQUIRED	3.00	2.80	1.00	95	21.5	7.0	28.5	.02	.05	.07
STATUS	.00	.00		90	.0	16.6	16.6	.00	.00	.00

MAINTENANCE LEVEL   DS

	DAILY INSP		PREOP INSP		POSTOP INSP		PERIODIC INSP		MSSN PROF CHG		UNSCH MAINT	
	ELAP	M-H	ELAP	M-H	ELAP	M-H	ELAP	M-H	ELAP	M-H	ELAP	M-H
REQUIRED	.00	.00	.00	.00	.00	.00	.95	1.01	1.10	1.50	3.00	3.00
STATUS	.00	.00	.00	.00	.00	.00	.00	.00	.00	.00	.80	.45

	TURNAROUND		MAX TIME TO REPAIR	PCT	ANNUAL M-H PER END ITEM			M-H PER OPER HOUR		
	ELAP	M-H			SCHED	UNSCHED	TOTAL	SCHED	UNSCHED	TOTAL
REQUIRED	5.00	5.10	4.00	95	30.0	18.0	48.0	.05	.01	.06
STATUS	.00	.00		100	6.8	6.8		.00	.00	.00

Fig. A-3. LSA-003—Maintenance Summary.

286

LSA-004   MAINTENANCE ALLOCATION CHART

89/03/22   PAGE   1
TM CODE TL DISP OPT

(1) GROUP NUMBER	(2) COMPONENT/ ASSEMBLY	(3) MAINT FUNCTION	(4) MAINTENANCE CATEGORY					(5) TOOLS AND EQUIP	(6) REMARKS
			C	O	F	H	D		
0	REFRIGERATION UNIT	INSPECT	.3	.0	.0	.0	.0		
		REPAIR	.3	.3	.0	.0	.0	2,16,	
001	DOOR-SCREEN ASSY	INSPECT	.0	.1	.0	.0	.0	15,	
00102	DOOR SIDE LEFT	REPLACE	.0	.2	.0	.0	.0	2,9,	
002	WIRE HARNESS ASSY	INSPECT	.1	.1	.0	.0	.0	6,11,	
		TEST	.0	.0	.0	.0	.4		
		REM/INS	.0	.0	.0	.0	.5		
		REPAIR	.0	.0	.0	.0	1.4	11,12,13, 14,19,	
005	COMPRESSOR ASSY	REPLACE	.0	.0	.8	.0	.1	4,5,8,9,10, 17,18,	
		REPAIR	.0	.0	.2	.0	.0	8,17,18,	
		OVERHAL	.0	.0	.0	.0	*****		
00501	VALVE PLATE ASSY	INSPECT	.0	.0	.1	.0	.0		
		REM/INS	.0	.0	.1	.0	.0	3,	
		REPAIR	.0	.0	.3	.0	.0	1,3,7,	
006	ENGINE ASSY	REPLACE	.0	1.5	.0	.0	.0	2,3,4,8,10, 15,	

LSA-004   RCC A   CYCLE 0010   LOGISTIC SUPPORT ANALYSIS RECORD
                                          MAINTENANCE ALLOCATION SUMMARY

89/03/22   PAGE   1
TM CODE TL DISP OPT

ITEM NAME   ENGINE ASSY
END   ENGINE ASSY

EIAC GROUP NUMBER	START LCN 006 ALC	STOP LCN	COMPONENT/ASSEMBLY	MAINTENANCE FUNCTION	MAINTENANCE LEVEL CODES							TOOL AND EQUIPMENT
						UDC DCY	SERV DES NAVY	ICC				
					C	O	F	H	G	L	D	
006			ENGINE ASSY	SERVICE	.00	.05	.00	.00	.00	.00	.00	
				REMOVE AND REPLACE	.00	1.54	.00	.00	.00	.00	.00	
00602			ENGINE BLOCK	INSTALL	.00	.00	.58	.00	.00	.00	.00	
0060201			PISTON ASSY	REPAIR	.00	.00	.56	.00	.00	.00	.00	
00607			CARBURETOR ASSY	REMOVE AND REPLACE	.00	.98	.00	.00	.00	.00	.00	
				REPAIR	.00	.00	1.00	.00	.00	.00	.00	
00607	B		SUPER CARB	REPAIR	.00	.00	1.50	.00	.00	.00	.00	
				DISASSEM/ASSEMBLE	.00	.00	.90	.00	.00	.00	.00	
00607	C		DELUXE CARB	ADJUST	.00	.70	.00	.00	.00	.00	.00	
				REMOVE AND REPLACE	.00	1.18	.00	.00	.00	.00	.00	

Fig. A-4. LSA-004—Maintenance Allocation Summary.

Appendix A   LSA Summary Reports

```
LSA-005   RCC A   CYCLE 0011              LOGISTIC SUPPORT ANALYSIS RECORD                      89/03/22  PAGE  1
                                          SUPPORT ITEM UTILIZATION SUMMARY

EIAC   ITEM NAME            START LCN  ALC STOP LCN  UDC SERV DES   ITEM CATEGORY CODE SELECTED   T/Q OPT  DISP OPT
END    REFRIGERATION UNIT   0              005       DCZ  ARMY       A  B  C                        Q

----------------------------------------------------------------------------------------------------------------
SUPPORT ITEM REFERENCE NUMBER: CC586T3692            SCC:       ITEM NAME: DITMCO STATION           ITEM CATEGORY CODE: G
M/L  LCN    ALC  ITEM NAME              TASK CD TASK IDENTIFICATION TASK FREQ MB ELAP TIME MAN HOURS  QTY/TA  UM WUC/TM FGC
ORG  002    A    WIRE HARNESS ASSY      BGDAAAA CONTINUITY TST OF CO   .300  0   .12(P)     .00( )     1.00   EA 02A
                                                MP MTR CONTROLLE                                        .30

TOTAL QUANTITY OF REPAIR PART FOR MAINTENANCE LEVEL: ORG
TOTAL QUANTITY OF REPAIR PART FOR ALL MAINTENANCE LEVELS:                                               .30

----------------------------------------------------------------------------------------------------------------
SUPPORT ITEM REFERENCE NUMBER: A135                  SCC:       ITEM NAME: SCREWDRIVER               ITEM CATEGORY CODE: 4
M/L  LCN    ALC  ITEM NAME              TASK CD TASK IDENTIFICATION TASK FREQ MB ELAP TIME MAN HOURS  QTY/TA  UM WUC/TM FGC
ORG  002    A    WIRE HARNESS ASSY      BGDAAAA CONTINUITY TST OF CO   .300  0   .12(P)     .00( )     1.00   EA 02A
                                                MP MTR CONTROLLE                                        .30

TOTAL QUANTITY OF REPAIR PART FOR MAINTENANCE LEVEL: ORG
M/L  LCN    ALC  ITEM NAME              SCC: TASK CD TASK IDENTIFICATION TASK FREQ MB ELAP TIME MAN HOURS  QTY/TA  UM WUC/TM FGC
DS   00218  A    COMP MTR CONTROLLER    JGFAGAA REPAIR COMP MTR CONT    .277  0   .38(P)     .38(P)    1.00   EA 0218A
                                                ROLLER

TOTAL QUANTITY OF REPAIR PART FOR MAINTENANCE LEVEL: DS                                                 .28
TOTAL QUANTITY OF REPAIR PART FOR ALL MAINTENANCE LEVELS:                                               .58

----------------------------------------------------------------------------------------------------------------
SUPPORT ITEM REFERENCE NUMBER: SN9                   SCC:       ITEM NAME: SCREW STARTER, HAND       ITEM CATEGORY CODE: 4
M/L  LCN    ALC  ITEM NAME              TASK CD TASK IDENTIFICATION TASK FREQ MB ELAP TIME MAN HOURS  QTY/TA  UM WUC/TM FGC
ORG  00102  A    DOOR SIDE LEFT         HGOABAA REPLACE DOOR           .572  0   .18(P)     .18(P)    1.00   EA 0102
                                                                                                       .57
TOTAL QUANTITY OF REPAIR PART FOR MAINTENANCE LEVEL: ORG
TOTAL QUANTITY OF REPAIR PART FOR ALL MAINTENANCE LEVELS:                                               .57
```

Fig. A-5. LSA-005—Support Item Utilization.

```
LSA-006   RCC A   CYCLE 0011              LOGISTIC SUPPORT ANALYSIS RECORD                      89/03/22  PAGE  1
                                          CRITICAL MAINTENANCE TASK SUMMARY

EIAC   ITEM NAME            START LCN  ALC STOP LCN    UOC    SERV DES              DISP OPT
END    REFRIGERATION UNIT   0              00201       DCY    ARMY
CRITICAL CRITERIA  1. THE FOLLOWING TASKS EXCEED   .300 FOR MANHOURS.
                   2. THIS REPORT COVERS: ALL                      MAINTENANCE LEVEL(S).
                   3. THIS REPORT COVERS: SCHEDULED AND UNSCHEDULED TASKS.

                                                                         TASK  ELAP              ANNUAL
LCN  ALC ITEM NAME         REFERENCE NUMBER FSCM  TASK CD TASK IDENTIFICATION  FREQ  MB TIME MAN-HOURS MAN-HRS WUC/TM FGC

002      WIRE HARNESS ASSY                        94833 JGDAGAA REPAIR WIRE HARNESS  .200  0  1.36   1.36     .27   02
                                                                ASSY
0        REFRIGERATION UNIT  F1000ORG-2           94833 HGOAAAA REPLACE REFRIGERATIO 4.054 0   .46    .63    2.55   00
                                                                N UNIT
002      WIRE HARNESS ASSY                        94833 RGDAGAA REMOVE WIRE HARNESS  .200  0   .50    .50     .10   02
                                                                ASSY
0        REFRIGERATION UNIT  F1000ORG-2           94833 NGCAAAC FAULT LOCATION - NOI 5.405 0   .37    .37    1.99   00
                                                                SY OPERATION
002      WIRE HARNESS ASSY                        94833 BGDAGAA TEST WIRE HARNESS AS .200  0   .37    .37     .07   02
                                                                SY
0        REFRIGERATION UNIT  F1000ORG-2           94833 JGOAAAA MINOR REPAIR ACTION  5.405 0   .33    .33    1.78   00
0        REFRIGERATION UNIT  F1000ORG-2           94833 NGCAAAB FAULT LOCATION-INSUF 3.041 0   .33    .33    1.00   00
                                                                FICIENT COOLING
```

Fig. A-6. LSA-006—Critical Maintenance Task Summary.

LSA-007   RCC A   CYCLE 0011   LOGISTIC SUPPORT ANALYSIS RECORD   89/03/22 PAGE 1
                                SUPPORT EQUIPMENT REQUIREMENTS

EIAC   SEQ OPT DISP OPT

END ITEM NAME   START LCN ALC STOP LCN UDC SERV DES ICC   SSC   ML   ALL   O

SSC ENGINE ASSY   006   007   DCY ALL   XQ4F

M/L	ITEM NAME	REFERENCE NUMBER	SCC	LCN	ALC	TASK CD	TASK IDENTIFICATION	WUC/TM FGC
52C10	O							
	ADJUSTABLE WRENCH	AT503		006		HGOXAAA	REPLACE ENGINE ASSY	06
	SCREWDRIVER	A135		006		HGOXAAA	REPLACE ENGINE ASSY	06
	SOCKET	A24		006		HGOXAAA	REPLACE ENGINE ASSY	06
	GAS CAN, 16 GAL	CCBX23		006		HGOXAAA	REPLACE ENGINE ASSY	06
	ENGINE	CCKA-MS/3834J		006		HGOXAAA	REPLACE ENGINE ASSY	06
	CLOTHS	E3727	A	006		HGOXAAA	REPLACE ENGINE ASSY	06
	PLIERS	GGG-P-471		006		HGOXAAA	REPLACE ENGINE ASSY	06
	EXT, SOCKET WRENCH	GGG-W-641		006		HGOXAAA	REPLACE ENGINE ASSY	06
	TAPE	H25732102		006		HGOXAAA	REPLACE ENGINE ASSY	06
	SCREW STARTER, HAND	SN9		006		HGOXAAA	REPLACE ENGINE ASSY	06
	TM5-4110-234-24	YOU GOT ME		006		HGOXAAA	REPLACE ENGINE ASSY	06
	TWINE	1191		006		HGOXAAA	REPLACE ENGINE ASSY	06

Fig. A-7. LSA-007—Support Equipment Requirements by Skill Specialty Code and Level of Maintenance.

LSA-008   RCC A   CYCLE 0012   LOGISTIC SUPPORT ANALYSIS RECORD   89/03/22 PAGE 1
                               SUPPORT ITEMS VALIDATION SUMMARY

EIAC   ITEM CATEGORY CODES SELECTED

END ITEM NAME   START LCN ALC STOP LCN UOC SERV DES M/L SELECTED   X B

    REFRIGERATION UNIT O   DCY ARMY   O

SUPPORT/TEST EQUIPMENT AND TOOLS

M/L	ICC	REFERENCE NUMBER	SCC	ITEM NAME	QTY/TASK	UM	SUPPORT LCN	ALC	TASK CD	TASK FREQ	MB	SSC	NO SSC	HMPC
ORG	4	AT503		WRENCH, ADJUSTABLE	1.00	EA	0		NGOAAAA	3.007	0	52C20	1	D
ORG	4	AT503		WRENCH, ADJUSTABLE	1.00	EA	002		ABOACAA	.300	0	52C10	1	D
ORG	4	AT503		ADJUSTABLE WRENCH	1.00	EA	006		HGOXAAA	3.337	0	52C20	1	B
ORG	4	AT503		ADJUSTABLE WRENCH	1.00	EA	006		HGOXAAA	3.337	0	52C10	1	B
ORG	4	A135		SCREWDRIVER	1.00	EA	006		HGOXAAA	3.337	0	52C20	1	B
ORG	4	A135		SCREWDRIVER	1.00	EA	006		HGOXAAA	3.337	0	52C10	1	B
ORG	4	A24		SOCKET	1.00	EA	006		HGOXAAA	3.337	0	52C20	1	B
ORG	4	A24		SOCKET	1.00	EA	006		HGOXAAA	3.337	0	52C10	1	B
ORG	4	B2502		SOCKET SET	1.00	EA	0		HGOAAAA	4.054	0	52C20	1	B
ORG	4	B2502		SOCKET SET	1.00	EA	006		HGOAAAA	4.054	0	52C10	1	B
ORG	4	B2502		SOCKET WRENCH	1.00	EA	006		NGOAABB	3.309	0	52C20	1	C
ORG	4	GGG-G-17 TY9CL2S		COMPRESSION GAUGE	1.00	EA	006		NGOAABB	3.309	0	52C20	1	C
ORG	4	GGG-P-471		PLIERS	1.00	EA	006		HGOXAAA	3.337	0	52C20	1	B
ORG	4	GGG-P-471		PLIERS	1.00	EA	006		HGOXAAA	3.337	0	52C10	1	B
ORG	4	GGG-S-121		SCREWDRIVER	1.00	EA	002		ABOACAA	.300	0	52C20	1	D
ORG	4	GGG-W-641		EXT, SOCKET WRENCH	1.00	EA	006		HGOXAAA	3.337	0	52C20	1	B
ORG	4	GGG-W-641		EXT, SOCKET WRENCH	1.00	EA	006		HGOXAAA	3.337	0	52C10	1	B
ORG	4	SN9		SCREW STARTER, HAND	1.00	EA	00102		HGOABAA	.572	0	52C20	1	D
ORG	4	SN9		SCREW STARTER, HAND	1.00	EA	006		HGOXAAA	3.337	0	52C20	1	B
ORG	4	SN9		SCREW STARTER, HAND	1.00	EA	006		HGOXAAA	3.337	0	52C10	1	D
ORG	5	1279979		BATTERY CHARGER	1.00	EA	0		NGOAAAA	3.007	0	52C20	1	D

Fig. A-8. LSA-008—Support Item Validation.

Appendix A LSA Summary Reports

```
LSA-009  RCC A   CYCLE 0012          LOGISTIC SUPPORT ANALYSIS RECORD                89/03/22  PAGE  1
                                            SUPPORT ITEMS LIST
```

EIAC	ITEM NAME	START LCN	ALC STOP LCN	UOC	ITEM CATEGORY CODES SELECTED				PTD SELECT			
END	PISTON ASSY	0060201	00608	DCY A B X Y					LPSCRIPTSD	SEQ PUC	DISP OPT	
LCN	ALC REFERENCE NUMBER SCC FSCM	PLISN I	ITEM NAME	SM PL SM	UM QTY/EI	UM PRICE	PS/QTY/					
WUC/TM FGC		PCCN C	NAT STOCK NUMBER	CC CC IC ICC	PLT QTY/REC NO OF	Y PUCS PUC	PC ASSY	SMR				SL

LCN	REF NUMBER	PLISN	ITEM NAME / NSN	SM PL SM / CC	UM QTY/EI	UM PRICE	PUCS PUC	PC ASSY	SMR	SL
0060201 068	BC1920	44940 0209 TESTPL	C PISTON ASSY	A X		.00 ( )			PAFZZ	
0060201AA 06801	112-0136	44940 0217 TESTPL	D PISTON, INT COMB EN 2805-00-647-0713	A Y EA 12		9.99 ( )	Y U	2	PAFZZ	0
0060201AB 06802	112-0003	44940 0221 TESTPL	D RING, RETAINING	A Y EA 06		.47 ( )	Y	4	XAFZZ	0
0060201AC 06803	112-0069	44940 0225 TESTPL	D PIN, PISTON	A Y EA 08		6.00 ( )	Y	2	XAFZZ	0
0060201AD 06804	114-0203	44940 0229 TESTPL	D CONNECTING ROD,PIST 2805-00-865-2333	A Y EA 18		36.35 ( )	Y U	2	PAFZZ	0
0060201AE 06805	805-0010	44940 0233 TESTPL	D BOLT, CONNECTINGROD	A Y EA 03		.98 ( )	N	4	XAFZZ	0
0060201AF 06806	114-0036	44940 0237 TESTPL	D BUSHING, CONNEC ROD	A Y EA 06		3.20 ( )	Y	2	XAFZZ	0
0060201AG 06807	114-0145	44940 0241 TESTPL	D BEARING, ROD (HALF)	A Y EA 08		4.20 ( )	Y	4	PAFZZ	0
0060201AH 06808	113-0153	44940 0245 TESTPL	D RING SET, PISTON 2805-01-045-3095	A Y EA 10		2.53 ( )	Y	2	PAFZZ	0

Fig. A-9. LSA-009—Support Item List.

LSA-010   RCC A   CYCLE 0012

89/03/22   PAGE   1

LOGISTIC SUPPORT ANALYSIS RECORD
PARTS STANDARDIZATION SUMMARY

EIAC																SEQ OPT
END	ITEM NAME													AMC		UM FY
	COMPRESSOR, ASSY													ALL		
REFERENCE NUMBER SCC REFNO DVFL		START LCN 005	ALC	STOP LCN								CTIC C G		FSCM(S)		
FSCM RNCC RNVC ITEM NAME					FSC	DAC	AMC	PPSL	UDC			AMSC CTIC UM PRICE		LOT QUANTITY FROM TO	CPC TUC PUC	

Reference Number	SCC	FSCM	RNCC	RNVC	Item Name	FSC	DAC	AMC	PPSL	UDC	CTIC/CG	UM Price	FSCM(S)	Lot Qty From–To	CPC/TUC/PUC	UM	FY	OPT
AA06BR200		25567	5	2	SCREW, CAP HEX HEAD	5305	1	1	A		CG	.10	96944 87350	1 1200	41370 93280	EA	84	Y
AA06BR200	A	10855	3	2	SCREW, CAP, HEX HD	5305	1	1	A		CG	.07	96944 87350	1 1200	41370 93280	EA	84	Y
A4544		41947	3	1	CAP, TUBE	4730	1	1	A		CG	4.51	96944 87350	1 1200	41370 93280	EA	84	Y
A4622		41947	3	2	COUPLING, FEMALE	4730	1	1	A		CG	.30	96944 87350	1 1200	41370 93280 Y C	EA	84	Y
A50407-481		41625	3	2	SCREW, CAP, HEX HD	5305	1	1	A		CG	.07	96944 87350	1 1200	41370 93280	EA	84	Y
A5051		41947	3	2	NUT, TUBE, COUPLING	4720	1	1	A		CG	.16	96944 87350	1 1200	41370 93280	EA	84	Y
END7AA271		06534	5	2	VALVE	4130	1	2	A		CG	10.15	96944 87350	1 5000	41370 93280	EA	84	N
END7AA348		10855	3	2	VALVE, SERVICE	4820	1	2	A		CG	13.89	96944 87350	1 5000	41370 93280	EA	84	N
MS20066-229		96906	2	2	KEY, SQUARE	5315	1	2	A		CG	.12	96944 87350	1 3000	41370 93280	EA	84	Y
MS27183-13		96906	2	2	WASHER, FLAT	5310	1	3	A		CG	.80	96944 87350	1 3000	41370 93280	EA	84	Y
MS90728-60	A	96906	2	2	SCREW, CAP	5305	1	3			CG	.11.	96944 87350	1 500	41370 93280	EA	84	Y
TH-WW3510		04643	3	2	WASHER, LOCK	5305	1	3	A		CG	.29	96944 87350	1 500	41370 93280	EA	84	N
05DA500143		66935	3	2	GASKET, CYL HEAD	5330	1	1	A		CG	.20		1 10000		EA		Y
05DA500153		10855	3	2	GASKET, VALVE PLATE	5330	1	1	A		CG	1.30		1 10000		EA		Y
142-0033		44940	3	9	GASKET KIT		1	4			CG	5.12		1 1500		EA		Y
3302		59730	3	2	BOX CONNECTOR	5975	1	3	N		CG	.22	96944 87350	1 1000		EA	84	Y

Fig. A-10. LSA-010—Parts Standardization Summary.

LSA-011 RCC A   CYCLE 0012   89/03/22 PAGE 1

EIAC
END   ITEM NAME
      COMPRESSOR ASSY

LOGISTIC SUPPORT ANALYSIS RECORD
REQUIREMENTS FOR SPECIAL TRAINING DEVICE

START LCN 005   STOP LCN 007

LCN	ALC	ITEM NAME	TASK CD	TASK IDENTIFICATION	TASK FREQ	MB	ELAPSED TIME	SSC	MAN-HOURS	UOC DCY SERV DES ARMY WUC/TM FGC	DISP OPT
00501		VALVE PLATE ASSY	AGFAGAA	INSPECT VALVE PLATE ASSY.	1.244	0	.10(M)	52C20	.10(M)	0501	
006		ENGINE ASSY	BGFAGAA	TEST ENGINE ASSY AFTER REPAIR	3.337	0	.77(P)	52C20	.77(P)	06	
		ENGINE ASSY	CBCACAA	CHECK ENGINE OIL LEVEL	900.000	0	.06(M)	76J10	.06(M)	06	
		ENGINE ASSY	HGOXAAA	REPLACE ENGINE ASSY	3.337	0	1.68(M)	52C20	1.51(M)	06	
		ENGINE ASSY	HGOXAAA	REPLACE ENGINE ASSY	3.337	0	1.68(M)	52C10	.03(M)	06	
		ENGINE ASSY	NGOAABB	FAULT LOCATION - ENGINE ASSY	3.309	0	.78(M)	52C20	.78(M)	06	
0060201		PISTON ASSY	JGFXGAA	REPAIR PISTON ASSY	.233	0	.56(P)	52C20	.56(P)	060201	
00614		STARTER ASSY	HGFAGAA	REPLACE STARTER ASSY	.333	0	.61(M)	52C20	.61(M)	0614	
		STARTER ASSY	JGFAGAA	REPAIR STARTER ASSY	.333	0	.35(M)	52C20	.35(M)	0614	

Fig. A-11. LSA-011—Requirements for Special Training Device.

LSA-012 RCC A   CYCLE 0012   89/03/22 PAGE 1

EIAC
END   ITEM NAME
      REFRIGERATION UNIT

LOGISTIC SUPPORT ANALYSIS RECORD
REQUIREMENTS FOR FACILITY

START LCN 0   STOP LCN 005

LCN	ALC	ITEM NAME	TASK CD	TASK IDENTIFICATION	TASK FREQ	MB	ELAPSED TIME	SSC	MAN-HOURS	UOC DCY SERV DES ARMY WUC/TM FGC	DISP OPT FAC
002		WIRE HARNESS ASSY	BGDAGAA	TEST WIRE HARNESS ASSY	.200	0	.37(M)	35B30	.37(M)	02	8
		WIRE HARNESS ASSY	JGDAGAA	REPAIR WIRE HARNESS ASSY	.200	0	1.36(P)	35B30	1.36(P)	02	A

Fig. A-12. LSA-012—Requirements for Facility.

```
LSA-013   RCC A    CYCLE 0013              LOGISTIC SUPPORT ANALYSIS RECORD                    89/03/22   PAGE    1
                                  SUPPORT EQUIPMENT GROUPING NUMBER UTILIZATION SUMMARY
EIAC
       ITEM NAME               START LCN   ALC   STOP LCN   UDC                      GROUP NO   M/L SELECTED   DISP OPT
END    COMPRESSOR ASSY         005               007        DCY   SERV DES           ALL        C   O   F
                                                                  ARMY

SUPPORT EQUIPMENT GROUPING INDENTIFICATION NUMBER 050
M/L    LCN   ALC   ITEM NAME          TASK CD   TASK IDENTIFICATION        TASK FREQ MB   ELAPSED TIME   MAN-HRS   WUC/TM FGC
ORG    006         ENGINE ASSY        HGOXAAA   REPLACE ENGINE ASSY        3.337   0      1.68(M)        .00       06

SUPPORT EQUIPMENT GROUPING INDENTIFICATION NUMBER 150
M/L    LCN   ALC   ITEM NAME          TASK CD
       006         ENGINE ASSY        HGOXAAA   REPLACE ENGINE ASSY        3.337   0      1.68(M)        .03(M)    06

SUPPORT EQUIPMENT GROUPING INDENTIFICATION NUMBER 200
M/L    LCN   ALC   ITEM NAME          TASK CD
CREW   006         ENGINE ASSY        CBCACAA   CHECK ENGINE OIL LEV       900.000 0      .06(M)         .06(M)    06
                                                EL

ORG    006         ENGINE ASSY        HGOXAAA   REPLACE ENGINE ASSY        3.337   0      1.68(M)        1.51(M)   06
       006         ENGINE ASSY        NGOABB    FAULT LOCATION - ENG       3.309   0      .78(M)         .78(M)    06
                                                INE ASSY

DS     006         ENGINE ASSY        BGFAGAA   TEST ENGINE ASSY AFT       3.337   0      .77(P)         .77(P)    06
                                                ER REPAIR
       00602       ENGINE BLOCK       RGFAGAA   REMOVE ENGINE FROM E       .337    0      .54(M)         .54(M)    0602
                                                NGINE ASSY
       0060201     PISTON ASSY        JGFXGAA   REPAIR PISTON ASSY         .233    0      .56(P)         .56(P)    060201
       00614       STARTER ASSY       HGFAGAA   REPLACE STARTER ASSY       .333    0      .61(M)         .61(M)    0614
       00614       STARTER ASSY       JGFAGAA   REPAIR STARTER ASSY        .333    0      .35(M)         .35(M)    0614

SUPPORT EQUIPMENT GROUPING INDENTIFICATION NUMBER 250
M/L    LCN   ALC   ITEM NAME          TASK CD
       005         COMPRESSOR ASSY    HGFAAAA   REPLACE COMPRESSOR A       2.000   0      .75(P)         .05(P)    05
                                                SSY.

SUPPORT EQUIPMENT GROUPING INDENTIFICATION NUMBER 300
M/L    LCN   ALC   ITEM NAME          TASK CD
       005         COMPRESSOR ASSY    HGFAAAA   REPLACE COMPRESSOR A       2.000   0      .75(P)         .70(P)    05
                                                SSY.
```

Fig. A-13. LSA-013—Support Equipment Grouping Number Utilization.

Appendix A   LSA Summary Reports

```
LSA-014   RCC A    CYCLE 0015            LOGISTIC SUPPORT ANALYSIS RECORD                89/03/22   PAGE   1
                                             TRAINING TASK LIST

EIAC          ITEM NAME          START LCN   ALC    STOP LCN                                    SERV DES    SSC      TRN REC
END           COMPRESSOR ASSY    005                007                                         ARMY        ALL
SSC    LCN    ALC ITEM NAME      TASK FREQ   MB   TASK CD   TASK IDENTIFICATION     UDC DCY  TRN RECOMMENDATION     WUC/TM FGC

52C10  005    COMPRESSOR ASSY    2.000       0    HGFAAAA   REPLACE COMPRESSOR A             OJT                        05
                                                            SSY.

TASK CONDITION:
PERFORMANCE STANDARD:  SUPERVISION REQUIRED
RATIONALE FOR TRN:     IMMEDIACY OF PERFORMANCE
RECOMMENDATION
RATIONALE FOR TRNG:    FIELD EQUIPMENT AVAILABLE FOR TRAINING PURPOSES
LOCATION

52C10  006    ENGINE ASSY        3.337       0    HGDXAAA   REPLACE ENGINE ASSY             OJT                        06

TASK CONDITION:
PERFORMANCE STANDARD:  SUPERVISION REQUIRED
RATIONALE FOR TRN:     IMMEDIACY OF PERFORMANCE
RECOMMENDATION
RATIONALE FOR TRNG:    FIELD EQUIPMENT AVAILABLE FOR TRAINING PURPOSES
LOCATION

52C20  005    COMPRESSOR ASSY    .200        0    HGDAAAA   REMOVE AND REPLACE A            OJT                        05
                                                            T DEPOT LVL

TASK CONDITION:
PERFORMANCE STANDARD:  SUPERVISION REQUIRED
RATIONALE FOR TRN:     FREQUENCY OF PERFORMANCE
RECOMMENDATION
RATIONALE FOR TRNG:    FIELD EQUIPMENT AVAILABLE FOR TRAINING PURPOSES
LOCATION

52C20  005    COMPRESSOR ASSY    2.000       0    HGFAAAA   REPLACE COMPRESSOR A            OJT                        05
                                                            SSY.

TASK CONDITION:
PERFORMANCE STANDARD:  SUPERVISION REQUIRED
RATIONALE FOR TRN:     IMMEDIACY OF PERFORMANCE
RECOMMENDATION
RATIONALE FOR TRNG:    FIELD EQUIPMENT AVAILABLE FOR TRAINING PURPOSES
```

Fig. A-14. LSA-014—Training Task List.

LSA-015   RCC D   CYCLE 0016   LOGISTIC SUPPORT ANALYSIS RECORD   89/03/22   PAGE   1
                                             SEQUENTIAL TASK DESCRIPTION

EIAC END	ITEM NAME COMPRESSOR ASSY	START LCN 005	ALC	STOP LCN 00507	UDC DCZ	SERVICE	SEQ	DO

MAINT LEVEL	LCN	ALC TASK ID	TASK-CD	TASK IDENTIFICATION	TSK-CD ALL	TSK-MG	SUP	SSC 52C20	MLS FO	PID	SSC
ORG	005	SATD	ABONCAA	INSPECT ASSY FOR LEAKAGE							

TASK FREQ 6.790   TASK-MG M / B / O   PRED ELAP MEAS TIME .10 (M)   PRED MAN MEAS .10 (M)   MEAN MAN MIN   MEAN ELAP MIN

TASK SLN INS ID	SLN INS	TASK CD	SEQUENTIAL TASK DESCRIPTION	WORK AREA	PERS ID	MEAN MAN MIN	MEAN ELAP MIN	PID	SSC
SATD	AAA	S	CHECK AND DETERMINE WHETHER VALVES ARE PROPERLY SET.		A	3.2	3.2	A	52C20
	AAB	S	CHECK FOR SIGNS OF OBVIOUS LEAKAGE, DAMAGE OR DEFEC-						
	AAC		TIVE PARTS.		A	3.0	3.0		
	AAD		REPORT ANY PROBLEMS TO DIRECT SUPPORT.						

MAINT LEVEL	LCN	ALC TASK ID	TASK-CD	TASK IDENTIFICATION	TASK FREQ 2.000	TASK-MG				PID	SSC
DS	005	SATF	HGFAAAA	REPLACE COMPRESSOR ASSY.		M / B / O					

PRED ELAP MEAS TIME .75 (P)   PREL MAN MEAS .70 / .05 (P)(P)   MEAN MAN MIN   MEAN ELAP MIN

TASK SLN INS ID	SLN INS	TASK CD	SEQUENTIAL TASK DESCRIPTION	WORK AREA	PERS ID	MEAN MAN MIN	MEAN ELAP MIN	PID	SSC
SATF	AAA	S	PUMP THE SYSTEM DOWN, TURN THE UNIT OFF AND DISCONNECT					A	52C20
	AAB		INPUT POWER	A	A	5.0	8.0	B	52C10
	AAC	S	LOOSEN THE IDLER ARM SCREW AND RELAX THE BELT TENSION.	A	A	1.5	1.5		
	AAD	S	REMOVE THE FAN DRIVE BELT FROM THE COMPRESSOR PULLEY						
	AAE		BY LOOSENING THE FOUR GASOLINE ENGINE BOLTS. THERE IS						
	AAF		AN ACCESS SLOT ON THE LOWER LEFT FRONT OF THE CABINET						
	AAG		FOR THE FRONT BOLTS.						
	AAH	S	USE A 3/4IN. SOCKET AND WRENCH WITH AN EXTENSION	A	A	4.0	4.0		
	AAI		AND TURN THE ENGINE MOUNT ADJUSTING SCREWS LOCATED						
	AAJ		UNDER THE COMPRESSOR MOUNT TO MOVE THE ENGINE AND						
	AAK		RELEASE BELT TENSION. BE CAREFUL TO TURN BOTH SCREWS						
	AAL		THE SAME NUMBER OF FULL TURNS.						
	AAM	S	REMOVE THE DRIVE BELTS.	A	A	2.5	2.5		
	AAN	S	CLOSE (FRONT SEAT) THE TWO COMPRESSOR SERVICE VALVES.	A	A	1.0	1.0		
	AAO	S	LOOSEN THE FLARE CAPS ON THE SUCTION AND DISCHARGE						
	AAP		VALVE TEE FITTINGS TO PERMIT THE REFRIGERANT TRAPPED						
	AAQ		IN THE COMPRESSOR TO ESCAPE.	A	A	.5	.5		
	AAR	S	REMOVE THE GAGE CONNECTIONS FROM THE SERVICE VALVES.	A	A	1.0	1.0		
	AAS	S	UNBOLT THE TWO SERVICE VALVES FROM THE COMPRESSOR	A	A	1.5	1.5		
	AAT		CAUTION: COMPRESSOR WEIGHS 112 POUNDS AND THUS						
	AAU		REQUIRES TWO PEOPLE TO REMOVE FROM THE UNIT.						
	AAV	S	REMOVE THE FOUR MOUNTING BOLTS AND PULL THE COMPRESSOR	A	A	3.0	3.0		
	AAW		FROM THE FRAME.		B	3.0			
	AAX	S	CHECK OIL CHARGE ON SUBSTITUTE COMPRESSOR.	A	A	1.5	1.5		
	AAY	S	PLACE COMPRESSOR IN POSITION IN THE UNIT. LINE UP THE						
	AAZ		COMPRESSOR PULLEY WITH THE ENGINE PULLEY.	A	A	2.0	2.0		
	AA0		USE ONLY MATCHED SETS OF TWO BELTS ON THE ENGINE TO						
	AA1		COMPRESSOR DRIVE.						

Fig. A-15. LSA-015—Sequential Task Description.

295

```
LSA-016  RCC A    CYCLE 0017                    LOGISTIC SUPPORT ANALYSIS RECORD                89/03/22  PAGE  1
                                          PRELIMINARY MAINTENANCE ALLOCATION SUMMARY
EIAC       ITEM NAME            START LCN    ALC STOP LCN   UOC SERV DES  ICC      PMAC STRUCTURE TOOL LIST  DISPLAY OPTION
END        REFRIGERATION UNIT      0         00615          DCZ  ARMY     BC            122220                    X
ITEM NO  LCN    ALC GENERAL BREAKDOWN                               QTY  REFERENCE                              E
                 A    B    C    D    E    F    G     H     J        ASSY NUMBER      SCC QUP   MRRI  C  WUC/TM  FGC
         TASK FUNCTION A    B    C    D    E   CALB INST REPL REP   ****** TOOLS ******         REC CD SRC CD  QRR
                 INSP TEST SERV ADJ  ALGN

0001  001                                                DOOR, SCREEN, ASSY         1 74639      001    .0000      01
          ORG .09

0002  00102                                              UNMATCHED PART/LCN           74639-1  0012,          .0000    0102
                                              ORG .18

0003  002                                                WIRE HARNESS ASSY          1 74601      001   1.5545 1   02A
          A    ORG .00

0004  00218                                              CONTROLLER, MOTOR          1 AH30-130-U-20  0002,0006,0011,  001
          A                                                                     DS                   0      XB   001
                                                                                                    1.6656 7   0218A

0005  005                                                COMPRESSOR, ASSY           1 5D43-139-A  0002,     001
                                              DEPOT .10                                .38  0002,                Z  PA  05  005
                                              DS    .75                                                         1.4545 7  05
                                                                                                    F      PA   003

0006  00501                                              VALVE PLATE ASSY           2 6D23-522    001
          DS .10                                                                DS     0003,0004,0008,0009,
                                                                                       0010,0013,           Z  PA  050
                                                                                                    1.5545 1   0501

0007  00607                                              GASKET, CYL HEAD            .25  0001,0002,0007,
          B    ORG 1.38                                  GASKET, VALVE PLATE    DS     05DA500143
                                                         CARBURETOR ASSY        DS     05DA500153
                                                                                DS   1 142-0431ALCB
                                                                                ORG  1.38  0005,0009,   1.3423 1   0602
                                                                                     1.50                       F  PA  001
```

Fig. A-16. LSA-016—Preliminary Maintenance Allocation Summary.

LSA-017   RCC A   CYCLE 0017

LOGISTIC SUPPORT ANALYSIS RECORD
PRELIMINARY MAINTENANCE ALLOCATION SUMMARY TOOL PAGE

89/03/22   PAGE   1

EIAC END	ITEM NAME	START LCN	ALC STOP LCN	UDC	SERV DES	ICC	PMAC	STRUCTURE TOOL LIST	DISPLAY OPTION
	00615	0	00615	DCZ	ARMY	BC	122220	X	

TOOL NO	MAINTENANCE LEVEL	ITEM NAME		REFERENCE NUMBER	SCC
0001	DS	TORQUE WRENCH	F	AA123C	
0002	ORG DS	SCREWDRIVER	O	A135	
0003	DS	3/4 INCH SOCKET	F	A24	
0004	ORG	WRENCH	F	B107-6	
0005	ORG	SOCKET SET 3/8 INCHO		B2502	
0006	DS	EXTMCO STATION	O	CC586T3692	
0007	DS	WORKBENCH	F	GA9473612	
0008	ORG DS	PLIERS	F	GGG-P-471	
0009	ORG	SCREWDRIVER	F	GGG-S-121	
0010	DS	SOCKET WRENCH	F	GGG-W-641	
0011	ORG	MULTIMETER	O	JG285	
0012	DS	SCREW STARTER, HANDO		SN9	
0013		PUMP, VACUUM	F	1400B	

Fig. A-17. LSA-017–Preliminary Maintenance Allocation Summary—Tool Page.

LSA-019   RCC A   CYCLE 0018

LOGISTIC SUPPORT ANALYSIS RECORD
MAINTENANCE TASK ANALYSIS VALIDATION SUMMARY

89/03/22   PAGE   1

EIAC END	ITEM NAME	START LCN	ALC STOP LCN	UDC	SERV DES	M/L SELECTED	ITEM CATEGORY CODES SELECTED	DISP OPT
	SUPER CARB	00607	B	DCZ	ARMY	C O	ALL	

LCN	ALC	TASK CODE	TASK IDENTIFICATION	HMPC	TASK FREQ	MB	LSAR	TASK ELAP TIME	MEASURED ELAPSED TIME
00607	B	HGOAGAA	REPLACE CARBURETOR ON	D	1.840	O	1.3B(P)		

MANUFACTURERS PART NUMBER   FSCM   WUC/TM FGC
ITEM NAME   142-0431ALCB   27567   0602
SUPER CARB

SSC   SS EVAL   NO SSC LSAR M-H   SSC   SS EVAL   NO SSC LSAR M-H   MEAS M-H   SSC   SS EVAL   NO SSC LSAR M-H   MEAS M-H

46810   E   01   1.3B(M)

SUPPORT/TEST EQUIPMENT AND TOOLS

ICC	ITEM NAME	REFERENCE NUMBER	SCC	QTY/TASK	UM	QTY USED	EVALUATION
4	SCREWDRIVER	GGG-S-121		1.00	EA		
4	SOCKET SET 3/8 INCH	B2502		1.00	EA		

SPARE AND REPAIR PARTS

ICC	ITEM NAME	REFERENCE NUMBER	SCC	QTY/TASK	UM	QTY USED	EVALUATION
X	CARBURETOR	142-0431		1.00	EA		
Y	KIT, GASKET	142-0033		1.00	EA		
Z	TOOL KIT GEN REFRIG	SC5180-90-CL-N14	A	1.00	EA		

OTHER

ICC	ITEM NAME	REFERENCE NUMBER	SCC	QTY/TASK	UM	QTY USED	EVALUATION
Q	SEALANT, GASKET	S023		.01	OZ		

SUPPORT ITEMS NOT IDENTIFIED IN LSAR

ICC	ITEM NAME	REFERENCE NUMBER	SCC	QTY/TASK	UM	QTY USED	EVALUATION

REVIEWERS NAME

Fig. A-18. LSA-019—Maintenance Task Analysis Validation.

Fig. A-19. LSA-020—Tool and Test Equipment Requirements.

TOOL/TEST EQUIPMENT REF CODE	MAINT CATEGORY	NOMENCLATURE	NATIONAL/NATO STOCK NUMBER	TOOL NUMBER
1	F	TORQUE WRENCH	- - -	AA123C
2	C,O	WRENCH, ADJUSTABLE	5120-00-449-8083	AT503
3	O,F	SCREWDRIVER	5120-00-278-1273	A135
4	O,F	3/4 INCH SOCKET	5120-00-189-7985	A24
5	F	WRENCH	5120-00-148-7917	B107-6
6	D	DITMCO STATION	- - -	CC586T3692
7	F	WORKBENCH	- - -	GA9473612
8	O,F	PLIERS	5120-00-293-0032	GGG-P-471
9	C,O,F	SCREWDRIVER	5120-00-222-8852	GGG-S-121
10	O,F	SOCKET WRENCH	5120-00-243-1697	GGG-W-641
11	D	CABLE FORMING TABLE	- - -	JC931H4257
12	D	SCISSORS	- - -	KT02463N2
13	D	LEAD TIN SOLDER	- - -	QQ-S-571
14	D	PMS6 VOLTMETER	- - -	SN517832105
15	O	SCREW STARTER, HAND	5120-00-832-6221	SN9
16	O	BATTERY CHARGER	2700-00-133-2000	1279979
17	F	PUMP, VACUUM	4310-00-098-5272	1400B
18	F,D	SET, SOLDERING	5820-00-347-8650	4003100
19	D	SOLDERING GUN	3439-00-930-1638	450K4

Fig. A-20. LSA-021—Task Referencing List.

LSA-021   RCC A   CYCLE 0018   LOGISTIC SUPPORT ANALYSIS RECORD   89/03/22   PAGE   1

EIAC	ITEM NAME	START LCN	STOP LCN	UDC	SERV DES	TASK CD
END	COMPRESSOR ASSY	005	007	DCZ	ARMY	

******************** REFERENCING ******************** ****************** REFERENCED TASK ******************

LCN	ALC TASK IDENTIFICATION	TASK CD TID	LCN	REF ALC TASK CD TID	LCN	SLN FROM	SILN TO	SILN	WUC/TM FGC	TASK CD
005	FAULT LOCATION – COMPRESSOR ASSY	NGFAGAA SATH	00501	RGFAGAA SATL	00501	AAA	AAI			05
00501	INSPECT VALVE PLATE ASSY.	AGFAGAA SATI	00501	JGFAGAA SATK	00501	AAA	AAD			0501
	REPAIR VALVE PLATE ASSY.	JGFAGAA SATK	00501	GGFFGAA SATJ	00501	AAA	AAZ			0501
	REMOVE VALVE PLATE ASSY	RGFAGAA SATL	00501	AGFAGAA SATI	00501	AAA	AAJ			0501
00607 B	REPAIR CARBURETOR	JGFXGAA SATZ	00607	SGFFGAA SAUK	00607	AAA	AAB			0602
	REPAIR CARBURETOR	JGFXGAA SATZ	00607	SGFFGAA SAUK	00607	AAC	AAD			0602

LSA-022 RCC A CYCLE 001B   LOGISTIC SUPPORT ANALYSIS RECORD   89/03/22 PAGE 1
                                         REFERENCED TASK LIST
EIAC   ITEM NAME   START LCN   ALC   STOP LCN   SERV DES   TASK CD
END   REFRIGERATION UNIT   002   00501   ARMY
********************************** REFERENCED TASK **REFERENCING**********

LCN   ALC TASK IDENTIFICATION   TASK CD TID   REF SLN   SLN   LCN   UOC   ALC TASK CD TID   WUC/TM FGC
                                                                    FROM SILN TO SILN

002   TEST WIRE HARNESS ASSY   BGDAGAA SASW AAA   AAF   002   002   RGDAGAA SASZ   02
002   REPAIR WIRE HARNESS ASSY   JGDAGAA SASY AAA   AAK   002   002   BGDAGAA SASW   02
00218 A REPAIR COMP MTR CONTROLLER   JGFAGAA SATB AAA   AAK   00218 00218 A HJDFEAA SATA   0218A
005   REPLACE COMPRESSOR ASSY.   HGFAAAA SATF AAA   ABL   0   0   NGOAAAB SASD   05
005   FAULT LOCATION - COMPRESSOR ASSY NGFAGAA SATH AAA   AAN   0   0   A NJDFEAA SASG   05

Fig. A-21. LSA-022—Referenced Task List.

LSA-023 RCC A CYCLE 001B   LOGISTIC SUPPORT ANALYSIS RECORD   89/03/22 PAGE 1
                                       MAINTENANCE PLAN SUMMARY
                             PART I SYSTEM/END ITEM R&M REQUIREMENT
EIAC   ITEM NAME   START LCN ALC STOP LCN   UOC   SERVICE   ICC   SELECTED   RPT PT   DISP OPT
END   REFRIGERATION UNIT   0   0   0   DCY   ARMY   QZC   FSCM   YYYY
LCN   ALC WUC/TM FGC   ITEM NAME   MFR PART NUMBER   ITEM DESIGNATOR CODE   SR SUFFIX   HCI   ICS
                                                                                      TYPE   MODEL   SR SUFFIX
0   00   REFRIGERATION UNIT   F10000RG-2   94833   TYPE001 MODEL00002 SUFFIX0   B

AOR   MB   AOR   MB   AOR   AA   AD   AOR   MB   MB   MSN DUR MEAS BASE
7200   D   300   D   90.0000   10   T   T   1   D

SERIAL NO EFFECTIVITY
   FROM   TO   AI   AA   AD
   0   97.0000   95.0000   90.0000

                                               MTBF   MTBMA   MTTR   MAMDT   MAX TTR
                                        MAV   350.0   75.0   .35   1.0   7.50
                                        BOC   500.0   90.0   .25   .7
                                        MAV   14.6   3.1   3.50   8.5   7.50
                                        BOC   12.0   2.9   .38   1.0   7.50
                                        MAV   0.5   0.1   1.00   .9
                                        BOC   .4   .1   .85   1.5   7.50

                                         MAINTENANCE CONCEPT
INSPECTION/FAULT LOCATION TO BE ACCOMPLISHED BY CREW MAINTENANCE, WITH FOLLOW-ON INSPECTION/FAULT LOCATION AND REPLACEMENT OF DOOR-SCREEN AND ENGINE ASSEMBLIES PERFORMED BY ORGANIZATIONAL MAINTENANCE. DIRECT SUPPORT TASKED WITH REPLACEMENT OF COMPRESSOR AND REPAIR OF ALL ASSEMBLIES EXCEPT THE WIRE HARNESS, WHICH REQUIRES THE ATTENTION OF DEPOT MAINTENANCE.

Fig. A-22. LSA-023—Maintenance Plan, Summary. (Continued to page 302).

Appendix A   LSA Summary Reports

MAINTENANCE PLAN SUMMARY
PART II RELIABILITY AND MAINTAINABILITY

EIAC	ITEM NAME	START LCN	ALC STOP LCN	UDC SERVICE	ICC SELECTED				RPT PT DISP OPT
END	REFRIGERATION UNIT	0	0	DCY ARMY	QZC				YYYY
LCN	ALC WUC/TM FGC	NSN AND RELATED DATA	MFR PART NUMBER	SCC FSCM	OP CONV FACTOR	MAOT MAC SMR	UI PRICE	QPA	

ITEM NAME

0	REFRIGERATION UNIT	00	-4110-01-074-5175-	F10000RG-2	94833 0001		5876.00	1

ALLOCATED	MTBF	GR	MTBMA	MTBM-INH	MTBM-IND	MTBM NO DEF	MTBPM	MB	MTTR	MAX TTR	PCTL
	426.2	7.1	7.1	7.1	7.2			MB H	5.18	5.30	95

MAINTENANCE PLAN SUMMARY
PART III SECTION B
CORRECTIVE MAINTENANCE REQUIREMENTS SUMMARY

EIAC	ITEM NAME	START LCN	ALC STOP LCN	UDC SERVICE	ICC SELECTED	RPT PT DISP OPT
END	REFRIGERATION UNIT	0	0	DCY ARMY	QZC	YYYY

MAINTENANCE LEVEL CREW

LCN	ALC TASK CODE	TASK FREQ	MB	HCP	NO SSC	M-H PER SSC	ELAP TIME	SKILL LEVEL	SSC	TRN REC	TRN EQP	WUC/TM FGC
0	AGCABAA	.845	0	N	01	.25	.25	B	76J20	N	N	00
	NGCAAAA	3.547	0	N	01	.27	.27	B	76J20	N	N	00
	NGCAAAB	3.041	0	N	01	.33	.33	B	76J20	N	N	00
	NGCAAAC	5.405	0	N	01	.37	.37	B	76J20	N	Y	00

MAINTENANCE LEVEL ORG

	HGOAAAA	4.054	0	N	01	.46	.46	I	52C20	J	Y	00
	HGOAAAA	4.054	0	N	01	.17	.46	I	52C10	J	Y	00
	JGOAAAA	5.405	0	N	01	.33	.33	I	52C20	J	Y	00
	NGOAAAA	3.007	0	N	01	.23	.23	I	52C20	J	Y	00
	NGOAAAB	2.801	0	N	01	.25	.25	I	52C20	J	N	00
	NGOAAAC	5.105	0	N	01	.25	.25	I	52C20	J	N	00

```
LSA-023  RCC A    CYCLE 0018                    LOGISTIC SUPPORT ANALYSIS RECORD                    89/03/22  PAGE  4

                                                   MAINTENANCE PLAN SUMMARY
                                               PART IV RESOURCE REQUIREMENTS                        RPT PT  DISP OPT
                                                                                                     YYYY

EIAC   ITEM NAME              START LCN  ALC   STOP LCN   UDC   SERVICE   ICC   SELECTED
END    REFRIGERATION UNIT         0               0      DCY    ARMY     QZC

MAINTENANCE LEVEL - CREW
LCN                           WUC/TM FGC              TASK CODE    TASK IDENTIFICATION                          FAC
0     ALC ITEM NAME              00                   AGCABAA      INSPECT DAMAGE                                N
      REFRIGERATION UNIT

MAINTENANCE LEVEL - CREW
LCN                           WUC/TM FGC              TASK CODE    TASK IDENTIFICATION                          FAC
0     ALC ITEM NAME              00                   NGCAAAA      FAULT LOCATION - UNIT INOPERABLE              N
      REFRIGERATION UNIT
      REQUIREMENTS FOR SUPPORT EQUIPMENT:
      ICC   ITEM NAME                         QTY/TASK    UM    REFERENCE NUMBER      SCC
      Q     FUEL, REG GASOLINE                  16.00     GL    VV-G-1690

MAINTENANCE LEVEL - CREW
LCN                           WUC/TM FGC              TASK CODE    TASK IDENTIFICATION                          FAC
0     ALC ITEM NAME              00                   NGCAAAB      FAULT LOCATION-INSUFFICIENT COOLING           N
      REFRIGERATION UNIT

MAINTENANCE LEVEL - CREW
LCN                           WUC/TM FGC              TASK CODE    TASK IDENTIFICATION                          FAC
0     ALC ITEM NAME              00                   NGCAAAC      FAULT LOCATION - NOISY OPERATION              N
      REFRIGERATION UNIT

MAINTENANCE LEVEL - ORG
LCN                           WUC/TM FGC              TASK CODE    TASK IDENTIFICATION                          FAC
0     ALC ITEM NAME              00                   HGOAAAA      REPLACE REFRIGERATION UNIT                    N
      REFRIGERATION UNIT
      REQUIREMENTS FOR SUPPORT EQUIPMENT:
      ICC   ITEM NAME                         QTY/TASK    UM    REFERENCE NUMBER      SCC
      Q     CLOTHS                               .10      PG    E3727                  A
      Q     SHIMS                               2.00      EA    E3727
      Z     TOOL KIT GEN REFRIG                 1.00      EA    SC5180-90-CL-N14       A

MAINTENANCE LEVEL - ORG
LCN                           WUC/TM FGC              TASK CODE    TASK IDENTIFICATION                          FAC
0     ALC ITEM NAME              00                   JGOAAAA      MINOR REPAIR ACTION                           N
      REFRIGERATION UNIT
```

```
LSA-023   RCC A   CYCLE 0018              LOGISTIC SUPPORT ANALYSIS RECORD                    89/03/22   PAGE  5

                                          MAINTENANCE PLAN SUMMARY
                                          PART IV RESOURCE REQUIREMENTS
EIAC      ITEM NAME            START LCN   ALC                STOP LCN   TASK CODE   UDC   SERVICE   ICC   SELECTED        RPT PT DISP OPT
END       REFRIGERATION UNIT   0                              0          NGOAAAA     DCY   ARMY      QZC                   YYYY
MAINTENANCE LEVEL - ORG                            WUC/TM FGC            TASK IDENTIFICATION
LCN       ALC ITEM NAME                            00                    FAULT LOCATION - UNIT INOPERABLE                  FAC
0         REFRIGERATION UNIT                                                                                              N
REQUIREMENTS FOR SUPPORT EQUIPMENT:
          ICC   ITEM NAME             QTY/TASK   UM    REFERENCE NUMBER        SCC

          P     HYDROMETER            1.00       EA    K252

          Q     FUEL, REG GASOLINE    16.00      GL    VV-G-1690
          Q     ACID, SULFURIC        1.00       PT    ACSUF26

          Z     TOOL KIT GEN REFRIG   1.00       EA    SC5180-90-CL-N14        A

MAINTENANCE LEVEL - ORG
LCN       ALC ITEM NAME                            WUC/TM FGC   TASK CODE   TASK IDENTIFICATION                            FAC
0         REFRIGERATION UNIT                        00          NGOAAAB     FAULT LOCATION-INSUFFICIENT COOLING           N
MAINTENANCE LEVEL - ORG
LCN       ALC ITEM NAME                            WUC/TM FGC   TASK CODE   TASK IDENTIFICATION                            FAC
0         REFRIGERATION UNIT                        00          NGOAAAC     FAULT LOCATION - NOISY OPERATION              N
```

```
LSA-024   RCC A   CYCLE 0018              LOGISTIC SUPPORT ANALYSIS RECORD                    89/03/22   PAGE  1

                                          MAINTENANCE PLAN
EIAC      ITEM NAME      START LCN   ALC STOP LCN   UDC SERV DES   PART 2 ICCS   PART 3 ICCS   EQUIP TYPE DISP OPT   PRT SEL
END       ENGINE BLOCK   00602                      DCY   ALL                                                  S

                                          PART I - GENERAL CONSIDERATIONS

HEADING INFORMATION
MANUFACTURERS PART NUMBER 110-1860            WUC/TMFGC 0602            TYPE EQUIP CODE T123
FSCM 44940 ITEM DESIGNATOR                    SMR CODE   PAFZZ         PREPARING ACTIVITY MRSA
NSN + RELATED DATA  -  -  -  -                NALC A1B                 PREPARED BY       FISHER
MAINTENANCE PLAN NUMBER                       DLSC SCREEN 10-10-86     REVIEWED BY    --------------
SERD NUMBER 437731                            DATE OF SUB/REV/DATE OF REV 10-17-79/D/08-14-83
                                        APPROVED BY ----------------        DATE OF APPROVAL ----------------
                                            TITLE -------------------

                                            NARRATIVE
LCN-ALC 00602     ITEM FUNCTION:    DRIVES COMPRESSOR, CONDENSER AND EVAPORATOR FANS.
                  MAINTENANCE CONCEPT:   REMOVE AND INSTALL TASKS OF SUBASSEMBLIES ACCOMPLISHED BY DIREC
                                         T SUPPORT MAINTENANCE.

                                            NARRATIVE
LCN-ALC 0060201   ITEM FUNCTION:    PISTON ASSY. MOVES UNDER PRESSURE (FUEL AND FUEL COMBUSTION) TO
                                    ULTIMATELY MOVE THE EVAPORATOR AND CONDENSER FANS.
                  MAINTENANCE CONCEPT:   PISTON ASSEMBLY TO BE REMOVED, REPAIRED AND INSTALLED BY DIRECT
                                         SUPPORT MAINTENANCE.
```

LSA-024   RCC A   CYCLE 0018   LOGISTIC SUPPORT ANALYSIS RECORD   89/03/22   PAGE   2
                                              MAINTENANCE PLAN

EIAC   ITEM NAME   START LCN   ALC STOP LCN   UDC SERV DES   PART 2 ICCS   PART 3 ICCS   EQUIP TYPE DISP OPT   PRT SEL
END   ENGINE BLOCK   00602   DCY   ALL   S

HEADING INFORMATION   PART II - REPAIR CAPABILITY
MANUFACTURERS PART NUMBER 110-1860
FSCM 44940 ITEM DESIGNATOR   -   - - -   WUC/TMFGC 0602   TYPE EQUIP CODE T123
NSN + RELATED DATA   -   -   -   -   SMR CODE   PAFZZ   PREPARING ACTIVITY MRSA
MAINTENANCE PLAN NUMBER   NALC A1B   PREPARED BY   FISHER
SERD NUMBER 437731   DLSC SCREEN 10-10-86   REVIEWED BY
                                                        DATE OF SUB/REV/DATE OF REV 10-17-79/D/08-14-83
                                            APPROVED BY ------------------------------------- DATE OF APPROVAL -------------
                                               TITLE

                        REPAIRABLE ITEMS/MAINTENANCE SIGNIFICANT CONSUMABLES
WUC/TM FGC   IND   MANUFACTURERS PT NO   SCC   SMR   DMIL   TECHNICAL FACTORS BASIS 1
LCN   I/R   NSN + RELATED DATA   WEAROUT   RIP   INTERVAL   MC
ALC   MB
                                                      AMC   AMSC
060201   C   BC1920   - - - - -   PISTON ASSY   PAFZZ   A   MRR   1.6656   NSO   P   1680
0060201   -   - -   - -   -   36000   MRF   00.0000   SAR   7209.2C
                                                      O   RPF   00.0000   RSR   T
                                                                          DSR   U
                                                                          BDSR 00.0000   RRR   .00

LSA-024   RCC A   CYCLE 0018   LOGISTIC SUPPORT ANALYSIS RECORD   89/03/22   PAGE   3
                                              MAINTENANCE PLAN

EIAC   ITEM NAME   START LCN   ALC STOP LCN   UDC SERV DES   PART 2 ICCS   PART 3 ICCS   EQUIP TYPE DISP OPT   PRT SEL
END   ENGINE BLOCK   00602   DCY   ALL   S

HEADING INFORMATION   PART III - MAINTENANCE REQUIREMENTS
MANUFACTURERS PART NUMBER 110-1860
FSCM 44940 ITEM DESIGNATOR   -   - - -   WUC/TMFGC 0602   TYPE EQUIP CODE T123
NSN + RELATED DATA   -   -   -   -   SMR CODE   PAFZZ   PREPARING ACTIVITY MRSA
MAINTENANCE PLAN NUMBER   NALC A1B   PREPARED BY   FISHER
SERD NUMBER 437731   DLSC SCREEN 10-10-86   REVIEWED BY
                                                        DATE OF SUB/REV/DATE OF REV 10-17-79/D/08-14-83
                                            APPROVED BY ------------------------------------- DATE OF APPROVAL -------------
                                               TITLE

                                        MAINTENANCE
WUC/TM FGC   REQ NO   TASK CD   TASK IDENTIFICATION   TASK FREQ INTERVAL MB   SUPPORT   EQUIPMENT   REQUIREMENTS
LCN   ALC   ITEM NAME   ICC MFR PART NO   SCC
060201   0001C JGFXGAA REPAIR PISTON ASSY   000.233   O LEAK DETECTION DEV M   4990866
0060201   PISTON RINGS   Y   113-0153
                                                                    RING, RETAINING   Y   112-0003
                                                                    PIN, PISTON   Y   112-0069
                                                                    PISTON   Y   112-0136
                                                                    RING SET, PISTON   Y   113-0153
                                                                    BUSHING, CONN ROD   Y   114-0036
                                                                    BEARING, ROD (HALF) Y   114-0145
                                                                    CONNECT ROD, PISTON Y   114-0203
                                                                    SPREADER,PISTONRING 4   JH25
                                                                    SET, SOLDERING   7   4003100
                                                                    COMPRESSOR, RING   7   4003100   A

Fig. A-23. LSA-024—Maintenance Plan.

Appendix A   LSA Summary Reports

LSA-025   RCC A   CYCLE 0018   LOGISTIC SUPPORT ANALYSIS RECORD
PACKAGING REQUIREMENTS DATA

EIAC	ITEM NAME		START LCN	ALC	STOP LCN					UOC	REFERENCE NUMBER	SCC	PCO	OPT
END	COUPLING, FEMALE										A4622			

CARD	RES (5 POS)	NSN AND MTL-MGT-CD	UNIT WEIGHT		UNIT SIZE LEN WID HEI	PKG CC	SPEC MKG	QUP	ICQ	CT	FSCM	REFERENCE NUMBER	SCC	SRC CD
A	-----	4730-00-090-0832 --	00001		0008 0005 0005	80A0	99	012	---		41947	A4622		SCI
CARD	RES (5 POS)	NSN AND MTL-MGT-CD	HC	QUP	ICQ MTH CD PRES	PRES MATL	WRAP MATL	CUSH MATL	YY	INT CONT	UNIT CONT	DOP	SPEC PK CD	UC LVL
B	-----	4730-00-090-0832 --	--	012		00	YY	YY	X YY	WR	C	11	99 MKG ABC	A 4

UNIT PACK SIZE LEN WID DEP
UNIT PACK WEIGHT 0040 0040 0030   CUBE RES OPI SCI
SPI NUMBER SPI REV 0000002B   (5 POS)   E 4

CARD	RES (5 POS)	NSN AND MTL-MGT-CD	FSCM				CONTAINER NSN
D	-----	4730-00-090-0832 --	45678		(8 POS)		

Fig. A-24. LSA-025—Packaging Requirements Data.

LSA-026   RCC A   CYCLE 0018   LOGISTIC SUPPORT ANALYSIS RECORD
PACKAGING DEVELOPMENTAL DATA

EIAC	ITEM NAME	START LCN	ALC	STOP LCN		UOC	REFERENCE NUMBER	SCC	PKG CAT CD
END	GASKET						12284-5-7437		41A0

REFERENCE NUMBER 12284-5-7437

SCC	FSCM	NSN	***** UNIT SIZE *****				UI	PRICE	PS/PC	QUP	HC
	94833						EA	.29	002		

UNIT WGT LENGTH WIDTH HEIGHT SL
.2   4.0   4.0   .1   0

UI PRICE .29   PS/PC 002

Fig. A-25. LSA-026—Packaging Development Data.

LSA-027   RCC B   CYCLE 0019   LOGISTIC SUPPORT ANALYSIS RECORD
FAILURE/MAINTENANCE RATE SUMMARY

EIAC	ITEM NAME	START LCN	ALC	STOP LCN			UDC DCY	SERV DES ARMY	
END	REFRIGERATION UNIT								

LCN		ALC ITEM NAME	AOR	M B	SMR CODE	TASK CODE	FAIL RATE	COMP TASK FR	TASK M FREQ B	MRRI	COMP MRRI	MRRII	COMP MRRII	MRR MOD
0		REFRIGERATION UNIT	7200	0		HGOAAAA	2346.1	------	4.054 0	.0000	------	.000	------	------
						JGDAAAA	------	------	5.405 0					
00102		DOOR SIDE LEFT	7200	0		HGOABAA	12.5	------	.572 0	.0000	------	.000	------	------
002		WIRE HARNESS ASSY	7200	0		JGDAGAA	694.4	------	.200 0	.0000	------	.000	------	------
005		COMPRESSOR ASSY	7200	0	PAFFF	HGDAAAA	1250.0	------	.200 0	.4545	------	1.334	------	01223
						HGFAAAA	------	------	2.000 0					
						KRDAAAA	------	------	2.000 0					
00501		VALVE PLATE ASSY	7200	0	PAFZZ	JGFAGAA	50.0	------	.000 0	1.5545	------	1.334	------	01223
006		ENGINE ASSY	7200	0	PAFZZ	HGDXAAA	1202.4	------	3.337 0	1.6656	------	1.445	------	12C67
0060201		PISTON ASSY	7200	0	PAFZZ	JGFXGAA	666.7	------	.233 0	1.6656	------	1.445	------	12367
00607	C	DELUXE CARB	7200	0		HGOXGAA	500.0	------	1.140 0	.0000	------	.000	------	------
00614		STARTER ASSY	7200	0	PAQFF	HGFAGAA	833.3	------	.333 0	1.3434	------	1.223	------	C0701
						JGFAGAA	------	------	.333 0					

Fig. A-26. LSA-027—Failure, Maintenance Rate Summary.

```
LSA-028  RCC A    CYCLE 0019                      LOGISTIC SUPPORT ANALYSIS RECORD                89/03/22  PAGE  1
EIAC                                  REFERENCE NUMBER/ADDITIONAL REFERENCE NUMBER CROSS REFERENCE LIST    SCC
         ITEM NAME
END      VALVE, SERVICE
                      START LCN   ALC       STOP LCN    UDC        REFERENCE NUMBER
                      00506                 00516
```

REFERENCE NUMBER	SCC	FSCM	RN VC	RN CC	LCN	ALC	ALC ITEM NAME	ADDITIONAL REFERENCE NUMBER(S)	FSCM	RN VC	RN CC
AA06BR200		25567	2	5	00513		SCREW, CAP HEX HEAD	1C544	12603	2	3
		25567	2	5	00513			13207E5471FN88	97403	2	5
		25567	2	5	00513			25401	40001	2	5
		25567	2	3	00513			262N870-03	40001	2	5
A4544		41947	1	3	00507		CAP, TUBE	J513	81343	1	3
		41947	1	3	00507			MILF15049	30327	9	5
END7AA271		06534	2	5	00515		VALVE	END7AA271	10855	2	3
		06534	2	5	00515			END7AA271	41947	2	5
		06534	2	5	00515			7332D	28193	2	3
END7AA348		10855	2	3	00506		VALVE, SERVICE	A2-503-16	15809	2	5
		10855	2	3	00506			B31771	41947	2	5
		10855	2	3	00506			7660J	28193	9	5
MS20066-229		96906	2	2	00509		KEY, SQUARE	00K220TYPE25TYLEGRADEB	81348	1	4
442827		24617	2	3	00508		NUT, SELF-LOCK HEX	NO ADD REF NO ON FILE			
5F20-1631		10855	2	3	00510		WASHER, FLAT	NO ADD REF NO ON FILE			
5F20-781		10855	2	3	00511		INDICATOR, SIGHT	NO ADD REF NO ON FILE			
6D40-112		10855	2	3	00512		STRAINER, SUCTION	NO ADD REF NO ON FILE			
6D40-2163		10855	2	5	00514		HEAD, COMPRESSOR	6D40-1023	10855	2	3
		10855	2	5	00514			7780-1	97450	2	5
850-0050		44940	2	3	00508AA		WASHER, LOCK	NO ADD REF NO ON FILE			

Fig. A-27. LSA-028—Reference Number/Additional Reference Number Cross Reference List.

029 SECTION II

DRAFT-RPSTL   DATE 89/03/22   PAGE 1

(1) ITEM NO	(2) SMR CODE	(3) FSCM	(4) PART NUMBER	(5) DESCRIPTION AND USABLE ON CODE (UOC)	(6) QTY	WUC/TM FGC	LCN	A L C TMC	C	FIG	PL CC	ICC	NSN
3	PAFFF	10855	5D43-139-A	COMPRESSOR, ASSY / UOC: DCY,DCZ,	1	05	005	TM1		1	F	X	Y
10	PAFFF	10855	5D43-139-A	COMPRESSOR, ASSY / UOC: DCY,DCZ,	1	05	005	TM1		6	F	X	Y
1	PAFZZ	10855	6D23-522	VALVE PLATE ASSY / UOC: DCY,DCZ,	1	0501	00501	TM2		1		Y	Y
2	PAFZZ	66935	5D40-1182	GASKET SCTN MANI / UOC: DCY,DCZ,	1	0502	00502	TM2		1	9		Y
3	PAFZZ	66935	6D40-1131	GASKET SCTN VALVE / UOC: DCY,DCZ,	1	0503	00503	TM2		1	9		Y
4	PAFZZ	96906	MS27183-13	WASHER, FLAT / UOC: DCY,DCZ,	4	0503AA	00503AA	TM2		1		Y	Y
5	PAFZZ	41947	A5051	NUT, TUBE, COUPLING / UOC: DCY,DCZ,	4	0505	00505	TM2		1		Y	Y
6	PAFZZ	10855	EN07AA348	VALVE, SERVICE / UOC: DCY,DCZ,	1	0506	00506	TM2		1		Y	Y
7	PAFZZ	41947	A4544	CAP, TUBE / UOC: DCY,DCZ,	1	0507	00507	TM2		1		Y	Y
8	PAFZZ	24617	442827	NUT, SELF-LOCK HEX / UOC: DCY,DCZ,	4	0508	00508	TM2		1		Y	Y
9	PAFZZ	44940	850-0050	WASHER,LOCK / UOC: DCY,DCZ,	4	0508AA	00508AA	TM2		1		Y	Y
10	PBFZZ	96906	MS20066-229	KEY, SQUARE / UOC: DCY,DCZ,	1	0509	00509	TM2		1		Y	Y
11	PAFZZ	10855	5F20-1631	WASHER, FLAT / UOC: DCY,DCZ,	2	0510	00510	TM2		1		Y	Y
12	PAFZZ	10855	5F20-781	INDICATOR,SIGHT / UOC: DCY,DCZ,	1	0511	00511	TM2		1		Y	Y
13	PAFZZ	10855	6D40-112	STRAINER, SUCTION / UOC: DCY,DCZ,	1	0512	00512	TM2		1		Y	Y
14	PAFZZ	25567	AA06BR200	SCREW, CAP HEX HEAD / UOC: DCY,DCZ,	5	0513	00513	TM2		1		Y	Y
15	PBFZZ	10855	6D40-2163	HEAD, COMPRESSOR / UOC: DCY,DCZ,	2	0514	00514	TM2		1		Y	Y
16	PAFZZ	06534	EN07AA271	VALVE / UOC: DCY,DCZ,	1	0515	00515	TM2		1		Y	Y

Fig. A-28. LSA-029—Repair Parts List.

SECTION III   TM-5-4110-300-24P   PROOF-RPSTL   DATE 89/03/24   PAGE 10

(1) ITEM NO	(2) SMR CODE	(3) FSCM	(4) PART NUMBER	(5) DESCRIPTION AND USABLE ON CODE (UDC)	(6) QTY	WUC/TM FGC	LCN	TMC	A L C FIG	PL CC	ICC	NSN
				GROUP: 95								
				FIG 10 SPECIAL TOOLS								
		73785	GA9473612	WORK BENCH..........		1T	0060T	TM3	10	D	4	N
		25752	K252	HYDROMETER..........		1T	0060T	TM3	10	D	5	N
				UOC:DCY,								
1		72777	RC100	RING COMPRESSOR........		1T	0060T	TM3	10	D	4	N
				UOC:DCY,								
2		44940	JH25	SPREADER,PISTON RNG........		1T	0060T	TM3	10	D	4	N
				UOC:DCY,								
3		22441	JC931H4257	TABLE,CABLE FORMING........		1T	0060T	TM3	10	D	5	N
				UOC:DCY,								
				BOI:9 PER HQ OF UNITS ABOVE BN LEVEL								
4		01762	SN517832105	PM56VOLTMETER........		1T	0060T	TM3	10	D	5	N
				UOC:DCY,								
				BOI:2 PER LETTERED COMPANY								
				BOI:9 BY NUMBERED BTRY/COMPANY AND SIMILIAR HQ PERFORMING ORG MAINT FOR OTHER UNITS								
5		33721	CC586T3692	DITMCO STATION........		1T	0060T	TM3	10	D	5	N
				UOC:DCY,								
				END OF FIGURE								

Fig. A-29. LSA-030—Special Tools List.

CROSS REFERENCE INDEXES
PART NUMBER INDEX

FSCM	PART NUMBER	STOCK NUMBER	FIGURE NO	ITEM NO
25567	AA06BR200	5305-00-225-8507	1	14
10855	AA06BR200	5305-00-378-2804	1	17
41947	A4544	4730-00-260-8284	1	7
41947	A4622	4730-00-090-0832	2	6
41625	A50407-481	5305-00-206-9952	1	20
41947	A5051	4720-00-189-2737	1	5
06534	EN07AA271	4130-00-453-6272	1	16
10855	EN07AA348	4820-00-316-2659	1	6
96906	MS20066-229	5315-00-956-5683	1	10
96906	MS27183-13	5310-00-087-7493	1	4
96906	MS27183-13	5310-00-087-7493	1	19
96906	MS90728-60	5305-01-000-0542	2	2
04643	TH-WW3510	5305-00-058-6330	2	5
66935	05DA500143	5330-01-111-9289	2	4
10855	05DA500153	5330-01-111-9276	2	1
44940	142-0033		1	8
59730	3302	5975-00-152-1144	2	7
24617	442827	5130-00-298-9284	1	8
66935	5D40-1182	5330-01-111-9288	1	2
10855	5D43-139-A	4130-01-091-9159	1	3
10855	5D43-139-A	4130-01-091-9159	6	10
10855	5F20-1631	5310-01-914-0429	1	11
10855	5F20-781	6680-00-818-3941	1	12
10855	6D23-1421	5330-00-809-9573	1	18
10855	6D23-522	4130-00-620-7000	1	1
10855	6D40-112	4130-00-785-5132	1	13
66935	6D40-1131	5330-01-111-9287	1	3
10855	6D40-2163	4130-00-795-0345	1	15
10855	6D48-1072	4130-00-791-5312	2	3
44940	850-0050	5310-01-060-9104	1	9

Fig. A-30. LSA-031—Part Number/National Stock Number/Reference Designation Cross Reference Index.

```
LSA-032  RCC A   CYCLE 0019              LOGISTIC SUPPORT ANALYSIS RECORD                    89/03/22  PAGE  5
                                               DLSC SUBMITTALS
EIAC         ITEM NAME                      PROVISIONING SCREENING
END          ENGINE
ACTIVITY  DESTINATION  OUT DATA  SGL/MULT  SOURCE  ARN SEL  TYPE SCREEN  PLISN SUBMIT   UOC   SERV DES   DLSC    PRI IND CD
CODE      CODE         REQ CODE  OUT CODE  SOURCE   SEL      TYPE SCREEN  CONTROL CODE                    IMAGE        4
MU        XMDSE        9910      4         CODE     CODE     CODE                                          1      DSR/RC   STAT
                                          P        X        F            P                                       OPTION  IND CODE
                                                                                                                          A

START LCN   ALC         STOP LCN
006
```

ERROR CODE
1 - MISSING RNCC/RNVC FOR P TYPE SCREEN.
2 - MORE THAN 25 REFERENCE NUMBERS IN SUBMISSION PACKET.
3 - MISSING FSCM.
4 - INVALID RNCC (1-8 AND A-G ALLOWED) FOR P TYPE SCREEN.
5 - INVALID RNVC (1-3 AND 9) FOR P TYPE SCREEN.
6 - SOURCE CODE NOT ON FILE.
7 - INVALID RNCC/RNVC COMBINATION FOR P TYPE SCREEN.
8 - MORE THAN 36 IDENTICAL LCN/ALC COMBINATIONS.
* - DUPE ON REF-NO & FSCM WILL NOT BE SENT TO DLSC. (FOR F & S TYPE SCREEN).

PART ONE
SUBMITTER'S CONTROL NUMBER - LCN CROSS REFERENCE LIST

REFERENCE NUMBER/ARN	SCC	CSC	RNCC	RNVC	FSCM	SUBMITTER CONTROL	LCN	ALC CT	SMR	ERROR CODE(S)
114-0145			4	2	44940	TESTPL0241	0060201AG		PAFZZ	
114-0203			3	2	44940	TESTPL0229	0060201AD		PAFZZ	
1144144		A	5	9	44940	TESTPL0229				
1144144		B	5	9	44940	TESTPL0229				
1191			2	2	10235	TESTPL0061	0060B			6
122-0323			2	2	44940	TESTPL0065	0060B			6
12799979			3	2	12204	TESTPL0197	0060T			6
1400B			3	2	64484	TESTPL0201	0060T			6
142-0431			3	2	44940	TESTPL0249	00607			
1424131		A	5	9	44940	TESTPL0249	00607		PAOFF	
191-0971			3	1	44940	TESTPL0625	00614AU		PAFZZ	
191-0987			3	2	44940	TESTPL0573	00614AF		PAFZZ	
191-1006			3	2	44940	TESTPL0585	00614AJ		PAFZZ	
191-1008			3	2	44940	TESTPL0593	00614AL			
ATESTREFND		A				TESTPL0593				3
191-1010			3	9	44940	TESTPL0629	00614AV		PAFZZ	
191-1052			3	2	44940	TESTPL0553	00614		PAOFF	6
191-1076			3	2	44940	TESTPL0565	00614AC			6

Fig. A-31. LSA-032—DLSC Submittals.

```
LSA-032   RCC A    CYCLE 0019                          LOGISTIC SUPPORT ANALYSIS RECORD          89/03/22   PAGE   7
PART TWO                CARD IMAGE DLSC SCREENING
CARD COL         DESCRIPTION                           CARD COL          DESCRIPTION
01-03   DOCUMENT IDENTIFIER CODE      LSR              32      TYPE SCREENING CODE        F
04-06   PACKAGE SEQUENCE NUMBER                        33-36   OUTPUT DATA REQ            9910
07      PRIORITY INDICATOR            4                37      STATISTICAL IND            A
08-09   ACTIVITY CODE                 MU               38      SINGLE/MULT OUTPUT         4
10-26   SUB CTL NUMBER                                 39      RNFC (LEFT BLANK)
10-13   JULIAN DATE                   9081             40      DIDS SEGMENT CODE          2
14      SER ID OR LCN CT                               41      RNCC (P TYPE SCREEN)
15-25   PCCN-PLISN OR LCN                              42      RNVC (P TYPE SCREEN)
26      ALC OR BLANK                                   43-47   FSCM
27-31   DESTINATION CODE              XMDSE            48-79   REFERENCE NUMBER/ARN
                                                       80      CONTINUATION IND           1

          1         2         3         4         5         6         7         8
12345678901234567890123456789012345678901234567890123456789012345678901234567890

LSR2014MU9081 TESTPL0209 XMDSEF9910A4 2 44940BC1920         1
LSR2014MU9081 AAAA01AABW XMDSEF9910A4 2 44940CCKA-MS/3834J  1
LSR2014MU9081 TESTPL0205 XMDSEF9910A4 2 44940110-1860       1
LSRA014MU9081 TESTPL0217 XMDSEF9910A4 2 44940112-0136       1
LSRA024MU9081 TESTPL0217 XMDSEF9910A4 2 96737A8916          1
LSRA034MU9081 TESTPL0217 XMDSEF9910A4 2 44730112-0179       1
LSRA044MU9081 TESTPL0217 XMDSEF9910A4 2 44730112-71         1
LSR2054MU9081 TESTPL0217 XMDSEF9910A4 2 44940112411STD      1
LSR2014MU9081 TESTPL0245 XMDSEF9910A4 2 44940113-0153       1
LSR2014MU9081 TESTPL0241 XMDSEF9910A4 2 44940114-0145       1
LSRA014MU9081 TESTPL0229 XMDSEF9910A4 2 44940114-0203       1
LSRA024MU9081 TESTPL0229 XMDSEF9910A4 2 44940144144         1
LSR2034MU9081 TESTPL0229 XMDSEF9910A4 2 44940144144         1
LSRA014MU9081 TESTPL0249 XMDSEF9910A4 2 44940142-0431       1
LSR2024MU9081 TESTPL0249 XMDSEF9910A4 2 44940142413         1
LSR2014MU9081 TESTPL0625 XMDSEF9910A4 2 44940191-0971       1
LSR2014MU9081 TESTPL0573 XMDSEF9910A4 2 44940191-0987       1
LSR2014MU9081 TESTPL0585 XMDSEF9910A4 2 44940191-1006       1
LSR2014MU9081 TESTPL0629 XMDSEF9910A4 2 44940191-1010       1
LSR2014MU9081 TESTPL0553 XMDSEF9910A4 2 44940191-1052       1
LSR2014MU9081 TESTPL0617 XMDSEF9910A4 2 44940191-1087       1
LSR2014MU9081 TESTPL0561 XMDSEF9910A4 2 44940B50-0050       1

                  TOTAL DLSC ITEMS      000022
```

Fig. A-3. (Continued.)

MARINE CORPS STOCK LIST
PART I - ITEM IDENTIFICATION LISTING
SL-4-88647D

DATE 89/03/22 PAGE 1 LSA-034

ITEM NO.	MODEL	NATIONAL STOCK NUMBER	REF DESIG FIG-KEY	D	ITEM IDENTIFICATION	UM	QUANTITY PER PER APPL EQUIP	SMR CODE	REPL FACTOR	LCN	A C TMC	FIG NO	REFERENCE NUMBER	S C
1	DCY	4130-00-620-7000		B	VALVE PLATE ASSY	EA	2	PAFZZ	1.554	00501	TM2	1	6D23-522	
2	DCY	5330-01-111-9288		*	GASKET SCTN MANI	EA	1	PAFZZ	1.454	00502	TM2	1	5D40-1182	
3	DCY	5330-01-111-9287		*	GASKET SCTN VALVE	EA	1	PAFZZ	1.554	00503	TM2	1	6D40-1131	
4	DCY	5310-00-087-7493			WASHER, FLAT	EA	4	PAFZZ	1.676	00503AA	TM2	1	MS27183-13	
5	DCY	4720-00-189-2737		B	NUT, TUBE, COUPLING	EA	4	PAFZZ	1.665	00505	TM2	1	A5051	
6	DCY	4820-00-316-2659	001-006	B	VALVE, SERVICE	EA	1	PAFZZ	1.675	00506	TM2	1	EN07AA348	
7	DCY	4730-00-260-8284		B	CAP, TUBE	EA	1	PAFZZ	1.665	00507	TM2	1	A4544	
8	DCY	5130-00-298-9284		B	NUT, SELF-LOCK HEX	EA	4	PAFZZ	1.454	00508	TM2	1	442827	
8	DCY			C	GASKET KIT	EA	1	PAFZZ	1.232	00540	TM2	1	142-0033	
9	DCY	5310-01-060-9104		C	WASHER,LOCK	EA	4	PBFZZ	1.665	0050BAA	TM2	1	850-0050	
10	DCY	5315-00-956-5683	001-010	B	KEY,SQUARE	EA	1	PAFZZ	1.676	00509	TM2	1	MS20066-229	
11	DCY	5310-00-914-0429		B	WASHER, FLAT	EA	2	PAFZZ	1.454	00510	TM2	1	5F20-1631	
12	DCY	6680-00-818-3941		B	INDICATOR,SIGHT	EA	1	PAFZZ	1.454	00511	TM2	1	5F20-781	
13	DCY	4130-00-785-5132		B	STRAINER, SUCTION	EA	1	PAFZZ	1.554	00512	TM2	1	6D40-112	
14	DCY	5305-00-225-8507		B	SCREW, CAP HEX HEAD	EA	5	PAFZZ	1.665	00513	TM2	1	AA06BR200	
15	DCY	4130-00-795-0345	001-005	B	HEAD, COMPRESSOR	EA	2	PBFZZ	1.554	00514	TM2	1	6D40-2163	
16	DCY	4130-00-453-6272		B	VALVE	EA	1	PAFZZ	1.675	00515	TM2	1	EN07AA271	A
17	DCY	5305-00-378-2804		B	SCREW, CAP, HEX HD	EA	1	PAFZZ	1.665	00517	TM2	1	AA06BR200	
18	DCY	5330-00-809-9573		*	GASKET	EA	1	PAFZZ	1.554	00518	TM2	1	6D23-1421	
19	DCY	5310-00-087-7493		B	WASHER, FLAT	EA	4	PAFZZ	1.676	00519	TM2	1	MS27183-13	
20	DCY	5305-00-206-9952		B	SCREW, CAP, HEX HD	EA	2	PAFZZ	1.665	00520	TM2	1	A50407-481	

Fig. A-32. LSA-034—Stockage List Type-Four Report.

Appendix A   LSA Summary Reports

```
PROVISIONING LIST FOR PCCN AAAB03 AND MODEL ENGINE ASSY
1........10.......20.......30.......40.......50.......60.......70.......80

AAAB03AAAA M  2805011089240                                         01B
AAAB03AAAA G                                                        01J
AAAB03AAAA MTM1   1    4    001006                                  01J

AAAB03AAAJ G                                                        01J
AAAB03AAAJ MTM3   1    2    0010604                                 01J

AAAB03AAAK G 44940112-0179                                          02A
AAAB03AAAK G 44940112-71                                            03A
AAAB03AAAK G 44940112A71STD                                         04A
AAAB03AAAK G 96787A8916                                             05A
AAAB03AAAK M 44730112-0179                                    32    02A
AAAB03AAAK M 44730112-71                                      59    03A
AAAB03AAAK M 44940112411STD                                   59    04A
AAAB03AAAK M 96737A8916                                       52    05A
AAAB03AAAK M 2805006470713                                          01B
AAAB03AAAK G                                                        01J
AAAB03AAAK MTM3   5    1    00206801                                01J

AAAB03AAAL G                                                        01J
AAAB03AAAL MTM3   5    2    00406802                                01J

AAAB03AAAM G                                                        01J
AAAB03AAAM MTM3   5    2    00206803                                01J

AAAB03AAAN G 44940114-144                                           02A
AAAB03AAAN G 44940148144                                            03A
AAAB03AAAN M 44940144144                                      59    02A
AAAB03AAAN M 44940144144                                      59    03A
AAAB03AAAN M 2805008652333                                          01B
AAAB03AAAN G                                                        01J
AAAB03AAAN MTM3   5    4    00206804                                01J

AAAB03AAAP G                                                        01J
AAAB03AAAP MTM3   5    5    00406805                                01J

AAAB03AAAQ G                                                        01J
AAAB03AAAQ MTM3   5    6    00206806                                01J

AAAB03AAAR G                                                        01J
AAAB03AAAR MTM3   5    7    00406807                                01J

AAAB03AAAS M  2805010453095                                         01B
AAAB03AAAS G                                                        01J
AAAB03AAAS MTM3   5    8    00206808                                01J

AAAB03AAAT G                                                        01J
AAAB03AAAT MTM3   5    1    068                                     01J
AAAB03AAAV G 44940142A431                                           02A

1........10.......20.......30.......40.......50.......60.......70.......80
```

Fig. A-33. LSA-036—Provisioning Requirements.

LSA-036   PCC A   CYCLE 0008

LOGISTIC SUPPORT ANALYSIS RECORD

86/11/19 Page 47

LSA-036 SUMMARY FOR AAAB03

PCCN	PLISN						
AAAB03	AABY						

	TO IND	REFERENCE NUMBER - OVERFLOW	RN RN DA PP E			S SL	CS CF
PCCN	CC CD FSCM	ADDITIONAL REFERENCE NUMBERS	CC VC C SL C	ITEM NAME		L AC	N I
AABY	C 44940	191-1008	3 2 1 A 1	BRUSH, NEGATIVE		0	01 A

	TO -----NSN RELATED DATA----			UI	DM PL HC PS PM ADP	CS CF
	CC PRE FSC NIIN	SUFF UM UM PRICE	UI UI PRICE	CONV QUP SMR C	IL T I PC IC EC	N I
		EA 00000001.10	EA 00000001.10	100	A 06 A	01 B

	TO NHA NHA QTY/ QTY/		TOT	SAME AS PRIOR	CS CF
	CC PLISN IND ORR ASSY EI	MRR I MRR I	MRR MOD R QTY	PLISN PLISN	N I
	AAAB C 100 0001	0001.3434 00001.223 C0701W		MAOT MAC NRTS LRU	01 C

	TO RD RD SM PL SM AI AIC	RMS RISS RTLL	CS CF
	OO UOC	OC C CC CC IC C QTY MRU SL BUY QTY RSR	N I
	DCY,FF, AAAAABBBBTTTTTBBBBBCCCCC111BE	A 004 015 030 010	01 D

	TO MAINT TASK DISTRIB	REPAIR CYCLE TIME--CON	REPLACEMENT TASK DIST	DES REMORK PT	CT AM AM IM RICS	CS CF
	CC O F H SRA D CB CA	O F H SRA D TAT	O F H SRA D	ONE TWO	IC C SC C P N I	N I
		030	070	CG 3		01 E

	TO CHANGE AUTHORITY	SEP NUMBER EFFECTIVITY	REP/SUP RS/ QUANTITY QUANTITY	CS CI
	CC NUMBER	IC FROM TO	TIC PLISN IND SHIPPED PROCURED DCN-UOC	N 1
	CHANGE-FIVE OR		03 AABV R 000333 000444	01 F
	CHG-AUTH-ONE TM		AABV R	02 F

	TO CHANGE AUTHORITY	PRORATED PRORATED	CS CF
	CC NUMBER	ELIN QUANTITY	N I
	CHANGE-FIVE	ELINBB 000400	01 G

	TO LCN		REMARKS	CS CF
	CC	ALC		N I
	00614AL			01 H

	TO TM FIG ITEM	TM TM QTY/	--BASIS OF ISSUE--	BASIS OF ISSUE	CS CF.
	CC CODE NO NO	CHG IND FIG	WUC/TM FGC	QTY-A EI LV CTR QTY-A	EI LV CTR	N I
			06911			01 J

PROVISIONING NOMENCLATURE

FIG 3, ITEM 21
PART OF KIT GROUP 70, ITEM 1

	TO TM FIG ITEM		CS CF
	CC CODE NO NO		N I
M	TM3		01 K
M	TM3 3 21		02 K

```
LSA-040   RCC A   CYCLE 0021        LOGISTIC SUPPORT ANALYSIS RECORD          89/03/23  PAGE  1
                                    COMPONENTS OF END ITEM LIST
EIAC
END               ITEM NAME            START LCN         STOP LCN          UOC
                  REFRIGERATION UNIT   0                                   DCY
(1)      (2)                           (3)
ILLUS NO NSN      DESCRIPTION, FSCM AND REFERENCE NUMBER      ALC   UOC    (4)  (5)
                                                                          UM   QTY REQD

  1   5975-00-152-1144   BOX CONNECTOR                       DCY,DCZ       EA    4
                         (59730), 3302
  2   5940-00-926-0085   CLAMP, ELECTRICAL                   DCY           EA    4
                         (00779), 42332-2
  3   6645-00-089-8842   METER,TIME                          DCY           EA    4
                         (16476), 56181
  4   5310-00-655-6534   NUT,PLAIN,ASSEMBLED                 DCY           EA    4
                         (78189), 511-101800-50
  5   5940-00-236-1573   TERM, QUICK DISCON                  DCY           EA    4
                         (00779), 32446
  6   5940-00-177-6760   TERMINAL LUG                        DCY           EA    4
                         (00779), 42565-1
```

Fig. A-34. LSA-040—Components of End Item List.

```
LSA-041   RCC A   CYCLE 0021        LOGISTIC SUPPORT ANALYSIS RECORD          89/03/23  PAGE  1
                                    BASIC ISSUE ITEMS LIST
EIAC
END               ITEM NAME            START LCN         STOP LCN          UOC
                  REFRIGERATION UNIT   0                                   DCY
(1)      (2)                           (3)
ILLUS NO NSN      DESCRIPTION, FSCM AND REFERENCE NUMBER      ALC   UOC    (4)  (5)
                                                                          UM   QTY REQD

  1   2910-01-044-8999   CARBURETOR ASSY     DCY,FFA,AAB,AAC,AAD,AAE,AAF,AAG,AAH,FFI,AAJ,     EA    2
                         (44940), 142-0431   AAK,AAL,AAM,AAN,AAO,AAP,AAQ,AAR,FAA,FAI
  2   2805-00-865-2333   CONNECTING ROD,PIST                 DCY,FF,FA     EA    2
                         (44940), 114-0203
  3   2910-00-358-5618   DISK,VALVE                          DCY,FF        EA    2
                         (44940), 142-0055
  4   5330-01-111-9276   GASKET, VALVE PLATE                 DCY,DCZ       EA    2
                         (10855), 05DA500153
  5   2805-00-647-0713   PISTON, INT COMB EN                 DCY,FF,FA     EA    2
                         (44940), 112-0136
```

Fig. A-35. LSA-041—Basic Issue Items List.

```
LSA-042   RCC A      CYCLE 0021          LOGISTIC SUPPORT ANALYSIS RECORD                        89/03/23  PAGE    1
                                         ADDITIONAL AUTHORIZATION LIST
                     ITEM NAME                   START LCN        ALC          STOP LCN     UOC
EIAC                 REFRIGERATION UNIT              0                                      DCY
END                    (2)
 (1)                 DESCRIPTION, FSCM AND REFERENCE NUMBER      UOC                              (3)      (4)
NSN                      ADDITIONAL AUTHORIZED LIST-MTOE AUTHORIZED                              UM       QTY REQD

4730-00-260-8284     CAP, TUBE                                  DCY,DCZ                          EA        8
                     (41947), A4544
4730-00-090-0832     COUPLING, FEMALE                           DCY,DCZ                          EA        8
                     (41947), A4622
4720-00-189-2737     NUT, TUBE, COUPLING                        DCY,DCZ                          EA        8
                     (41947), A5051
5120-00-189-7933     SOCKET WRENCH                              DCY                              EA        8
                     (30106), A26

                         ADDITIONAL AUTHORIZED LIST-OTHER AUTHORIZED

4130-00-453-6272     VALVE                                      DCY,DCZ                          EA       10
                     (06534), EN07AA271
5120-00-148-7917     WRENCH SET, COMB                           DCY                              EA       10
                     (B0204), B107-6
```

Fig. A-36. LSA-042—Additional Authorization List.

```
LSA-043   RCC A      CYCLE 0021          LOGISTIC SUPPORT ANALYSIS RECORD                        89/03/23  PAGE    1
                                   EXPENDABLE/DURABLE SUPPLIES AND MATERIALS LIST
                     ITEM NAME                   START LCN        ALC          STOP LCN     UOC
EIAC                 REFRIGERATION UNIT              0                                      DCY
END                    (2)                       (4)
 (1)                       (3)       DESCRIPTION, FSCM AND REFERENCE NUMBER                       (5)
ITEM NO              LEVEL   NSN                                                                  UM

 1                          7920-00-205-1711    CLOTHS                                           EA
                                                (58536), A-A-531
 2                          5120-00-227-8074    EXT-SOCKET WRENCH                                EA
                                                (30106), A610
 3                    F     4130-00-795-0345    HEAD, COMPRESSOR                                 EA
                                                (10855), 6D40-2163
 4                    F     5305-00-225-8507    SCREW, CAP HEX HEAD                              EA
                                                (25567), AA06BR200
 5                          5120-00-278-1273    SCREWDRIVER                                      EA
                                                (79061), A135
 6                          5120-00-189-7985    SOCKET, WRENCH                                   EA
                                                (30106), A24
 7                    F     4130-00-791-5312    VALVE, SUCTION                                   EA
                                                (10855), 6D48-1072
 8                          5120-00-449-8083    WRENCH,ADJUSTABLE                                EA
                                                (11599), AT503
```

Fig. A-37. LSA-043—Expendable/Durable Supplies and Materials List.

MARINE CORPS STOCK LIST   SL-3-88643D   DATE 89/03/22   PAGE LSA-045
LIST OF COMPONENTS
SUPPLY SYSTEM RESPONSIBILITY

ITEM NO.	NATIONAL STOCK NUMBER	REF DESIG FIG-KEY	MODEL	ITEM IDENTIFICATION	UM	QTY USED IN UNIT	REFERENCE NUMBER	SCC	LCN	ALC	AIC	FSCM
1	5905-00-900-7753	DCZ		RESISTOR, 50 OHM	EA		2004		00214	A	AA	44655
2	5330-01-111-9276	DCY		GASKET, VALVE PLATE	EA		05DA500153		00501AE		AA	10855
3	4130-00-791-5312	DCY		006-VALVE, SUCTION	EA		6D48-1072		00501AY		AD	10855
4	5305-00-225-8507	DCY		010-SCREW, CAP HEX HEAD	EA		AA06BR200		00513		AD	25567
5	4130-00-795-0345	DCY	001-005	006-HEAD, COMPRESSOR	EA		6D40-2163		00514		AD	10855
6	7920-00-205-1711	DCY		006-CLOTHS	EA		A-A-531		0060B		AD	58536
7	5120-00-449-8083	DCY		010-WRENCH,ADJUSTABLE	EA		AT503		0060T		AD	11599
8	5120-00-278-1273	DCY		006-SCREWDRIVER	EA		A135		0060T		AD	79061
9	5120-00-189-7985	DCY		006-SOCKET, WRENCH	EA		A24		0060T		AD	30106
10	5120-00-227-8074	DCY		008-EXT,SOCKET WRENCH	EA		A610		0060T		AD	30106
11	2805-00-647-0713	DCY		PISTON, INT COMB EN	EA		112-0136		0060201AA		AA	44940
12	2805-00-865-2333	DCY		CONNECTING ROD,PIST	EA		114-0203		0060201AD		AA	44940
13	2910-01-044-8999	DCY		CARBURETOR ASSY	EA		142-0431		00607		AA	44940
14	2910-00-358-5618	DCY		DISK,VALVE	EA		142-0055		00607AC		AA	44940

MARINE CORPS STOCK LIST   SL-3-88643D   DATE 89/03/22   PAGE LSA-045
LIST OF COMPONENTS
USING UNIT RESPONSIBILITY

ITEM NO.	NATIONAL STOCK NUMBER	REF DESIG FIG-KEY	MODEL	ITEM IDENTIFICATION	UM	QTY USED IN UNIT	REFERENCE NUMBER	SCC	LCN	ALC	AIC	FSCM
15	6645-00-089-8842	DCY		METER,TIME	EA		56181		00203		AC	16476
16	5310-00-655-6534	DCY		NUT,PLAIN,ASSEMBLED	EA		511-101800-50		00208		AC	78189
17	5940-00-926-0085	DCY		CLAMP, ELECTRICAL	EA		42332-2		00213		AC	00779
18	5940-00-236-1573	DCY		TERM, QUICK DISCON	EA		32446		00216		AC	00779
19	5940-00-177-6760	DCY		TERMINAL LUG	EA		42565-1		00217		AC	00779
20	5975-00-152-1144	DCY		BOX CONNECTOR	EA		3302		00501BB		AC	59730

MARINE CORPS STOCK LIST   SL-3-88643D   DATE 89/03/22   PAGE LSA-045
LIST OF COMPONENTS
COLLATERAL EQUIPMENT

ITEM NO.	NATIONAL STOCK NUMBER	REF DESIG FIG-KEY	MODEL	ITEM IDENTIFICATION	UM	QTY USED IN UNIT	REFERENCE NUMBER	SCC	LCN	ALC	AIC	FSCM
21	4730-00-090-0832	DCY		COUPLING, FEMALE	EA		A4622		00501BA		AE	41947
22	4720-00-189-2737	DCY		NUT, TUBE, COUPLING	EA		A5051		00505		AE	41947
23	4730-00-260-8284	DCY		CAP, TUBE	EA		A4544		00507		AE	41947
24	5120-00-189-7933	DCY		SOCKET WRENCH	EA		A26		0060T		AE	30106

MARINE CORPS STOCK LIST   SL-3-88643D
FEDERAL SUPPLY CODES FOR MANUFACTURER

00779   10855   11599   16476   25567   30106   41947   44655   44940   58536   59730
78189   79061

Fig. A-38. LSA-045—Stockage List Type-Three Report.

```
LSA-050   RCC A   CYCLE 0021          LOGISTIC SUPPORT ANALYSIS RECORD              89/03/23   PAGE   1
                                   RELIABILITY CENTERED MAINTENANCE SUMMARY

EIAC    ITEM NAME           START LCN        ALC   STOP LCN   UDC    SHSC SEL   PART I   PART II   RCM DISP
END     REFRIGERATION UNIT     0                             DCY    1 2 3 4      Y         Y          X

                                          PART I
                            FAILURE MODES WITH RCM ANALYSIS

                               DISP       LOGIC RESULTS
                                          00000000011111111112   PREVENTIVE MAINTENANCE           TASK    FM CRIT
                                          1234567890123456789 0                                   TIME    OR          LOGIC
ALC  ITEM NAME        SHSC FMI ABCDE MPC                        LCN   ALC TSK CD                           FAIL PROB   UTILIZED
LCN
0     REFRIGERATION UNIT  2  AB   Y    B    Y   N       N N Y                                              418.7800    750-16
00501 VALVE PLATE ASSY    3  AA   Y         NY  N       N N Y                                                8.6300    750-16
006   ENGINE ASSY         2  AB   Y    B    Y   N       N N Y                                              110.3400    750-16
006   ENGINE ASSY         3  AC   Y    B    Y   N       N YY                                             LEVEL A       750-16
00602 ENGINE BLOCK        3  AA   Y    B    NY  N       N YY                                              107.3400    750-16
0060201 PISTON ASSY       3  AA   Y    B    NY YYY                                                        110.4100    750-16
0060201 PISTON ASSY       2  AB   Y    B    Y  YYY                                                         30.6700    750-16
00607 CARBURETOR ASSY     3  AA   Y    B    NY  N    NN  Y                                                 32.2000    750-16
00607 CARBURETOR ASSY     3  AB   Y    B    NY  N    NN  Y                                                 39.1000    750-16
00607 CARBURETOR ASSY     3  AC   Y    B    NY  N    NN  Y                                                 20.7000    750-16
00614 STARTER ASSY        2  AA   Y    B    Y   N       N YY                                                 8.3300    750-16
0     REFRIGERATION UNIT  2  AA   Y    A    Y   N       YY        005   ABCACAA              .27          358.9500    750-16
                                                                 005   ABDACAA              .10
0     REFRIGERATION UNIT  4  AC   Y    A    NY  N      YY         006   CBCACAA              .06          638.1400    750-16
                                                                 006   CBDAAAA              .37
0     REFRIGERATION UNIT  3  AD   Y    A    NY  N      YN         002   AACACAA              .13          378.9000    750-16
                                                                 002   ABDACAA              .10
002   WIRE HARNESS ASSY   3  AA   Y    A    NY  N      YN         002   AACACAA              .13          599.9600    750-16
                                                                 002   ABDACAA              .10
005   COMPRESSOR ASSY     3  AA   Y         NY  N      YY         005   ABCACAA              .27          218.5000    750-16
                                                                 005   ABDACAA              .10
006   ENGINE ASSY         3  AA   Y    B    NY YYY                006   CBCACAA              .06            8.3000    750-16
                                                                 006   CBDAAAA              .37
```

Fig. A-39. LSA-050—Reliability Centered Maintenance Summary.

317

LSA-051   RCC A   CYCLE 0021

LOGISTIC SUPPORT ANALYSIS RECORD   89/03/23   PAGE   1
RELIABILITY SUMMARY - REDESIGN

EIAC	ITEM NAME	START LCN	ALC	STOP LCN	UOC	DISP OPT	FAILURE MODE AND CAUSE	
END	ENGINE ASSY	006		006	DCY		SYSTEM REDESIGN	Y
							LOGISTIC CONSIDERATIONS	Y
							LOGISTIC CONSIDERATION NARRATIVE	Y

LCN	ALC	FMI	ITEM NAME	MFR PART NUMBER	FSCM	SHSC	FM CRIT NO/FAIL PROB LVL
006	AA		ENGINE ASSY	CCKA-MS/3834J	44940	3	8.3000

FAILURE MODE AND CAUSE:
 POOR ENGINE PERFORMANCE DUE TO PISTON ASSEMBLY FAILURE.
 LOGISTIC CONSIDERATIONS:

STANDARDIZATION	Y	ACCESSIBILITY	Y	MAINTENANCE EASE	Y	SAFETY	Z	TEST POINTS	Y	SKILLS	Y	TRAINING	Y
CONN REMOVAL	Y	PKG AND TRANSP	Y	FAULT LOCATION	Y	LABELING	Y	DAMAGE PROTECT	Y	CORR AND RUST CONT	Y		

Fig. A-40. LSA-051—Reliability Summary—Redesign.

LSA-052   RCC D   CYCLE 0021

LOGISTIC SUPPORT ANALYSIS RECORD   89/03/23   PAGE   1
CRITICALITY ANALYSIS SUMMARY

EIAC	ITEM NAME	START LCN	ALC	STOP LCN	UOC	SHSC SEL	FM CRIT SEL	FAIL PROB SEL
END	REFRIGERATION UNIT	0		LCN	DCY		10.0000	

SAFETY HAZARD SEVERITY CODE - (CRITICAL)

FM CRIT	LCN	ALC FMI	WUC/TM FGC	ITEM NAME	MFR PART NUMBER	FSCM	FAIL RATE SOURCE
418.7800	0	AB 00		REFRIGERATION UNIT	F10000RG-2		GIDEP
358.9500	0	AA 00		REFRIGERATION UNIT	F10000RG-2	94833	GIDEP
FM CRIT	LCN	ALC FMI	WUC/TM FGC	ITEM NAME	MFR PART NUMBER	94833 FSCM	FAIL RATE SOURCE
110.3400	006	AB 06		ENGINE ASSY	CCKA-MS/3834J	44940	GIDEP
FM CRIT	LCN	ALC FMI	WUC/TM FGC	ITEM NAME	MFR PART NUMBER	FSCM	FAIL RATE SOURCE
30.6700	0060201	AB	060201	PISTON ASSY	BC1920	44940	GIDEP

Fig. A-41. LSA-052—Criticality Analysis Summary.

318

LSA-053 RCC B CYCLE 0021   89/03/23 PAGE 1

LOGISTIC SUPPORT ANALYSIS RECORD
MAINTAINABILITY SUMMARY – LEVEL OF REPAIR

EIAC		
END	ITEM NAME	
LCN	ENGINE ASSY	
006		

START LCN 006   ALC   STOP LCN 00614   UDC DCY   ALC

ALC M/L	FMI	SHSC	WUC/TM FGC	LCN	UDC DCY	ALC	TASK CD	REPAIR TIME	FM CRIT NO
D	AA	3	06	006			HGDXAAA	1.67	8.3000
	AA	3	06	006			NGDAABB	.78	8.3000
	AB	2	06	006			HGDXAAA	1.67	110.3400
	AB	2	06	006			NGDAABB	.78	110.3400
	AB	2	06	00607			HGDAGAA	.98	110.3400
	AC	3	06	00607			HGDAGAA	.98	110.3400
	AC	3	06	00607			NGDAABB	.78	110.3400
F	AA	3	06	006			DGDAAAA	.50	8.3000
	AB	2	06	006			BGFAGAA	.77	110.3400
	AB	2	06	006			BGFAGAA	.77	110.3400
				00614			HGFAGAA	1.03	110.3400

LCN 00602 ALC M/L	FMI	SHSC	WUC/TM FGC	LCN	UDC DCY	ALC	TASK CD	REPAIR TIME	FM CRIT NO
D	AA	3	0602	006			NGDAABB	.78	107.3400
F	AA	3	0602	00602			GGFAGAA	.59	107.3400
	AA	3	0602	00602			RGFAGAA	.59	107.3400
	AA	3	0602	0060201			GGFAGAA	.92	107.3400
	AA	3	0602	0060201			JGFXGAA	1.00	107.3400
	AA	3	0602	0060201			RGFAGAA	1.08	107.3400

LCN 0060201 ALC M/L	FMI	SHSC	WUC/TM FGC	LCN	UDC DCY	ALC	TASK CD	REPAIR TIME	FM CRIT NO
F	AA	3	060201	00602			GGFAGAA	.59	110.4100
	AA	3	060201	00602			RGFAGAA	.59	110.4100
	AA	3	060201	0060201			GGFAGAA	.92	110.4100
	AA	3	060201	0060201			JGFXGAA	1.00	110.4100
	AA	3	060201	0060201			RGFAGAA	1.08	110.4100
	AB	2	060201	00602			GGFAGAA	.59	30.6700
	AB	2	060201	00602			RGFAGAA	.59	30.6700
	AB	2	060201	0060201			GGFAGAA	.92	30.6700
	AB	2	060201	0060201			JGFXGAA	1.00	30.6700
	AB	2	060201	0060201			RGFAGAA	1.08	30.6700

LCN 00607 ALC M/L	FMI	SHSC	WUC/TM FGC	LCN	UDC DCY	ALC	TASK CD	REPAIR TIME	FM CRIT NO
D	AA	3	0607	006			NGDAABB	.78	32.2000
	AB	3	0607	00607			HGDAGAA	.98	32.2000
	AB	3	0607	006			NGDAABB	.78	39.1000
	AB	3	0607	00607			DGDAAAA	.50	39.1000
	AC	3	0607	00607			HGDAGAA	.98	39.1000
	AC	3	0607	006			NGDAABB	.78	20.7000
F	AA	3	0607	00607			HGDAGAA	.98	20.7000
	AA	3	0607	00607			CGFAGAA	1.68	32.2000
	AC	3	0607	00607			SGFAGAA	.50	32.2000
	AC	3	0607	00607			JGFXGAA	1.00	20.7000
			0607	00607			SGFAGAA	.50	20.7000

Fig. A-42. LSA-053—Maintainability Summary—Level of Repair.

319

Appendix A   LSA Summary Reports

LSA-054   RCC A   CYCLE 0021   LOGISTIC SUPPORT ANALYSIS RECORD
FAILURE MODE ANALYSIS SUMMARY

EIAC
END   ITEM NAME   START LCN   ALC   STOP LCN
LCN   REFRIGERATION UNIT   O   003

ALC	PRT F-RATE	OP TIME	MPC	SHSC	FMI	FAIL EFF PROB	F-MODE RATIO	F-MODE CRIT	WUC/TM FGC	SHSC 1 2 3
0	2346.1	1.00	A	2	AA	.85	.18	358.9500	00	
		1.00	B	2	AB	.85	.21	418.7800	00	
		1.00	A	3	AD	.85	.19	378.9000	00	
						TOTAL	.58			
001	50.0	1.00	A	3	01	.70	.92	32.2000	01	
						TOTAL	.92			
00102	12.5	1.00	A	3	01	.70	.50	4.3800	0102	
		1.00	A	3	02	.85	.30	3.1900	0102	
						TOTAL	.80			
002	694.4	1.00	A	3	AA	.90	.96	599.9600	02	
						TOTAL	.96			

UOC DCY

Fig. A-43. LSA-054—Failure Mode Analysis Summary.

LSA-055   RCC A   CYCLE 0021   LOGISTIC SUPPORT ANALYSIS RECORD
FAILURE MODE DETECTION SUMMARY

EIAC
END   ITEM NAME   START LCN   ALC   STOP LCN   UOC
LCN   PISTON ASSY   0060201   00615   DCY

FAILURE MODE AND CAUSE	Y
FAILURE DETECTION METHOD	Y
COMPENSATING PROVISIONS	Y
FAILURE PREDICTABILITY	Y

LCN	FM	ITEM NAME	MFR PART NUMBER	FSCM
00607	AA	SUPER CARB	142-0431ALCB	27567
	ALC B			

FAILURE MODE AND CAUSE
    CARBURETOR FAILS DUE TO FORMATION OF GUM DEPOSITS INSIDE CARBURETOR JETS.
FAILURE DETECTION METHOD
    VISUAL INSPECTION OF CARBURETOR REVEALS GUM DEPOSITS.
FAILURE PREDICTABILITY
    REFRIGERATION UNIT ENGINE RUNS LESS SMOOTHLY THAN NORMAL.

LCN	FM	ITEM NAME	MFR PART NUMBER	FSCM
00607	AB	SUPER CARB	142-0431ALCB	27567
	ALC B			

FAILURE MODE AND CAUSE
    CARBURETOR OPERATES IMPROPERLY DUE TO A MALADJUSTMENT.
FAILURE DETECTION METHOD
    ANALYSIS OF OPERATING CHARACTERISTICS INDICATES THE NEED FOR READJUSTMENT.
FAILURE PREDICTABILITY
    UNIT'S FUEL CONSUMPTION INCREASES AND IT WILL RUN LESS SMOOTHLY.

Fig. A-44. LSA-055—Failure Mode Detection Summary.

```
LSA-060  RCC C   CYCLE 0022          LOGISTIC SUPPORT ANALYSIS RECORD                              89/03/23  PAGE  1
                                     LSA CONTROL NUMBER MASTER FILE
  EIAC    ITEM NAME                  START LCN  ALC    STOP LCN    UDC   SERV DES   B-SHEET OPT  HDR OPT  TAPE OPT
  END     ENGINE ASSY                   006            00615       DCY
  LCN     ALC    TASK   CARD        1.......10........20........30........40........50........60........70........80

  006                    A01    A01006   END          A12345                          DCY,FF,                        A
                         A03    A03006   ENGINE ASSY              FFM-BB0-IIR777-KANJ4603S1C42333                     A
                         A04    A04006   CCKA-MS/3B34J   4494014033                4494006                            A
                         B06    B06006   YYYZYYYYYYYY                      NB 99430082BB008272000720000D003A          A
                         B07    B07006   A0008317000000074  0000074          0000074H004750049090                    A
                                         C0008317000000074090000074100005000000000074H004750049090                   A
                                         M0008317000000074090000074100005000000000074H004750049090                   A
                                         P0008317000000074090000074100005000000000074H004750049090                   A
                         B08    B08006   ADRIVES COMPRESSOR, CONDENSER FAN, AND EVAPORATOR FAN.                       A
                         B09    B09006   AOPERATION IN EXTREME HEAT-INSURE THAT THERE ARE NO OBSTRUCTIONSA
                                         B OF AIR FLOW TO AND FROM ENGINE ASSEMBLY.                                   A
                         B10    B10006   AFAULT LOCATE, REPLACE AND TEST ACCOMPLISHED BY ORGANIZATIONAL MA
                                         BAINTENANCE.                                                                 A
                         B11    B11006   AAANY YYY            Y   006             CBCACAA00006750-16                  A
                                         AAB                      006             CB0AAAA00037                        A
                         B13    B13006   AAA     POOR ENGINE PERFORMANCE DUE TO PISTON ASBFAILURE OCCURS B3A
                                         AAB     SEMBLY FAILURE.                         DURING COOLING               A
                                         AAC                                             PHASE.                       A
                         B14    B14006   AAA     POOR ENGINE PERFORMANCE CAUSES THE REFRIGERATION UNIT TO PRA
                                         AAB     OVIDE INSUFFICIENT COOLING AND RESULTS IN DEGRADED MISSION A
                                         AAC     PERFORMANCE.                                                         A
                         B15    B15006   AAA     FAILURE DETECTABLE THROUGH RO                                        A
                                         AAB     UTINE MONITORING OF TEMPERATU                                        A
                                         AAC     RE AND ENGINE OPERATING CHARA                                        A
                                         AAD     CTERISTICS.                                                          A
                         B16    B16006   AAAGIDEP          B31000030012024000023000000B3000000B3000A                 A
                                         AAA006   NG0AABB00078006          HG0XAAA00167                               A
                         B18    B18006   AAB006   BGFAGAA00077                                                        A
                         B11    B11006   ABAY    N  N N Y                                         750-16             A
                         B13    B13006   ABA     ENGINE ASSEMBLY WILL NOT START DUE TO A BFAILURE OCCURS B2A
                                         ABB     FAILURE IN THE STARTER ASSEMBLY.        AT START OF THE              A
                                         ABC                                             COOLING PHASE.               A
                         B14    B14006   ABA     FAILURE OF THE ENGINE ASSY TO START CAUSES A COMPLETE LOSS A
                                         ABB     OF MISSION CAPABILITY WITH POSSIBLE MAJOR LOSS OF MATERIEL.A
                         B15    B15006   ABA     FAILURE DETECTABLE THROUGH RO                                        A
                                         ABB     UTINE MONITORING OF TEMPERATU                                        A
                                         ABC     RE AND ENGINE OPERATING CHARA                                        A
                                         ABD     CTERISTICS.                                                          A
                         B16    B16006   ABAGIDEP          B2030042001202400002300001103400001103400A                A
                         B17    B17006   ABAFAILURE TO START IS PRECEEDED BY INSTANCES OF PROLONGED CRANKA
                                         ABBING PRIOR TO ENGINE START-UP AND A TRIPPED UNIT CIRCUIT BREAKA
                                         ABCER.                                                                       A
                         B18    B18006   ABA006   HG0XAAA0167000607         HG0AGAA00098                              A
                                         ABB006614 HGFAGAA00103006          BGFAGAA00077                              A
                                         ABC006   NG0AABB0007800607         HG0AGAA00098                              A
                         B11    B11006   ACAY    N  N YY Y                                         750-16             A
                         B13    B13006   ACA     ENGINE OPERATES INTERMITTENTLY DUE TO MABFAILURE OCCURS A3A
                                         ACB     LADJUSTED CARBURETOR.                   DURING COOLING               A
                                         ACC                                             PHASE.                       A
                         B14    B14006   ACA     THE BURNING OF AN IMPROPER FUEL MIXTURE RESULTS IN GREATER A
```

Fig. A-45. LSA-060—LCN Master File.

```
LSA-060  RCC C    CYCLE 0022

                         LOGISTIC SUPPORT ANALYSIS RECORD
                         LSA CONTROL NUMBER MASTER FILE
                                                              89/03/23   PAGE   2

          START LCN   ALC    STOP LCN    UDC      SERV DES    B-SHEET OPT  HDR OPT  TAPE OPT
          006                00615       DCY
          1........10........20........30........40........50........60........70........80

EIAC  006
END LCN
ITEM NAME
ENGINE ASSY
ALC TASK  CARD

          B14006   ACB  FUEL CONSUMPTION AND INTERMITTENT OPERATION WHICH DEGRADES          A
B14       B14006   ACC  MISSION PERFORMANCE.                                                A
          B15006   ACA  FAILURE DETECTABLE THROUGH RO                                       A
B15       B15006   ACB  UTINE MONITORING OF TEMPERATU                                       A
          B15006   ACC  RE AND ENGINE OPERATING CHARA                                       A
B18       B18006   ACD  CTERISTICS.                                                         A
C06       C06006   ACA006        NGOABB0007B00607        DGOAAA00050                        A
          C06006   BGFAGAA0033370TEST ENGINE ASSY AFTER REPAIR      SATMNYS  DNTM2A
          C06006   CBCACAA9000000DCHECK ENGINE OIL LEVEL            SATNNYC  DNTM2A
          C06006   CBONAAA072000DCHANGE OIL AND OIL FILTER          SATONYC  DNTM2A
          C06006   HGOXAAA0033370REPLACE ENGINE ASSY                SATP5YC  BNTM1A
          C06006   NGOABB0033090FAULT LOCATION - ENGINE ASSY        SATQNYC  CNTM2A

BGFAGAA   D03006   BGFAGAAAAA 006            NGOAABBSATQAAD AA3                              A
D03       D06006   BGFAGAA00077      200AI52C20  A0100077       A  JF  A    N               A
D06       D06006   CBCACAA      00006200AB76J10 A01   00006     N           N               A
CBCACAA   D07006   CBCACAAAMIL-L-2140-DHEDO QOIL, LUBRICATING        00100EA                A
D06       D06006   CBONAAA000370037200AI52C20 A01000050005           00100GL               A
D07       D07006   CBONAAAAMIL-L-2140-DHEDO QOIL-LUBRICATING         00100GL                A
CBONAAA   D07006   CBONAAAB122-0323        YFILTER, OIL              00100EA                A
D06       D07006   CBONAAACSC5180-90-CL-N14AZTOOL KIT GEN REFRIG00100EA                     A
D07       D07006   CBONAAAADFW25           4WRENCH, FILTER           00100EA                A

HGOXAAA   D06006   HGOXAAA      0016B200AI52C20 A01   00151     A  JF  A    Y               A
D06       D06006   HGOXAAAB         150BB52C10 A01    00003     A  JF  A    Y               C
          D06006   HGOXAAAC         050                                                     C
          D07006   HGOXAAAASC5180-90-CL-N14AZTOOL KIT GEN REFRIG00100EA                     A
D07       D07006   HGOXAAABGGG-W-641       4EXT, SOCKET WRENCH   00100EA                    A
          D07006   HGOXAAACSN9             4SCREW STARTER, HAND00100EA                      A
          D07006   HGOXAAADCBX23           QGAS CAN, 16 GAL      00100EA                    A
          D07006   HGOXAAAEE3727           AQCLOTHS              0001OPG                    A
          D07006   HGOXAAAFH25732102       QTAPE                 00100FT                    A
          D07006   HGOXAAAGCKA-MS/3B34J    XENGINE               00100EA                    A
          D07006   HGOXAAAHAI35            4SCREWDRIVER          00100EA                    A
          D07006   HGOXAAAIAT503           4ADJUSTABLE WRENCH    00100EA                    A
          D07006   HGOXAAAJGGG-P-471       4PLIERS               00100EA                    A
          D07006   HGOXAAAK1191            QTWINE                01200FT                    A
          D07006   HGOXAAALA24             4SOCKET               00100EA                    A
          D07006   HGOXAAAMYOU GOT ME      FTM5-4110-234-24      00100EA                    A

NGOABB    D03006   NGOAABBAAA3 006           HGOXAAASATPAAA ACB                             A
D03       D06006   NGOABBA0007B00007B200AI52C20 A01000780007B     A  JF  A   Y             A
D06       D07006   NGOABBAASC5180-90-CL-N14AZTOOL KIT GEN REFRIG00100EA                    A
D07       D07006   NGOABBABB2502           4SOCKET WRENCH        00100EA                    A
          D07006   NGOABBADGGG-G-17 TY9CL2S 4COMPRESSION GAUGE    00100EA                   A
```

Fig. A-45. (Continued).

```
LSA-061   RCC C   CYCLE 0022              LOGISTIC SUPPORT ANALYSIS RECORD                   89/03/23  PAGE  1
                                                  PARTS MASTER FILE
EIAC                        START LCN     ALC   STOP LCN   UOC     REFERENCE NUMBER   SCC   DATA REC
       ITEM NAME                                                         BC1920
END    PISTON ASSY
REFERENCE NUMBER   SCC        LCN         ALC
                                                       RECORD IMAGE
                                          1........10........20........30........40........50........60........70........80
BC1920              0060201

                                          H01BC1920            44940 2A21 PISTON ASSY            Y                A A A
                                          H09BC1920            0060201  ADCY,FF,                                      A
                                          H10BC1920            0060201  ATESTPLC0209         0205                     A
                                          H11BC1920            0060201  XPAFZZ A000016556000014451 2367                A
                                          H15BC1920            0060201  ATM3   5   1         06B                      A


LSA-061   RCC A   CYCLE 0028              LOGISTIC SUPPORT ANALYSIS RECORD                   89/03/24  PAGE  1
                                                  PARTS MASTER FILE
EIAC                        START LCN     ALC   STOP LCN   UOC     REFERENCE NUMBER   SCC   DATA REC
       ITEM NAME                                                         35-8742
END    ENDPLATE,FRONT

*** H DATA SHEET ***
                                          RN PP RN
CD-NO  REFERENCE NUMBER   SCC   PSIC   FSCM   CC SL VC DAC   ITEM NAME                       L P S CB R IS PC TT SC D   TOT    PL SM PL SM HC PM
H01    35-8742            PSIC   05472  2  N  2    1  ENDPLATE,FRONT                        - Y - Y - - - - - -    QUP R QTY  T  CC CC IC I  IC UC
                                                        NSN RELATED DATA                                           001 ------  07 - F  -  -  A  A

CD-NO  REFERENCE NUMBER   SCC   PSIC   REFERENCE NO OVFL    PRE   FSC   NIIN    SUFF      UI  UI PRICE   CONV FAC  SL  SLAC               UC
H02    35-8742            PSIC   0000000132                  ---   ---   ---------  ----   EA  0000000132   ------   0  ------              A
                                                                                                            AIC AIC     DLSC

CD-NO  REFERENCE NUMBER   SCC   PSIC   CSC  ADDITIONAL REFERENCE NUMBER        FSCM   RNCC  RNVC MADT MAC PSPC ADP   AIC AIC   A B QTY IMC SCREEN   UC
H03    35-8742            PSIC        -                                        -----   -     -    -    -    -    -    -  -       -            I

                                                                 LOT QUANTITY
CD-NO  REFERENCE NUMBER   SCC   PSIC   CSC  UM PRICE        FROM  TO    CPC  TUC  PUC  FY  UM  CTIC  AMC   AMSC   FSCM  FSCM   FSCM   UM
H04    35-8742            PSIC   A     0000000132    000001 001000  -    -    -    N  84  EA  CG   4    -      96944 87350  41370  ------
                                       BASIS OF ISSUE                                          BASIS OF ISSUE

CD-NO  REFERENCE NUMBER   SCC   PSIC   QTY-A      EI   LVL CTL   QTY-A      EI   LVL CTL        QTY-A      EI   LVL CTL                  UC
H05    35-8742            PSIC   ----       ---   ----      ----       ---   ----              ----       ---   ----                     I

                                       PKG  MT  PR  WR  CUS   UN INT          SP  UNIT   UNIT PACK SIZE           SP   PK CD
CD-NO  REFERENCE NUMBER   SCC   PSIC   CC   PR  CD  MTL MTL MTL  CT  CN  CN   ICQ DOP  MKG WT  LEN  WID  DEP    SPI NO   REV A B C        UC
H06    35-8742            PSIC   C   82A0  --  0  00  00  00   0  EV  11  -     C  99  00010  0055 0055 0020    ------   -  -  -  Y        A
                                       UC  CONTAINER NSN               UNIT SIZE        UNIT

CD-NO  REFERENCE NUMBER   SCC   PSIC   CSC  LVL FSC  NIIN      OPI  LEN  WID  HEI   WEIGHT FSCM  HC SUPPLEMENTAL PKG DATA                UC
H07    35-8742            PSIC   C    -    ---  ---------       M   0050 0050 0015  00008  33130 -  --------------                        A

CD-NO  REFERENCE NUMBER   SCC   PSIC   CSC  SUPPLEMENTAL PACKAGING DATA OVERFLOW                                                         UC
H08    35-8742            PSIC   C    ----TEST NARRATIVE----                                                                              A
```

Fig. A-46. LSA-061—Parts Master File.

LSA-061 RCC A   CYCLE 0028   LOGISTIC SUPPORT ANALYSIS RECORD   89/03/24 PAGE 2

PARTS MASTER FILE

EIAC   ITEM NAME   START LCN ALC STOP LCN UDC   REFERENCE NUMBER SCC DATA REC

END   ENDPLATE,FRONT   35-8742

*** H1 DATA SHEET ***

USABLE ON CODES

CD-NO REFERENCE NO SCC   LCN   ALC PSIC CSC DCZ,   SAME AS PRIOR QTY/ LCN UC

H09 35-8742   0090123   A   A

                                        IND   TO QTY/ NHA NHA   ORR PLISN ASSY IC SIC UC

CD-NO REFERENCE NO SCC   LCN   ALC PSIC CSC PCCN CD PLISN CC EI   IND   005   0001   A

H10 35-8742   0090123   A

                                        MAINTENANCE TASK DISTRIBUTION

CD-NO REFERENCE NO SCC   LCN   ALC PSIC ICC SMR MRRI MRRII MRR MOD O F H SRA D CBD CAD UC

H11 35-8742   0090123   Y   XBOZZ A 00014434 00001223 C0781   - - -   - -   - A

                                        RISS RMSS

CD-NO REFERENCE NO SCC   LCN   ALC PSIC EC LRU NRTS RSR MRU BUY LVL RTLL   DESIGNATED REWORK RIP STAT UC

H12 35-8742   0090123   1 -   -   001 030 020 005   - A

                                   REPAIR CYCLE TIME   REPLACEMENT TASK DISTRIBUTION

CD-NO REFERENCE NO SCC   LCN   ALC PSIC O F H SRA D CON TAT   O F H SRA D UC

H13 35-8742   0090123   -   -   -   015   085 UC

H14 35-8742   0090123   A   REFERENCE DESIGNATION   RDC   RDC   A

                                   AAAAABBBBMMMMMAZ

LSA-061 RCC A   CYCLE 0028   LOGISTIC SUPPORT ANALYSIS RECORD   89/03/24 PAGE 3

PARTS MASTER FILE

EIAC   ITEM NAME   START LCN ALC STOP LCN UDC   REFERENCE NUMBER SCC DATA REC

END   ENDPLATE,FRONT   35-8742

*** H1 DATA SHEET ***

CD-NO REFERENCE NO SCC   LCN   ALC PSIC CSC TM CODE FIG NO ITEM NO TM CHG NO TM IND QTY/FIG WUC/TM FGC UC

H15 35-8742   0090123   A   TM1   4   24   -   2   001   090123   A

H16   LCN   ALC PSIC TMI CSC   PROVISIONING NOMENCLATURE   UM

                                   SERIAL NUMBER EFFECTIVITY REPL/SUP RS/

CD-NO REFERENCE NO SCC   LCN   ALC PSIC CSC CHANGE AUTHORITY NUMBER IC   FROM TO PLISN IND UC

H17

CD-NO REFERENCE NO SCC   LCN   ALC PSIC CSC CHANGE AUTHORITY NUMBER TIC QTY QTY PRORATE PRORATED

H18   SHIPPED PROCURED ELIN QTY UC

CD-NO REFERENCE NO SCC   LCN   ALC PSIC CSC CHANGE AUTHORITY NUMBER   DCN UDC

H19

CD-NO REFERENCE NO SCC   LCN   ALC PSIC CSC   REMARKS   UC

H20

Fig. A-46. LSA-061 Parts Master List.

```
LSA-070   RCC A   CYCLE 0022                                          89/03/23  PAGE  1

                          LOGISTIC SUPPORT ANALYSIS RECORD
                     SUPPORT EQUIPMENT RECOMMENDATION DATA (SERD)
                            SECTION 1. ADMINISTRATIVE DATA

SE ITEM NAME           GOVT. TYPE DESIGNATION    SUPPORT EQUIPMENT FULL ITEM NAME      SIASCN    SKETCH
COMPRESSOR, RING                                 COMPRESSOR, RING, BAND                0853421
   -----NATIONAL STOCK NUMBER-----                        ------RESPONSIBLE AGENCIES------
   PREFIX FSC   NIIN    SUFFIX     CONTRACT NUMBER         ADO         LDO          PE       PSICP
          5480  001239876          N00019-85-X-0999        NAEC 924XX  NAEC 928XX   SNS      KE
ICC  GFE/CFE   CAL ITEM  CAL REQD  USING SERVICE           CTIC        SMR       USABLE ON CODE(S)
 7      C          N         Y                             CG          PEDDL     DCY,DCZ,
TEC  TECHEVAL PRIORITY    TECH MANUAL CODES   PROD LEAD TIME   DATE FIRST ARTICLE   SPECIAL MGT   MGT PLAN REQ
WXZY      II                                        24            1087                  N             Y
      -----OPERATING CHARACTERISTICS-----              -----STORAGE CHARACTERISTICS-----
      LN    WD    HT    UM   WT      UM                 LN    WD    HT    UM   WT      UM
     004.0 005.0 005.0 IN  00003.5  LB                 004.0 003.0 003.0 IN  00003.5  LB
      * * * * * * SYSTEM EQUIPMENT REQUIRED * * * * * *
   ---LCN---    ALC   FSCM      PART NUMBER                     ---------NOMENCLATURE---------       QTY    PRICE
   ----NATIONAL STOCK NUMBER----                                       TYPE DESIGNATOR
   PREFIX FSC   NIIN    SUFFIX
      * * * * * * PRICE DATA * * * * * *
                              ----ITEM NAME----    ----ILS----    RECURRING     ---TOTAL---
HDWR DEV    DESIGN DATA   PASS THRU                 10000          10000          30000
 10000       10000

SERD                   ---------ITEM NAME---------          ---------NOMENCLATURE---------
 NO                    REFRIGERATION UNIT                         TYPE DESIGNATOR
 0727                                                      TYPE001MODEL00002SRSUFFIX0
```

Fig. A-47. LSA-070—Support Equipment Recommendation Data (SERD).

```
LSA-070   RCC A   CYCLE 0022              LOGISTIC SUPPORT ANALYSIS RECORD                 89/03/23   PAGE   2
                                   SUPPORT EQUIPMENT RECOMMENDATION DATA (SERD)
                                           SECTION 1. ADMINISTRATIVE DATA

                          * * * * * * ARTICLES REQUIRING SUPPORT * * * * * *
   ---LCN----    ALC    TASK CODE    ----MAINTENANCE PLAN---    FSCM    ------------PART NUMBER------------
   005                  HGDAAAA                                 10855   5D43-139-A
   ----NATIONAL STOCK NUMBER-----    ---------NOMENCLATURE--------    TYPE DESIGNATOR     --MTBF--     ---AI---
   PREFIX  FSC    NIIN    SUFFIX         ITEM NAME                                        000800.0     99.8300
           4130  010919159           COMPRESSOR ASSY
           CMRS STATUS    --WUC----    --SMR---    EQUIP ALLOWANCE    WORK PKG REFERENCE
                N         05           PAFFF

   ---LCN----    ALC    TASK CODE    ----MAINTENANCE PLAN---    FSCM    ------------PART NUMBER------------
   005                  NGFAGAA                                 10855   5D43-139-A
   ----NATIONAL STOCK NUMBER-----    ---------NOMENCLATURE--------    TYPE DESIGNATOR     --MTBF--     ---AI---
   PREFIX  FSC    NIIN    SUFFIX         ITEM NAME                                        000800.0     99.8300
           4130  010919159           COMPRESSOR ASSY
           CMRS STATUS    --WUC----    --SMR---    EQUIP ALLOWANCE    WORK PKG REFERENCE
                N         05           PAFFF

                             * * * * * * REMARKS * * * * * *
   CARD REFERENCE 1004: ACCURACY IS NOT APPLICABLE TO THE RING COMPRESSOR.
   ---LCN----    ALC    ----PREPARING ACTIVITY----    SUBMIT DATE    SERD NO    SERD STATUS    REV    FSCM
   00S02                MRSA                          101285         0727       R              AB     99999
                        ----PART NUMBER----                                    ACTION DATE
                        4003100                                                021086


   SERD    ------------NOMENCLATURE-----------    TYPE DESIGNATOR
   NO          ITEM NAME
   0727     REFRIGERATION UNIT    TYPE001MODEL00002SRSUFFIX0
```

Fig. A-47. (Continued).

```
LSA-070    RCC A    CYCLE 0022                    LOGISTIC SUPPORT ANALYSIS RECORD                    89/03/23    PAGE    3
                                          SUPPORT EQUIPMENT RECOMMENDATION DATA (SERD)
                                               SECTION 2. DESCRIPTION OF REQUIREMENTS

          FUNCTIONAL ANALYSIS OF END ARTICLE:    THE RING COMPRESSOR MUST SUCCESSFULLY SEAT SAE 4130 FREON CO
                                                 MPRESSOR RINGS.
          SE NON-PROLIFERATION SEARCH:           THE PROPOSED RING COMPRESSOR IS OF SUFFICIENT CAPACITY TO CO
                                                 MPLY WITH ALL PRESENT DESIGN CRITERIA AND FOR THOSE CRITERIA
                                                 FORSEEABLE IN THE NEAR FUTURE.
          DESCRIPTION AND FUNCTION OF SE:        A BAND TYPE SLEEVE WITH A MECHANICAL LEVERAGE MECHANISM TO F
                                                 ACILITATE EASY REDUCTION OF RING RADII.
          INSTALLATION FACTORS FOR SE:           NONE REQUIRED.
          ADDITIONAL SKILL REQUIREMENTS FOR SE:  OPERATORMUST BE SKILLED IN INTERNAL COMBUSTION ENGINE AND CO
                                                 MPRESSOR PISTON REPAIR.


          SERD    ------------NOMENCLATURE------------
          NO        ITEM NAME            TYPE DESIGNATOR
          0727    REFRIGERATION UNIT    TYPE001MODELO0002SRSUFFIX0
```

Fig. A-47. (Continued).

LSA-070   RCC A   CYCLE 0022

LOGISTIC SUPPORT ANALYSIS RECORD
SUPPORT EQUIPMENT RECOMMENDATION DATA (SERD)
SECTION 3. SUPERSEDURE/ALLOCATION

89/03/23   PAGE   4

SERD NO   * * * * * * SUPERSEDURE DATA * * * * * * *
           SERD REV   FSCM   --PART NUMBER---   SUPERSEDURE TYPE
                      * * * * * ALLOCATION DATA * * * * * * *

			1-4	5-8	9-12	13-16	ALLOWANCE RANGE 17-24	25-32	33-64	65-125	126-250	251-450	EXT RANGE

EQUIPMENT
ALLOWANCE

MAINT LVL
FUNCTION   LVC   1-4   5-8   9-12   13-16   17-24   25-32   33-64   65-125   126-250   251-450
                L   001   001   001   001   002   002   004   007   012   020

PRE POS   MOBILE FACILITY   SPARE FACTOR   REVOLVING ASSET
PP5   V   Q000   Q000

                     * * * * * SPECIFIC AUTHORIZATIONS * * * * * *
NUMBER OF ACTIVITIES   TYPE OF ACTIVITY   NAME/LOCATION OF ACTIVITY   QUANTITY PER ACTIVITY
     002   DEPOT   RRAD TEXARKANA TX   010

SERD   --------------NOMENCLATURE--------------
NO   ITEM NAME   TYPE DESIGNATOR
0727   REFRIGERATION UNIT   TYPE001MODEL00002SRSUFFIX0

Fig. A-47. (Continued).

328

```
LSA-070   RCC A   CYCLE 0022                    LOGISTIC SUPPORT ANALYSIS RECORD                89/03/23   PAGE   5
                                       SUPPORT EQUIPMENT RECOMMENDATION DATA (SERD)
                                                    SECTION 4. DESIGN DATA

                                          CONTRACTOR    GOVERNMENT    ESTIMATED
           REQUIREMENTS                   RECOMMENDED    REQUIRED       PRICE       SCOPE
           SE STANDARDIZATION                  Y            Y           1200     STANDARDIZATION
           SE STANDARDIZATION                  Y            Y           2200     STANDARDIZATION
           SAFETY                              Y            N            400     SAFETY

           SERD                   ---------ITEM NAME--------   --------NOMENCLATURE--------   TYPE DESIGNATOR
           NO                       REFRIGERATION UNIT              TYPE001MODEL00002SRSUFFIX0
           0727


LSA-070   RCC A   CYCLE 0022                    LOGISTIC SUPPORT ANALYSIS RECORD                89/03/23   PAGE   6
                                       SUPPORT EQUIPMENT RECOMMENDATION DATA (SERD)
                                                  SECTION 5. ILS REQUIREMENTS

                                          CONTRACTOR    GOVERNMENT    ESTIMATED
           REQUIREMENTS                   RECOMMENDED    REQUIRED       PRICE       SCOPE
           MAINTENANCE PLAN                    Y            Y            500         LSA
           LSA                                 Y            Y            900         LSA

           SERD                   ---------ITEM NAME--------   --------NOMENCLATURE--------   TYPE DESIGNATOR
           NO                       REFRIGERATION UNIT              TYPE001MODEL00002SRSUFFIX0
           0727


LSA-070   RCC A   CYCLE 0022                    LOGISTIC SUPPORT ANALYSIS RECORD                89/03/23   PAGE   7
                                       SUPPORT EQUIPMENT RECOMMENDATION DATA (SERD)

           SERD                   ---------ITEM NAME--------   --------NOMENCLATURE--------   TYPE DESIGNATOR
           NO                       REFRIGERATION UNIT              TYPE001MODEL00002SRSUFFIX0
           0727
                                  * * * * * * SIGNATURES * * * * * * *
           PROGRAM MANAGER  ------------------   ENGINEERING  ------------------   LOGISTICS  ------------------
```

Fig. A-47. (Continued).

```
LSA-072   RCC A    CYCLE 0019
                              LOGISTIC SUPPORT ANALYSIS RECORD              89/03/22   PAGE   1
                              TMDE TECHNICAL DESCRIPTION
EIAC          ITEM NAME            START LCN     ALC    STOP LCN     UOC          SERV DES
END           REFRIGERATION UNIT   00S02

LCN    ALC   ITEM NAME          TYPE DESIGNATOR                    NARRATIVE DESCRIPTION
00S02        COMPRESSOR, RING                     A BAND TYPE SLEEVE WITH A MECHANICAL LEVERAGE MECHANISM TO F
                                                  ACILITATE EASY REDUCTION OF RING RADII.
       I/O   PARAMETER              RANGE                        ACCURACY
                              FROM  UNIT    TO   UNIT            RANGE IS IN INCHES
             DIAMETER IN.       2     0      5    0       VOLTS   AC/DC   FREQUENCY  PHASE  WATTS   PERCENT MAX RIPPLE
                                                         MIN MAX         MIN   MAX

       DEPTH   WIDTH   HEIGHT   UM   WEIGHT   UM
       4.0     5.0     5.0     IN    3.5 LB
       ITEMS THIS WILL REPLACE:   MFR. PART NUMBER    SCC  FSCM
       SKILL SPECIALTY   PUBLICATIONS        FSCM     MFR. PART NUMBER          SCC   NSN AND RELATED DATA
         CODE
         52C10                    99999     4003100
       MAINT LVL  TYPE CLASS  LIN  LOG CONTROL  SELF TESTING  CAL INTERVAL  LIFE CYCLE   A   5820-003478650
                                   CODE                                     STATUS           UNIT COST
                                    T            N                720       D            75.75
       END ITEM NSN AND RELATED DATA         TMDE RAM CHARACTERISTICS   MANAGING COMMAND/ACTIVITY
                                             MTBF    MTTR   CAL TIME
         4110-010745175                      300.0   .50    1          MRSA
       CARD REF   SLN  SILN                                 REMARKS
       1004  AAA      ACCURACY IS NOT APPLICABLE TO THE RING COMPRESSOR.
       DESCRIPTION OF OPERATING PROCEDURE:
```

Fig. A-48. LSA-072—Test Measurement and Diagnostic Equipment (TMDE) Requirements Summary Report.

LSA-072   RCC A   CYCLE 0019   LOGISTIC SUPPORT ANALYSIS RECORD   89/03/22   PAGE   2
                                              TMDE REQUIREMENTS REVIEW

EIAC   ITEM NAME   START LCN   ALC   STOP LCN   UOC   SERV DES
END   REFRIGERATION UNIT   00S02

LCN   ALC   SUPPORTED ITEM NAME   TMDE NON-PROFILERATION SEARCH
00S02   MOTOR INTERNAL COMB   THE PROPOSED RING COMPRESSOR IS OF SUFFICIENT CAPACITY TO CO
                  COMPRESSOR   MPLY WITH ALL PRESENT DESIGN CRITERIA AND FOR THOSE CRITERIA
                                            FORSEEABLE IN THE NEAR FUTURE.
                                                                                          TMDE REG NO   TMDE CODE
                  SKILL SPECIALTY   MAINT   JUSTIFICATION SUMMARY
                           CODE   LVL   IAJ3114   E
                           52C10   ITEM NAME   TYPE DESIGNATOR   NATIONAL STOCK NUMBER
                  QUANTITY OF TMDE ITEMS TO BE PROCURED
                  QUANTITY DATE REQUIRED   ESTIMATED TOTAL COST   COMPRESSOR, RING   5820-003478650
                     20   1087
                                       CHARACTERISTICS TO BE MEASURED/STIMULUS REQUIRED
                  I/O   PARAMETER   RANGE
                                      FROM   UNIT   TO   UNIT   ACCURACY
                        DIAMETER IN.   32   D   45   D   NOT APPLICABLE
                        DIAMETER   32   D   42   D   NOT APPLICABLE
                                    INTERFACE ADAPTERS/SIGNAL CONDITIONING CIRCUITRY
                                                                        APPORTIONED UNIT COST
                  ITEM NAME   MFRS PART NO   SCC   FSCM   RECURRING   NONRECURRING
                                    ATE SOFTWARE REQUIRED
                  ITEM NAME   MFRS PART NO   SCC   FSCM   APPORTIONED UNIT COST   TEST PLAN
                                                               RECURRING   NONRECURRING
                                                          REMARKS
                  CARD REF   SLN SILN   DATE: /   /
                  ESTIMATED TYPE CLASSIFICATION STANDARD DATE: ___/___/___
                  PREPARED BY:

Fig. A-48. (Continued).

LSA-074   RCC A   CYCLE 0019   LOGISTIC SUPPORT ANALYSIS RECORD   89/03/22   PAGE   1
                                              SUPPORT EQUIPMENT TOOL LIST

EIAC   ITEM NAME   START LCN   ALC   STOP LCN   UOC   SERV DES
END   REFRIGERATION UNIT   00S10   00S20

                                                  PART I - STOCK LISTED TOOLS
LCN   ALC ITEM NAME   ACQ DEC OFFICE   SERD REFERENCE NUMBER   SCC ICC-1 ICC-2 ICC-3 ICC-4
00S10   N   4   *   B

LCN	ALC	ITEM NAME	ACQ DEC OFFICE	SERD	REFERENCE NUMBER	SCC	FSCM	NSN	MAINT LEVELS			ICC
00S10		SCISSORS	USATROSCOM	6020	KTO24683N2		44940		O	F	D	Z
00S1001		DOLLIE, 4WH	USATROSCOM	6010	CB9234569		44940				D	Z
00S1004		WRENCH SET, COMB	USATROSCOM	6007	B107-6		44940	5120-00-148-7917				Z
00S1006		KIT, SOLDERING GUN	USAAMCCOM	6005	450K4		12345	3439-00-930-1638				Z
00S1010		HYDROMETER	USAAMCCOM	6001	K252		44940					Z
00S12		TORQUE WRENCH	USAAMCCOM	6018	AA123C		13579		H		D	Z
00S15		SCREWDRIVER	USAAMCCOM	6015	A135		44940	5120-00-278-1273	C	O	F	H	L	D	Z

Fig. A-49. LSA-074—Support Equipment Tool List.

LSA-074
LOGISTIC SUPPORT ANALYSIS RECORD
89/03/22 PAGE 2

RCC A   CYCLE 0019
EIAC
SUPPORT EQUIPMENT TOOL LIST

ITEM NAME	START LCN	ALC	STOP LCN	UDC	SERV DES	ICC-1	ICC-2	ICC-3	ICC-4
END REFRIGERATION UNIT	00S10		00S20			N	4	*	8

PART II - COMMERCIALLY AVAILABLE TOOLS

LCN	ALC	ITEM NAME	ACQ DEC OFFICE	SERD	REFERENCE NUMBER	SCC	FSCM	SIASCN	SKETCH	MAINT LEVELS	ICC
00S1003		TONGS, 7 IN	USATROSCOM	6008	B25		44940	N1389XX		F	4
00S1005		EXT, SOCKET WRENCH	USATROSCOM	6006	A610		12345	N4509BX			4
00S11		WELDER	USATROSCOM	6019	45021		44940	N453-0X	N		4
00S14		WRENCH, SOCKET	USAMCCOM	6016	A24		34521	MAR-09B	N		4

LSA-074
LOGISTIC SUPPORT ANALYSIS RECORD
89/03/22 PAGE 3

RCC A   CYCLE 0019
EIAC
SUPPORT EQUIPMENT TOOL LIST

ITEM NAME	START LCN	ALC	STOP LCN	UDC	SERV DES	ICC-1	ICC-2	ICC-3	ICC-4
END REFRIGERATION UNIT	00S10		00S20			N	4	*	8

PART III - MODIFIED TOOLS - STOCK LISTED AND COMMERCIAL

LCN	ALC	ITEM NAME	ACQ DEC OFFICE	SERD	REFERENCE NUMBER	SCC	FSCM	SIASCN	SKETCH	MAINT LEVELS	ICC
00S100B		VOLTMETER,1/3AMP	USACECOM	6003	SN517B32105		44940	G-CE2/9	Y		*

MAKE FROM:

ITEM NAME	REFERENCE NUMBER	SCC	FSCM
SPRING	142-0035	NSN 5360-01-066-3450	44940
SLEEVE, CHOKE COVER	142-205		44940
SPRING SET	191-0984		44940
ARMATURE	191-10BB		44940

LCN	ALC	ITEM NAME	ACQ DEC OFFICE	SERD	REFERENCE NUMBER	SCC	FSCM	SIASCN	SKETCH	MAINT LEVELS	ICC
00S18		SHIM, 1/4 CM	USATROSCOM	6012	E3727		44940	N129(2)	N		D

MAKE FROM:

ITEM NAME	REFERENCE NUMBER	SCC	FSCM
DISK,VALVE	142-0055	NSN 2910-00-358-5618	
SLEEVE, CHOKE COVER	142-205		44940

LCN	ALC	ITEM NAME	ACQ DEC OFFICE	SERD	REFERENCE NUMBER	SCC	FSCM	SIASCN	SKETCH	MAINT LEVELS	ICC
00S19		BUCKET, 3 GAL	USATROSCOM	6011	CTB1		44940	N3412XX	N		F

LSA-074
LOGISTIC SUPPORT ANALYSIS RECORD
89/03/22 PAGE 4

RCC A   CYCLE 0019
EIAC
SUPPORT EQUIPMENT TOOL LIST

ITEM NAME	START LCN	ALC	STOP LCN	UDC	SERV DES	ICC-1	ICC-2	ICC-3	ICC-4
END REFRIGERATION UNIT	00S10		00S20			N	4	*	8

PART IV - TOOLS REQUIRING DEVELOPMENT

LCN	ALC	ITEM NAME	ACQ DEC OFFICE	SERD	REFERENCE NUMBER	SCC	FSCM	SIASCN	SKETCH	MAINT LEVELS	ICC
00S1002		SET, SOCKET	USATROSCOM	6009	B2502		44940	NR123XX	Y	F H	8
00S1007		DITCMO STATION	USATROSCOM	6004	CC5B6T3692			N39B7XX	N	D	8
00S1009		WRENCH, FILTER	USACECOM	6002	FW25		44940	G-CE5/7	N		8
00S13		WRENCH, SOCKET	USAMCCOM	6017	A26		44940	MAR-005	Y		8
00S16		WRENCH, ADJUSTABLE	USAMCCOM	6014	AT503		44940	MAR-023	N	F	8
00S17		BRUSH, WIRE	USATROSCOM	6013	FC1036921		44940	N238/2X	Y	H	8

Fig. A-49. (Continued).

LSA-075   RCC A   CYCLE 0019   LOGISTIC SUPPORT ANALYSIS RECORD   89/03/22   PAGE   1
                                               LSAR MANPRINT REPORT PART I

EIAC   ITEM NAME   START LCN   ALC   STOP LCN   UOC   SERV DES   TASK CODE   ML CODES   SSC   STRUCTURE
END   REFRIGERATION UNIT   0   DCY   ARMY   12

                NUMBER   ANNUAL   ANNUAL   MEAN
                SYSTEMS   M/H PER HR   ANNUAL M/H   OPERATING   NO. OF   MISSION
LCN   ALC   SUPPORTED   O/M LEVEL   SCHED   UNSCHED   SCHED   UNSCHED   DAYS   MISSIONS   DURATIONS   MB
0   000030   D   000.02   000.05   00021.5   00007.0   300   000300   00001   D
0   000150   F   000.05   000.01   00030.0   00018.0
0   000300   D   000.03   000.06   00035.0   00018.0
0   000001   C   000.02   000.05   00075.0   00300.0

                                        NO. OPER   CREW   ACHIEVED   OPER
ITEM NAME   LCN   EIAC   LOCATIONS   SIZE   AOR   MB   AOR   MB   AOR   AVAIL   AVAIL   ALDT
REFRIGERATION UNIT   0   END   0100   0002   007200   D   000300   D   000010   T   95.0000   90.0000   003

                                ITEM FUNCTION
            PROVIDES REFRIGERATED AIR FOR AN ENCLOSED SPACE, MAINTAINING A
            TEMPERATURE OF BETWEEN 0 AND 50 DEGREES F(-18 AND 10 DEGREES C)

                                                         MB   MTBM   MTBM   MTBM NO
MTTR   MTBMA   MTBF   MAMDT   MTBPM   MB   MTBPM   INDUCED   INHERENT   DEFECT   MB
000.35   000075.0   000350.0   00001.0   H   000007.2   MB
003.50   000003.1   000014.6   00008.5   D   000007.1   H
001.00   000000.1   000000.5   00000.9   T   000007.2

                                           FAILURE/DAMAGE EFFECTS
FMI AA   MISSION DEGRADATION - INSUFFICIENT COOLING.
        FAILURE MODE AND CAUSE/DAMAGE MODE   FAILURE DETECTION METHOD   SHSC   FAIL RATE   OPERTIME
        POOR PERFORMANCE DUE TO INSUFFICIENT COO   OBSERVANCE OF OPERATIONAL CHA   2   002346.1   0001.00
        LING.   RACTERISTICS-HUMAN DETECTION.

                                           FAILURE/DAMAGE EFFECTS
FMI AB   MISSION LOSS WITH POSSIBLE DAMAGE TO REFRIGERATED MATERIEL
        FAILURE MODE AND CAUSE/DAMAGE MODE   FAILURE DETECTION METHOD   SHSC   FAIL RATE   OPERTIME
        UNIT INOPERABLE DUE TO ENGINE FAILURE.   PERFORMANCE CHARACTERISTICS-   2   002346.1   0001.00
                                                    UNIT WILL NOT OPERATE.

                                           FAILURE/DAMAGE EFFECTS
        POOR PERFORMANCE DUE TO EXCESSIVE NOISE.   HUMAN DETECTION.   4   002346.1   0001.00
                                           FAILURE/DAMAGE EFFECTS
FMI AD   MISSION DEGRADATION - LOSS OF CONTROL DUE TO INSTRUMENTS

Fig. A-50. LSA-075—LSAR MANPRINT Report.

LSA-075   RCC A   CYCLE 0019

LOGISTIC SUPPORT ANALYSIS RECORD
LSAR MANPRINT REPORT PART II

89/03/22   PAGE   10

EIAC	ITEM NAME	START LCN	ALC	STOP LCN	UOC	SERV DES	TASK CODE	ML CODES	SSC	STRUCTURE
END	REFRIGERATION UNIT	0			DCY	ARMY				12

DUTY POSITION REQUIRING A NEW OR REVISED SKILL

RECOMMENDED RANK/RATE/GRADE
MIL RANK   CIVILIAN GRADE

SAFETY   Y

FAC CAT CODE

SE GROUP 300

MEAN M/H PER SSC	MEAN ELAP TIME	SSC	PERS ID	NO. SSC	AVAIL M/H	QTY SSC AVAIL	PERF STD	TRG RAT	TRG REC	TRG LOC RAT	TASK COND
000.09	000.09	76J10	A	01					N		

LCN 002   ALC   TASK FREQ 000.350   TASK IDENTIFICATION   CREW INSPECTION OF WIRES AND CABLES
TASK CODE AACACAA
REQUIREMENTS FOR NNC

SE GROUP 300

MEAN M/H PER SSC	MEAN ELAP TIME	SSC	SLC	PERS ID	NO. SSC	AVAIL M/H	QTY SSC AVAIL	PERF STD	TRG RAT	TRG REC	TRG LOC RAT	TASK COND
000.13	000.13	76J10		A	01					N		

LCN 002   ALC   TASK FREQ 000.300   TASK IDENTIFICATION   ORGANIZATIONAL INSP OF WIRES/CABLES
TASK CODE ABQACAA
REQUIREMENTS FOR NYC

SE GROUP 300

MEAN M/H PER SSC	MEAN ELAP TIME	SSC	SLC	PERS ID	NO. SSC	AVAIL M/H	QTY SSC AVAIL	PERF STD	TRG RAT	TRG REC	TRG LOC RAT	TASK COND
000.10	000.10	52C10	I	A	01	000300	00500	A	A	J	A	

LCN 002   ALC   TASK FREQ 000.200   TASK IDENTIFICATION   TEST WIRE HARNESS ASSY
TASK CODE BGDAGAA
REQUIREMENTS FOR BYB

SE GROUP 300

MEAN M/H PER SSC	MEAN ELAP TIME	SSC	SLC	PERS ID	NO. SSC	AVAIL M/H	QTY SSC AVAIL	PERF STD	TRG RAT	TRG REC	TRG LOC RAT	TASK COND
000.37	000.37	35B30		A	01			A	B	B	D	BC

LCN 002   ALC   TASK FREQ 000.200   TASK IDENTIFICATION   REPAIR WIRE HARNESS ASSY
TASK CODE JGDAGAA
REQUIREMENTS FOR ANC

SE GROUP 300

MEAN M/H PER SSC	MEAN ELAP TIME	SSC	SLC	PERS ID	NO. SSC	AVAIL M/H	QTY SSC AVAIL	PERF STD	TRG RAT	TRG REC	TRG LOC RAT	TASK COND
001.36	001.36	35B30		A	01			A	B	B	D	C

LCN 002   ALC   TASK FREQ 000.200   TASK IDENTIFICATION   REMOVE WIRE HARNESS ASSY
TASK CODE RGDAGAA
REQUIREMENTS FOR NYC

SE GROUP 300

MEAN M/H PER SSC	MEAN ELAP TIME	SSC	SLC	PERS ID	NO. SSC	AVAIL M/H	QTY SSC AVAIL	PERF STD	TRG RAT	TRG REC	TRG LOC RAT	TASK COND
000.50	000.50	35B20		A	01			A	B	J	C	

Fig. A-50. (Continued).

```
LSA-077   RCC A   CYCLE 0019              LOGISTIC SUPPORT ANALYSIS RECORD                    89/03/22   PAGE   1
                                     DEPOT MAINTENANCE INTERSERVICE DATA SUMMARY
EIAC      ITEM NAME              START LCN   ALC   STOP LCN   UDC   SERV DES
END       REFRIGERATION UNIT     0                           DCY   ARMY

HEADER DATA:                                                 TOTAL SYSTEMS    ORIGINATING
   ITEM DESIGNATOR CODE                                       SUPPORTED        COMMAND          NSN
TYPE  MODEL      SERIES  SUFFIX   FSCM    MANUFACTURERS PART NUMBER    003000
TYPE001 MODEL00002  SR   SUFFIX0  94833
PART I   JLC 28/29 DATA                    DEPOT REPARABLE ITEMS/ENGINEERING DRAWINGS
LCN       ALC  ITEM NAME          MANUFACTURERS PART NUMBER     FSCM  DAC     QTY/ASSY-QTY/EI
           WIRE HARNESS ASSY      ENGINEERING DRAWING           94833          DWG/CLASS   SMR   TASK CODE   RQMT FOR
002            NSN                                                                                            FAC TRN TOOL
                                                                                               BGDAGAA       B   Y   B

                                                                                               GGDFGAA       N   N   C
                                                                                               JGDAGAA       A   N   C
                                                                                               RGDAGAA       N   Y   C

                          ITEM FUNCTION
          WIRE HARNESS SERVES AS THE NETWORK OF POWER TRANSMISSION.

LCN       ALC  ITEM NAME          MANUFACTURERS PART NUMBER     FSCM  DAC     QTY/ASSY-QTY/EI
               COMPRESSOR ASSY    ENGINEERING DRAWING           10855  A      1                 DWG/CLASS   SMR   TASK CODE   RQMT FOR
005            NSN   5D43-139-A                                                                                  FAC TRN TOOL
                     4130-01-091-9159                                                           HGDAAAA       N   N   C
                                                                                                    PAFFF
                                                                                               KRDAAAA       N   N   C
                          ITEM FUNCTION
          COMPRESSES THE REFRIGERANT GAS AND PUMPS IT THROUGH THE SYSTEM.
```

Fig. A-51. LSA-077—Depot Maintenance Interservice Data Summary.

```
LSA-077  RCC A   CYCLE 0019           LOGISTIC SUPPORT ANALYSIS RECORD              89/03/22   PAGE   2
                                 DEPOT MAINTENANCE INTERSERVICE DATA SUMMARY
EIAC          ITEM NAME          START LCN   ALC   STOP LCN   UDC   SERV DES
END           REFRIGERATION UNIT      O                      DCY   ARMY

PART II
SECTION A.        FACILITY REQUIREMENT AND SUPPORT EQUIPMENT LIST
SECTION A.   SUPPORT EQUIPMENT LIST
SE LCN   ALC ITEM NAME          SUPPORT EQUIPMENT FULL ITEM NAME          GOVERNMENT DESIG   SERD ST REV TRD NUMBER
00S01        SET, SOLDERING HP   REPAIR SET, VACUUM/TEMPERATURE CONTROL    ANUSF1624          0726  R  AC  JJR83M
00S02        COMPRESSOR, RING    COMPRESSOR, RING, BAND                                       0727  R  AB  JJR83M
00S04        MULTIMETER          MULTIPLE USE ELECTRICAL MEASUREMENT DEV.                     0728  R  AB
00S05        LEAK DETECTION DEV. FREON LEAK DETECTION DEVICE, REFRIGERATIO                    0731  R  AC
00S10        SCISSORS                                                                         6020
00S1001      DOLLIE, 4WH                                                                      6010
00S1002      SET, SOCKET                                                                      6009
00S1003      TONGS, 7 IN                                                                      6008
00S1004      WRENCH SET, COMB                                                                 6007
00S1005      EXT, SOCKET WRENCH                                                               6006
00S1006      KIT, SOLDERING GUN                                                               6005
00S1007      DITCMO STATION                                                                   6004
00S1008      VOLTMETER,1/3AMP                                                                 6003
00S1009      WRENCH, FILTER                                                                   6002
00S1010      HYDROMETER                                                                       6001
00S11        WELDER                                                                           6019
00S12        TORQUE WRENCH                                                                    6018
00S13        WRENCH, SOCKET                                                                   6017
00S14        WRENCH, SOCKET                                                                   6016
00S15        SCREWDRIVER                                                                      6015
00S16        WRENCH, ADJUSTABLE                                                               6014
00S17        BRUSH, WIRE                                                                      6013
00S18        SHIM, 1/4 CM                                                                     6012
00S19        BUCKET, 3 GAL                                                                    6011
00S21        DYNOMOMETER         DEVICE, POWER MEASUREMENT, PRECISION                         8231  U  SS
00S22        EXHAUST ANALYZER    ANALYZER, EXHAUST GAS                                        8232  C  AA
00S23        LEAK DOWN BENCH     COMPRESSION LEAK DOWN TEST BENCH                             8233  C  AA

SECTION B.   DEPOT FACILITIES REQUIREMENT LIST
FAC LCN         FUNCTIONS REQUIREMENT FACILITY
                ALC   TASK CODE   LCN   ALC   TASK CODE   LCN   ALC   TASK CODE
00F01    005          ABCACAA                 JGDAGAA     006
         00614        JGDACAA

          FACILITY REQUIREMENT:   THE FREON FACILITY IS REQUIRED TO PERFORM REPAIR ON THE REFRIGE
                                  RATION UNITS BEING DEVELOPED TO SUPPORT THE ARMY MISSION INTO T
                                  HE TWENTY-FIRST CENTURY.  NEW WEAPON DEVELOPMENTS REQUIRE THAT
                                  155 MM ROUNDS BE KEPT AT A TEMPERATURE OF 10 DEGREES CELCIUS.
                                  THE REFRIGERATION UNIT REPAIRS WORKLOAD WILL INCREASE BY THRE
                                  E MILLION PERCENT THUS REQUIRING THAT AN ORGANIC REPAIR FACILIT
                                  Y BE DEVELOPED.  THE ENTIRE FREE WORLD WILL DEPEND ON THESE NEW
                                  AMMUNITION ROUNDS TO COUNTER THE RED THREAT.
```

Fig. A-51. (Continued).

LSA-077   RCC A   CYCLE 0019   LOGISTIC SUPPORT ANALYSIS RECORD   89/03/22   PAGE 3
                                    DEPOT MAINTENANCE INTERSERVICE DATA SUMMARY

EIAC   ITEM NAME   START LCN   ALC   STOP LCN   UOC   SERV DES
END   REFRIGERATION UNIT   0   DCY   ARMY

              FACILITY DESIGN CRIT: THE FREON FACILITY MUST HAVE A CLEAN ROOM (0.00023 PARTICULES P
                                      ER MILLION) AND 3000 SQUARE FT. CAPACITY.
                                      007   A   JGDAGAB
                        JGDAGAA   007
00F02   FACILITY REQUIREMENT: FACILITY ENLARGEMENT REQUIRED IN ELECTRIC MOTOR REWIND FACILITY
                                      DUE TO THE PROJECTED LARGE WORKLOAD INCREASE.

LSA-077   RCC A   CYCLE 0019   LOGISTIC SUPPORT ANALYSIS RECORD   89/03/22   PAGE 4
                                    DEPOT MAINTENANCE INTERSERVICE DATA SUMMARY

EIAC   ITEM NAME   START LCN   ALC   STOP LCN   UOC   SERV DES
END   REFRIGERATION UNIT   0   DCY   ARMY

PART III   JLC 30 DATA   NEW/UNIQUE DEPOT SUPPORT EQUIPMENT

SE LCN   ITEM NAME   MFR P/N   SCC   FSCM   SERD   ST REV   CFE   YR   QUANTITY
                                                                                GFE   FIELD   RECOMMENDED
00S1007   DITCMO STATION   CC586T3692   33721   6004   NSN
                                                            GOVERNMENT DESIG
-------- NONRECURRING COST --------   RECURRING
HDWR DEV   DESIGN   PASS-THRU   ILS

                                    TASKS REQUIRING SUPPORT EQUIPMENT
       ALC   TASK CODE   TASK COND   SLC   SSC   NO SSC   ST REV   M-H SSC   ELAPS TIME
LCN   .37(M)   .37(M)
002   BGDAGAA   BC   A   35B30   01

SE LCN   ITEM NAME   MFR P/N   SCC   FSCM   SERD   ST REV   CFE   YR   QUANTITY
                                                                                GFE   FIELD   RECOMMENDED
00S10   SCISSORS   KT02468J3N2   33201   6020   NSN
                                                            GOVERNMENT DESIG
-------- NONRECURRING COST --------   RECURRING
HDWR DEV   DESIGN   PASS-THRU   ILS

                                    TASKS REQUIRING SUPPORT EQUIPMENT
       ALC   TASK CODE   TASK COND   SLC   SSC   NO SSC   ST REV   M-H SSC   ELAPS TIME
LCN   1.36(P)   1.36(P)
002   JGDAGAA   C   A   35B30   01

SE LCN   ITEM NAME   MFR P/N   SCC   FSCM   SERD   ST REV   CFE   YR   QUANTITY
              VOLTMETER,1/3AMP   GFE   FIELD   RECOMMENDED
00S1008   SNS17832105   01762   6003   NSN
                                                                   GOVERNMENT DESIG
-------- NONRECURRING COST --------   RECURRING
HDWR DEV   DESIGN   PASS-THRU   ILS

Fig. A-51. (Continued).

```
LSA-077   RCC A   CYCLE 0019                    LOGISTIC SUPPORT ANALYSIS RECORD                    89/03/22   PAGE   5
                                        DEPOT MAINTENANCE INTERSERVICE DATA SUMMARY
EIAC      ITEM NAME                START LCN    ALC  STOP LCN      UDC   SERV DES
END       REFRIGERATION UNIT       0                              DCY   ARMY

                                    TASKS REQUIRING SUPPORT EQUIPMENT
          LCN       ALC  TASK CODE   TASK COND    SLC  SSC  NO SSC   M-H SSC      ELAPS TIME
          002            JGDAGAA     C            A    35B30 01      1.36(P)      1.36(P)
                                                                                          CFE  YR     QUANTITY
SE LCN    ALC  ITEM NAME             MFR P/N           SCC  FSCM  SERD  ST REV  NSN        GFE  FIELD  RECOMMENDED
00S01          SET, SOLDERING HP     4003100                99999 0726  R  AC   5820-00-347-8650  C   92
          ---- NONRECURRING COST ---------         RECURRING         GOVERNMENT DESIG
HDWR DEV  DESIGN  PASS-THRU   ILS
00001000  00015000 00000200          00004000        00002355  ANUSF1624
                                    TEST PROGRAM SETS

          LCN (UUT)  ALC  ITEM NAME             MFR P/N          SCC  FSCM            APPORTIONED UNIT COST
          005             LOW VACUUM ALARM                                           NON REC        RECURRING
                                    TASKS REQUIRING SUPPORT EQUIPMENT                 7000000.00
          LCN       ALC  TASK CODE   TASK COND    SLC  SSC  NO SSC   M-H SSC      ELAPS TIME
          005            HGDAAAA     C            I    52C20 01      .10(M)       .10(M)
                                                                                          CFE  YR     QUANTITY
SE LCN    ALC  ITEM NAME             MFR P/N           SCC  FSCM  SERD  ST REV  NSN        GFE  FIELD  RECOMMENDED
00S1006        KIT, SOLDERING GUN    450K4                  11103 6005            3439-00-930-1638
          ---- NONRECURRING COST ---------         RECURRING         GOVERNMENT DESIG
HDWR DEV  DESIGN  PASS-THRU   ILS

                                    TASKS REQUIRING SUPPORT EQUIPMENT
          LCN       ALC  TASK CODE   TASK COND    SLC  SSC  NO SSC   M-H SSC      ELAPS TIME
          002            JGDAGAA     C            A    35B30 01      1.36(P)      1.36(P)
```

Fig. A-51. (Continued).

```
LSA-080   RCC A   CYCLE 0019                    LOGISTIC SUPPORT ANALYSIS RECORD                    89/03/22   PAGE   1
                                                BILL OF MATERIALS
                                                PART 1 PARTS LIST
EIAC      ITEM NAME            START LCN   ALC STOP LCN    LCN-CD   LCN STRUCTURE
END       ENGINE               006                        1        12222
LINE PLISN IC FSCM REFNO       SCC ITEM NAME     UDC SERV DES   QTY/ASSY  SMR    NHA-PLISN   MRRI     MRRII   LCN        ALC ERROR
                                                 DCY
```

LINE	PLISN	IC	FSCM	REFNO	ITEM NAME	QTY/ASSY	SMR	NHA-PLISN	MRRI	MRRII	LCN	ALC ERROR
	0209	D	44940	BC1920	PISTON ASSY		PAFZZ	0205	1.6656	1.445	0060201	***
1	0217	E	44940	112-0136	PISTON, INT COMB EN	2	PAFZZ	0209	1.2230	1.000	0060201AA	
2	0221	E	44940	112-0003	RING, RETAINING	4	XAFZZ	0209	1.2230	1.000	0060201AB	
3	0225	E	44940	112-0069	PIN, PISTON	2	XAFZZ	0209	1.2230	1.000	0060201AC	
4	0229	E	44940	114-0203	CONNECTING ROD,PIST	2	PAFZZ	0209	1.2340	1.120	0060201AD	
5	0233	E	44940	B05-0010	BOLT, CONNECTINGROD	4	XAFZZ	0209	1.5656	1.445	0060201AE	
6	0237	E	44940	114-0036	BUSHING, CONNEC ROD	2	XAFZZ	0209	1.2340	1.120	0060201AF	
7	0241	E	44940	114-0145	BEARING, ROD (HALF)	4	PAFZZ	0209	1.2340	1.120	0060201AG	
8	0245	E	44940	113-0153	RING SET, PISTON	2	PAFZZ	0209	1.2340	1.120	0060201AH	

Fig. A-52. LSA-080—Bill of Materials.

89/03/22   PAGE   6

LOGISTIC SUPPORT ANALYSIS RECORD
BILL OF MATERIALS
PART 2   ERROR LISTING

LSA-080   RCC A   CYCLE 0019

		START LCN	ALC STOP LCN	UDC SERV DES	LCN-CD	LCN STRUCTURE
EIAC	ITEM NAME	006		DCY	1	12222
END	ENGINE					

NUMBER OF ITEMS IN END ITEM   57
NUMBER OF ITEMS ON PARTS LIST   56
NUMBER OF ITEMS ON ERROR LIST ONLY 50
NUMBER OF ITEMS ON ERROR LIST   60

ERROR CODES:

1 ITEM SMR CODED NONREPAIRABLE WCOMPONENT BREAKDOWN
2 PART OF THE END ITEM BUT NOT ATTACHED TO ANY ASSEMBLY OR PART
3 NO INDENTURE CODE
4 SMR CODE BLANK OR CONTAINS BLANKS
5 INDENTURE CODE INCONSISTENT WITH LCN STRUCTURE
6 DUPLICATE LCNS WHEN CLASSICAL ASSIGNMENT IS USED
7 RECOVERABILITY CODE IN ERROR
8 REPAIRABLE ASSEMBLY WITH NO PARTS

PLISN	IC	FSCM	REFERENCE NUMBER	SCC	ITEM NAME	QTY	SMR	NHA-PLISN	MRRI	MRRII	LCN	ALC	ERROR REASON ERR 1 2 3 4 5 6 7 8
AABW	B	44940	CCKA-MS/3834J		ENGINE	1	PAFZZ		1.6656	1.445	006	Y	Y
0005		35281	ACSUF26		ACID,SULFURIC			AAAA	0.0000	0.000	0060B		Y Y
0009		10235	CCBX23		METAL CONTAINER			AAAA	0.0000	0.000	0060B		Y Y
0013		05820	CK51		ACETONE			AAAA	0.0000	0.000	0060B		Y Y
0017		33307	EI8247921		SANDPAPER			AAAA	0.0000	0.000	0060B		Y Y
0021		32507	HI9358711		PAINT			AAAA	0.0000	0.000	0060B		Y Y
0025		10252	HK21		WIRE			AAAA	0.0000	0.000	0060B		Y Y
0029		10235	H25732102		TAPE			AAAA	0.0000	0.000	0060B		Y Y
0033		77231	MIL-L-2140-0HEDD		OIL,LUBRICATING			AAAA	0.0000	0.000	0060B		Y Y
0037		81348	P-D-680		DRY CLEANING SOLVNT			AAAA	0.0000	0.000	0060B		Y Y
0041		33201	PC54276734		WAXED STRING			AAAA	0.0000	0.000	0060B		Y Y
0045		81348	00-S-571		LEAD TIN SOLDER,SB5			AAAA	0.0000	0.000	0060B		Y Y
0049		72236	RC54217003		WIRE			AAAA	0.0000	0.000	0060B		Y Y
0053		37023	S023		SEALANT,GASKET			AAAA	0.0000	0.000	0060B		Y Y
0057		27240	VV-G-1690		GASOLINE,AUTOMOTIVE			AAAA	0.0000	0.000	0060B		Y Y
0061		10235	1191		TWINE			AAAA	0.0000	0.000	0060B		Y Y
0065		44940	122-0323		FILTER, OIL			AAAA	0.0000	0.000	0060B		Y Y
0069		77222	3352		WELDING RODS			AAAA	0.0000	0.000	0060B		Y Y
0001	C	58536	A-A-531		CLOTHS			AAAA	0.0000	0.000	0060B		
0085		11599	AT503		WRENCH,ADJUSTABLE			AAAA	0.0000	0.000	0060T		Y Y
0089		79061	A135		SCREWDRIVER			AAAA	0.0000	0.000	0060T		Y Y

Fig. A-52. (Continued).

LOGISTIC SUPPORT ANALYSIS RECORD   PAGE   1

CHRONOLOG INFORMATION

LSA-100   CYCLE   LOGISTIC

SYSTEM PARAMETERS

SYSTEM CYCLE NO.	0001
SYSTEM DATE	84/07/30
SYSTEM START TIME	13:19:03:40
SYSTEM RUN INDICATOR	T
SYSTEM UTILITY INDICATOR	
SYSTEM START TID	AAAA
SYSTEM END ITEM CODE	REFRIG UNT
SYSTEM SERVICE DESIGNATOR	A
SYSTEM FSCM	94388
SYSTEM DLSC CONTROL	
SYSTEM PRINT LINES	060
SYSTEM LCN MASTER IND	
SYSTEM PART MASTER IND	
SYSTEM DESC MASTER IND	

LSA-100   CYCLE

```
13:18:56:60 SYSTEM COMMENCES EXECUTION
13:19:01:60  MODULE ISUP01       BEGIN
13:19:04:00  MSG FROM MODULE ISUP01
13:19:04:50  MSG FROM MODULE ISUP01
13:19:05:00  MSG FROM MODULE ISUP01
13:19:05:50  MSG FROM MODULE ISUP01
13:19:06:00  MSG FROM MODULE ISUP01
13:19:06:40  MSG FROM MODULE ISUP01
13:19:07:20  MSG FROM MODULE ISUP01
13:19:07:70  MSG FROM MODULE ISUP01
13:19:08:20  MSG FROM MODULE ISUP01
13:19:08:60  MSG FROM MODULE ISUP01
13:19:09:10  MSG FROM MODULE ISUP01
13:19:09:70  MSG FROM MODULE ISUP01
13:19:11:50  MSG FROM MODULE ISUP01
13:19:12:00  MSG FROM MODULE ISUP01
13:19:13:90  MSG FROM MODULE ISUP01
13:19:15:40  MSG FROM MODULE ISUP01
13:19:21:40  MSG FROM MODULE ISUP01
13:19:23:70  MSG FROM MODULE ISUP01
13:19:24:70  MSG FROM MODULE ISUP01
13:19:25:30  MSG FROM MODULE ISUP01
13:19:25:70  MSG FROM MODULE ISUP01
13:19:26:80  MSG FROM MODULE ISUP01
13:19:27:30  MSG FROM MODULE ISUP01
13:19:27:70  MSG FROM MODULE ISUP01
13:19:28:20  MODULE ISUP01       ENDED
13:19:33:70  ISUP00  CANCELS ISUP01
```

Fig. A-53. LSA-100—Chronolog.

LSA-101   RCC   CYCLE 0004   LOGISTIC SUPPORT ANALYSIS RECORD   84/07/30   PAGE   1

TRANSACTION EDIT RESULTS - SELECTION CARDS

```
                    TRANSACTION IMAGE                                    ACTION TAKEN
1.........10.........20.........30.........40.........50.........60.........70.........80

S004CA        00608       DCYAD            TM2              ERROR IN GROUP                                  ...REJ...
              .......     .......                           IF START LCN BLANK STOP LCN MUST BE BLANK       ...ERR...
S004DA                    DCYAD            TMI              START LCN-00C COMBINATION NOT ON FILE           ...REJ...
S004EA        0       A   DCZAD4       X                    SELECTION VALID   REPORT GENERATED
S004FA        006         FF APABC4ZQXY9FJ  X   TM 5-4110-234-24   SELECTION VALID   REPORT GENERATED
S004GA        006         FF AD                             SELECTION VALID   REPORT GENERATED
S004HA        006     00608  FF AD                          SELECTION VALID   REPORT GENERATED
S004HB        00607   A                                     SELECTION VALID   REPORT GENERATED
S004IA        006         FF FD4        .............       ERROR IN GROUP                                  ...REJ...
                                                            IF TOOL IND BLANK ICCS MUST BE BLANK            ...ERR...
S004JA        006         FF AP                             SELECTION VALID   REPORT GENERATED
S004KA        006         FF H                              ERROR IN GROUP                                  ...REJ...
S004LA        006         FF AD             X               DRAFT/PROOF INDICATOR NOT D OR P                ...ERR...
                                                            SELECTION VALID   REPORT GENERATED
S004MA        00607   A   FF AD4        X   TM 5-4110-234-24   EXCEEDS 10 SEL CARDS                         ...REJ...
S004MA        00607   A   AD4           X                    EXCEEDS 10 SEL CARDS                           ...REJ...
```

Fig. A-54. LSA-101—Transaction Edit Results—Selection Cards.

```
LSA-102   RCC    CYCLE 0006              LOGISTIC SUPPORT ANALYSIS RECORD                        89/03/21   PAGE  1
                                         TRANSACTION EDIT RESULTS - LCN MASTER

                      TRANSACTION IMAGE                                                        ACTION TAKEN
1........10.........20.........30.........40.........50.........60.........70.........80

R 0         ANGCABAA
C060        ANGCABAA0034580FAULT LOCATION-INSUFFICIENT COOLING AAAANYCH DNTM1A   L   REMOVE CARD VALID MASTER LINE(S) REMOVED
D060        ANGCABAAA00022          BZZZZZ A01              KTO24683N2        N    A   MASTER LINE ERASED BY REMOVE TRANSACTION
                                                                                  A   MASTER LINE ERASED BY REMOVE TRANSACTION
E0100S10    A                                                                     A   ALL SPECIFIED FIELDS VALID MASTER UPDATED
E0200S10    6020      44940               N6233XX                         N    A   ALL SPECIFIED FIELDS VALID MASTER UPDATED
E0300S10    USATROSCOM                                                            A   ALL SPECIFIED FIELDS VALID MASTER UPDATED
E1100S10    SCISSORS                                                              A   ALL SPECIFIED FIELDS VALID MASTER UPDATED
E1200S10    A   O                                                                 A   ALL SPECIFIED FIELDS VALID MASTER UPDATED
E1200S10    B   F                                                                 A   ALL SPECIFIED FIELDS VALID MASTER UPDATED
            C   D                                                                 A   ALL SPECIFIED FIELDS VALID MASTER UPDATED
E0100S1001  44940                                      CB9234569                  A   ALL SPECIFIED FIELDS VALID MASTER UPDATED
E0200S1001  6010                        N980/21                          N    A   ALL SPECIFIED FIELDS VALID MASTER UPDATED
E0300S1001  USATROSCOM                                                            A   ALL SPECIFIED FIELDS VALID MASTER UPDATED
E1100S1001  DOLLIE, 4WH                                                           A   ALL SPECIFIED FIELDS VALID MASTER UPDATED
E1200S1001  A   O                                                                 A   ALL SPECIFIED FIELDS VALID MASTER UPDATED
E0100S1002  44940                                 B2502                      Y    A   ALL SPECIFIED FIELDS VALID MASTER UPDATED
E0200S1002  6009                        NR123XX                          8    A   ALL SPECIFIED FIELDS VALID MASTER UPDATED
E0300S1002  USATROSCOM                                                            A   ALL SPECIFIED FIELDS VALID MASTER UPDATED
E1100S1002  SET, SOCKET                                                           A   ALL SPECIFIED FIELDS VALID MASTER UPDATED
E1200S1002  A   F                                                                 A   ALL SPECIFIED FIELDS VALID MASTER UPDATED
E1200S1002  B   H                                                                 A   ALL SPECIFIED FIELDS VALID MASTER UPDATED
E0100S1003  44940                                 B25                            A   ALL SPECIFIED FIELDS VALID MASTER UPDATED
E0200S1003  6008                        N1389XX                          4    A   ALL SPECIFIED FIELDS VALID MASTER UPDATED
E0300S1003  USATROSCOM                                                            A   ALL SPECIFIED FIELDS VALID MASTER UPDATED
E1100S1003  TONGS, 7 IN                                                           A   ALL SPECIFIED FIELDS VALID MASTER UPDATED
E1200S1003  A   F                                                                 A   ALL SPECIFIED FIELDS VALID MASTER UPDATED
```

Fig. A-55. LSA-102—Transaction Edit Results—LCN Master.

```
LSA-103  RCC    CYCLE 0006              LOGISTIC SUPPORT ANALYSIS RECORD                89/03/21   PAGE  1
                                        TRANSACTION EDIT RESULTS - PARTS MASTER

             1........10........20........30........40........50........60........70........80
                                        TRANSACTION IMAGE                                    ACTION TAKEN

H15A4622          00501BA    ATM2  2  6     05906                        C  ALL SPECIFIED FIELDS VALID MASTER UPDATED
H05CC586T3692     000011-2500  1                            F            C  ALL SPECIFIED FIELDS VALID MASTER UPDATED
H14EN07AA34B      00506    B001-006                                      A  ALL SPECIFIED FIELDS VALID MASTER UPDATED
H05A9A473612      000011-100  100002101-350  2                           C  ALL SPECIFIED FIELDS VALID MASTER UPDATED
H053C931H4257     000031-2700  1                                         C  ALL SPECIFIED FIELDS VALID MASTER UPDATED
H05K252                      5                                           D  ALL SPECIFIED DATA DELETED
H05K252           000011-5    1000026-50      20000351-150  3            C  ALL SPECIFIED FIELDS VALID MASTER UPDATED
H14MS200066-229   00509    B001-010                         F            A  ALL SPECIFIED FIELDS VALID MASTER UPDATED
R MS27183-13      004144AA                                               P  REMOVE CARD VALID MASTER LINE(S) REMOVED
H09MS27183-13     004144AA   ADCY,DCZ,                                   A  MASTER LINE ERASED BY REMOVE TRANSACTION
H10MS27183-13     004144AA   A              005             0001         A  MASTER LINE ERASED BY REMOVE TRANSACTION
H11MS27183-13     004144AA   YPAFZZ A00016767000015563467               A  MASTER LINE ERASED BY REMOVE TRANSACTION
H12MS27183-13     004144AA   3     001010005020                         A  MASTER LINE ERASED BY REMOVE TRANSACTION
H14MS27183-13     004144AA   AAAAAABBBBBCCCCCBBBBBEEEEE1111111           A  MASTER LINE ERASED BY REMOVE TRANSACTION
H15MS27183-13     004144AA   ATM1  5 112   00104144AA                   A  MASTER LINE ERASED BY REMOVE TRANSACTION
H15MS27183-13     004144AA   ATM2  1  4  2  0503AA                       A  MASTER LINE ERASED BY REMOVE TRANSACTION
                  00503AA                                               C  ALL SPECIFIED FIELDS VALID MASTER UPDATED
R MS90728-60      0040201AA                                             P  REMOVE CARD VALID MASTER LINE(S) REMOVED
H09MS90728-60     0040201AA  ADCY,DCZ,                                  A  MASTER LINE ERASED BY REMOVE TRANSACTION
H10MS90728-60     0040201AA  A              005             0008        A  MASTER LINE ERASED BY REMOVE TRANSACTION
H11MS90728-60     0040201AA  YPAFZZ A00010767000015563421              A  MASTER LINE ERASED BY REMOVE TRANSACTION
H12MS90728-60     0040201AA  3     001010005005                        A  MASTER LINE ERASED BY REMOVE TRANSACTION
H14MS90728-60     0040201AA  AAAAAABBBBBCCCCCAAAAAACCCCCAAAAABB         A  MASTER LINE ERASED BY REMOVE TRANSACTION
H14MS90728-60     0040201AA  BBBB1111122222                            A  MASTER LINE ERASED BY REMOVE TRANSACTION
H15MS90728-60     0040201AA  ATM3  5  1    00B0040201AA                A  MASTER LINE ERASED BY REMOVE TRANSACTION
R ND37046-024     0040201AA                                            P  REMOVE CARD VALID MASTER LINE(S) REMOVED
H01ND37046-024    ZZZZZ3 2AWASHER,LOCK          Y Y    100    04  A A A A  MASTER LINE ERASED BY REMOVE TRANSACTION
```

Fig. A-56. LSA-103—Transaction Edit Results—Parts Master.

343

Appendix A LSA Summary Reports

```
LSA-104   RCC     CYCLE 0006              LOGISTIC SUPPORT ANALYSIS RECORD                          89/03/21   PAGE   1
                                     TRANSACTION EDIT RESULTS - NARRATIVE MASTER
                      TRANSACTION IMAGE                                                        ACTION TAKEN

1........10........20........30........40........50........60........70........80

AAAA
DO2AAAA       O       ANGCABAAFAULT LOCATION-INSUFFICIENT COOLING          T    TID MASTER AND DESCRIPTION REMOVED
R AAAG                                                                          MASTER REMOVED BY LCN/TASK CODE REMOVE
DO2AAAGAAA  S LIST ALL SUBTASKS AND ELEMENTS FOR REPAIR                    A    DESCRIPTION REMOVED BY THIS TRAN
DO2AAAGAAB    END OF TASK                                                  A    MASTER LINE REMOVED BY DO2 TRAN
DO2AACBAAA  SPLACE PARTS IN COVERED BUCKET CONTAINING ACETONE              A    MASTER LINE REMOVED BY DO2 TRAN
DO2AACBAAB    TO REMOVE GUM DEPOSITS-LET SOAK ABOUT 90MIN.        A 601020A    MASTER UPDATED VIA DO2 CARD
DO2AACBAAC  SREMOVE PARTS FROM ACETONE USING TONGS.              A  10  10A    MASTER UPDATED VIA DO2 CARD
DO2AACBAAD  SCLEAN JETS USING A FINE SOFT WIRE.                  A  50  98A    MASTER UPDATED VIA DO2 CARD
DO2AACCAAA  SLIST DETAILED SUBTASKS AND ELEMENTS.               A 420 420A    MASTER UPDATED VIA DO2 CARD
DO2AACDAAA  SREMOVE AIR CLEANER BY LOOSENING THE SCREW AT ITS BASE. A 30 30A    MASTER UPDATED VIA DO2 CARD
DO2AACDAAB  SREMOVE THE MANIFOLD FROM THE ENGINE.              A 150 150A    MASTER UPDATED VIA DO2 CARD
DO2AACDAAC  SREMOVE TWO SCREWS SECURING THE CABURETOR TO THE       A        MASTER UPDATED VIA DO2 CARD
DO2AACDAAD    MANIFOLD.                                        A 100 100A    MASTER UPDATED VIA DO2 CARD
DO2AACDAAE  SINSTALL SERVICEABLE CARBURETOR                        A        MASTER UPDATED VIA DO2 CARD
DO2AACDAAF    USE A NEW CARBURETOR GASKET.                     A 248 248A    MASTER UPDATED VIA DO2 CARD
DO2AACDAAG  SINSTALL THE MANIFOLD-USING NEW GASKETS- ON THE       A        MASTER UPDATED VIA DO2 CARD
DO2AACDAAH    ENGINE.                                          A 160 160A    MASTER UPDATED VIA DO2 CARD
DO2AACDAAI  SINSTALL THE AIR CLEANER ONTO THE CARBURETOR AND      A        MASTER UPDATED VIA DO2 CARD
DO2AACDAAJ    TIGHTEN THE SCREW AT ITS BASE.                   A  20  20A    MASTER UPDATED VIA DO2 CARD
DO2AACEAAA  SDISASSEMBLE CARBURETOR.                              A        MASTER UPDATED VIA DO2 CARD
DO2AACEAAB  REFERENCE LCN 00607 ALC A TASK CODE SGFFG.         A 720 720A    MASTER UPDATED VIA DO2 CARD
DO2AACEAAC  SRELACE NONREPAIRABLE ITEMS AS NECESSARY               A        MASTER UPDATED VIA DO2 CARD
DO2AACEAAD  SREASSEMBLE CARBURETOR.                               A        MASTER UPDATED VIA DO2 CARD
DO2AACEAAE  REFERENCE LCN 00607 ALC A TASK CODE SGFFG.            A        MASTER UPDATED VIA DO2 CARD
DO2AACFAAA  SSPECIFY DETAILED SUBTASKS AND ELEMENTS               A        MASTER UPDATED VIA DO2 CARD
```

Fig. A-57. LSA-104—Transaction Edit Results—Task Narrative Master.

```
LSA-105   RCC     CYCLE 0009          LOGISTIC SUPPORT ANALYSIS RECORD                89/03/21   PAGE   1
                                          KEY FIELD CHANGE REPORT
                             1........10........20........30........40........50........60........70........80

CHANGE TRANSACTION   7SASE
         OLD  D02AAAB        0           ANGOABAAFAULT LOCATION-INSUFFICIENT COOLING
         NEW  D02SASE        0           ANGOABAAFAULT LOCATION-INSUFFICIENT COOLING
         OLD  D02AAABAAA  SCHECK FOR CLOSED RECEIVER VALVES.                              A00100010A
         NEW  D02SASEAAA  SCHECK FOR CLOSED RECEIVER VALVES.                              A00100010A
         OLD  D02AAABAAB  SOPEN RECEIVER VALVES.                                          A
         NEW  D02SASEAAB  SOPEN RECEIVER VALVES.                                          A
         OLD  D02AAABAAC  SCHECK EVAPORATOR AIR INTAKE AND OUTLET SCREENS TO MAKE         A
         NEW  D02SASEAAC  SCHECK EVAPORATOR AIR INTAKE AND OUTLET SCREENS TO MAKE         A
         OLD  D02AAABAAD  SURE THEY ARE NOT OBSTRUCTED.                                   A00250025A
         NEW  D02SASEAAD  SURE THEY ARE NOT OBSTRUCTED.                                   A00250025A
         OLD  D02AAABAAF  SCHECK FOR DEFECTS OF THE EVAPORATOR FAN.                       A00100010A
         NEW  D02SASEAAF  SCHECK FOR DEFECTS OF THE EVAPORATOR FAN.                       A00100010A
         OLD  D02AAABAAGA IF DEFECTIVE-REPLACE.                                           A
         NEW  D02SASEAAGA IF DEFECTIVE-REPLACE.                                           A
         OLD  D02AAABAAGB (TASK NOT DOCUMENTED.)                                          A
         NEW  D02SASEAAGB (TASK NOT DOCUMENTED.)                                          A
         OLD  D02AAABAAGC IF EVAPORATOR FAN CHECKS OK, BUT WILL NOT OPERATE,              A
         NEW  D02SASEAAGC IF EVAPORATOR FAN CHECKS OK, BUT WILL NOT OPERATE,              A
         OLD  D02AAABAAGD DEFECTIVE ELECTRIC MOTOR IS INDICATED. REPLACE PER              A
         NEW  D02SASEAAGD DEFECTIVE ELECTRIC MOTOR IS INDICATED. REPLACE PER              A
         OLD  D02AAABAAH  REFERENCE LCN 00901          TASK CODE HGOAA.                   A
         NEW  D02SASEAAH  REFERENCE LCN 00901          TASK CODE HGOAA.                   A
         OLD  D02AAABAAI  SCHECK EVAPORATOR AND CONDENSER COIL FOR DIRT OR ANY            A
         NEW  D02SASEAAI  SCHECK EVAPORATOR AND CONDENSER COIL FOR DIRT OR ANY            A
         OLD  D02AAABAAJ  OBSTRUCTION THAT WOULD BLOCK AIR FLOW.                          A
         NEW  D02SASEAAJ  OBSTRUCTION THAT WOULD BLOCK AIR FLOW.                          A
         OLD  D02AAABAAK  SCLEAN COILS.                                                   A00300030A
         NEW  D02SASEAAK  SCLEAN COILS.                                                   A00300030A
         OLD  D02AAABAAL  SCHECK THERMOSTAT FOR DEFECTS.                                  A00700070A
         NEW  D02SASEAAL  SCHECK THERMOSTAT FOR DEFECTS.                                  A00700070A
         OLD  D02AAABAAM  SREPLACE DEFECTIVE THERMOSTAT. (TASK NOT DOCUMENTED)            A
         NEW  D02SASEAAM  SREPLACE DEFECTIVE THERMOSTAT. (TASK NOT DOCUMENTED)            A
         OLD  D02AAABAAN  XXXXXXXXXXXXXXXXXXXXXXXXXXXXXXXXXXXXXXXXXXXXXXX                  A
         NEW  D02SASEAAN  XXXXXXXXXXXXXXXXXXXXXXXXXXXXXXXXXXXXXXXXXXXXXXX                  A
```

Fig. A-58. LSA-105—Key Field Change Transactions.

345

Appendix A LSA Summary Reports

```
LSA-106  RCC A   CYCLE 0006              LOGISTIC SUPPORT ANALYSIS RECORD                    89/03/21  PAGE  1
                                         REFERENCE NUMBER DISCREPANCY LIST
EIAC            ITEM NAME        START LCN        ALC                  STOP LCN        PMF-LCN OPT
END             DOOR-SCREEN ASSY    001                                   006             X

     ERROR CODE:
          1 - LCN MASTER WITH BLANK PART NUMBER
          2 - REFERENCE NUMBERS STORED ON LCN MASTER FILE, BUT NOT ON PARTS MASTER FILE (WITHIN SELECT LCN RANGE)
          3 - REFERENCE NUMBERS STORED ON PARTS MASTER FILE, BUT WITHOUT LCN DATA
          4 - REFERENCE NUMBERS STORED ON PARTS MASTER FILE, BUT NOT ON LCN MASTER FILE
          5 - REFERENCE NUMBERS STORED ON LCN MASTER FILE AND PARTS MASTER FILE, BUT DO NOT MATCH ON LCN/ALC

REFERENCE NUMBER   SCC   REFERENCE NUMBER OVFL   LCN      ALC   TASK CODE   RECORD TYPE   ERROR CODE
```

REFERENCE NUMBER	SCC	REFERENCE NUMBER OVFL	LCN	ALC	TASK CODE	RECORD TYPE	ERROR CODE
AA06BR200			005		HGFAAAA	D07	1
AA06BR200	A		005		HGFAAAA	D07	1
AA123C						H01	4
AD44BS			00501		JGFAGAA	D07	2
AHP-304						H01	4
A135			00501		RGFAGAA	D07	2
A24			005		HGFAAAA	D07	2
A4544			00507AA			A04	5
A4622						H01	4
A50407-481						H01	4
A5051						H01	4
BEPY2						H01	3
BH30-130-U-20			00218	A	HJOFEAA	D07	2
B107-6			005		HGFAAAA	D07	2
CB9234569			00102		JGFFGAA	D07	2
CC586T3692			002	A	BGOAAAA	D07	2
C60-3						H01	4
DB-11						H01	4
EIB247921			00102		JGFFGAA	D07	2
EN07AA271						H01	4

Fig. A-59. LSA-106—Reference Number Discrepancy List.

LSA-107   RCC A   CYCLE 0019   89/03/22   PAGE   1

LCN – TASK IDENTIFICATION CODES CROSS REFERENCE LIST

LOGISTIC SUPPORT ANALYSIS RECORD

EIAC
ITEM NAME REFRIGERATION UNIT

START LCN   STOP LCN   DISPLAY OPTION   TID SEQUENCE X

TASK-ID	TASK CODE	LCN	ALC	WUC/TM FGC
SASE	NGOABAA	0	A	00A
SASF	NJCAEAA	0	A	00A
SASG	NJOFEAA	0	A	00A
SASH	AGCABAA	0		00
SASI	HGOAAAA	0		00
SASJ	JGOAAAA	0		00
SASK	NGCAAAA	0		00
SASL	NGCAAAB	0		00
SASM	NGCAAAC	0		00
SASN	NGOAAAA	0		00
SASO	NGOAAAB	0		00
SASP	NGOAAAC	0		00
SASQ	AGOABAA	001		01
SASR	HGOABAA	00102		0102
SASS	JGFFGAA	00102		0102
SAST	BGOAAAA	002	A	02A
SASU	AACACAA	002		02
SASV	ABOACAA	002		02
SASW	BGOAGAA	002		02
SASX	GGDFGAA	002		02
SASY	JGOAGAA	002		02
SASZ	RGOAGAA	002		02
SATA	HJOFEAA	00218	A	0218A
SATB	JGFAGAA	00218	A	0218A
SATC	ABCFCAA	005		05
SATD	ABONCAA	005		05
SATE	HGOAAAA	005		05
SATF	HGFAAAA	005		05
SATG	KRDAAAA	005		05
SATH	NGFAGAA	005		05
SATI	AGFAGAA	00501		0501
SATJ	GGFFGAA	00501		0501

TASK-ID	TASK CODE	LCN	ALC	WUC/TM FGC
SATK	JGFAGAA	00501		0501
SATL	RGFAGAA	00501		0501
SATM	BGFAGAA	006		06
SATN	CBCACAA	006		06
SATO	CBONAAA	006		06
SATP	HGOXAAA	006		06
SATQ	NGOABB	006		06
SATR	GGFNGAA	00602		0602
SATS	RGFAGAA	00602		0602
SATT	GGFMGAA	0060201		060201
SATU	JGFXGAA	0060201		060201
SATV	RGFFGAA	0060201		060201
SATW	CGFMGAA	00607	B	0602
SATX	DGOFAAA	00607	B	0602
SATY	HGOAGAA	00607	B	0602
SATZ	JGFXGAA	00607	B	0602
SAUA	SGFNGAA	00607	B	0602
SAUB	CGFAGAA	00607	C	0601
SAUC	DGONAAA	00607	C	0601
SAUD	HGOXGAA	00607	C	0601
SAUE	JGFMGAA	00607	C	0601
SAUF	SGFFGAA	00607	C	0601
SAUG	CGFAGAA	00607	C	0601
SAUH	DGOAAAA	00607		0607
SAUI	HGONGAA	00607		0607
SAUJ	JGFXGAA	00607		0607
SAUK	SGFFGAA	00607		0607
SAUL	HGFAGAA	00614		0614
SAUM	JGFAGAA	00614		0614
SAUN	BGFAGAA	00701	A	0901
SAUO	HGOAAAA	00701	A	0901
SAUP	JGFAGAA	00701	A	0901

Fig. A-60. LSA-107—LCN-Task Identification Code Cross-Reference.

LSA-108   RCC*   CYCLE 0006   LOGISTIC SUPPORT ANALYSIS RECORD   87/01/07   PAGE

CRITICAL DATA CHANGES

TRANSACTION IMAGE

1.........10.........20.........30.........40.........50.........60.........70.........80

						DATA ELEMENT	FROM	TO
H15A 4622	00501BA	ATM2	2	6	05906	C TM CODE	TM4	TM2
H15MS27183-13	00503AA	ATM2	1	4 2	0503AA	C TM CODE	TM4	TM2
H15TH-WW3510	00501AZ	ATM2	2	5	05905	C TM CODE	TM4	TM2
H153302	00501BB	ATM2	2	7	05907	C TM CODE	TM4	TM2
H155D40-1182	00502	ATM2	1	2	0502	C TM CODE	TM4	TM2
H156D40-1131	00503	ATM2	1	3	0503	C TM CODE	TM4	TM2

Fig. A-61. LSA-108—Critical Data Changes.

LSA-109   RCC   CYCLE 0004   LOGISTIC SUPPORT ANALYSIS RECORD   84/07/30   PAGE   1

UNIDENTIFIED TRANSACTIONS

TRANSACTION IMAGE

1.........10.........20.........30.........40.........50.........60.........70.........80

ACTION TAKEN

X004AA	FF AD	TM2		...REJ...
X004BA				...REJ...

Fig. A-62. LSA-109—Unidentified Transactions.

LSA-150 RCC A CYCLE 0003

DATE 84/02/29   PAGE 1

LOGISTIC SUPPORT ANALYSIS RECORD

PROVISIONING ERROR LIST

ERROR CODE	NARRATIVE	ERROR CODE	NARRATIVE
A01	PCCN MISSING--RECORD NOT PROCESSED	B22	SMR MISSING
A02	PLISN MISSING--RECORD NOT PROCESSED	C29	NHA PLISN MISSING
A04	INDENTURE CODE MISSING	C34	MRRI MISSING
A05	FSCM MISSING--RECORD NOT PROCESSED		
A12	ITEM NAME MISSING	E58	MTD MISSING
B16	UM MISSING	E59	RCT MISSING
B17	UM PRICE MISSING	E60	RTD MISSING

```
          1         2         3         4         5         6         7         8
1234567890123456789012345678901234567890123456789012345678901234567890123456789012345678901234567890

E84B8B1AA    449401120003                                               A  A04
E84B8B92E    D449401120040                                              A  A12
E84B8BDAA0   96906MS90278-60          RING,RETAINING                    A  A04
E84B8BDAA0                            SCREW,CAP HEX HEAD                 B  B17
E84B8BDAA0   EA                       PAFZZ                              C  C29
                00001140   11111
```

Fig. A-63. LSA-150—Provisioning Error List.

349

Appendix A LSA Summary Reports

LSA-151 RCC A   CYCLE 0031

LOGISTIC SUPPORT ANALYSIS RECORD
PROVISIONING PARTS LIST INDEX

PCCN AAAC02

SEQ OPT   PTD SEL OPT

REFERENCE NUMBER	C	FSCM	PCCN	PLISNC	LCN	A LI CC	ITEM NAME	QTY ASSY	QTY EI	UM	SMR	UOC	UOC	MRRI	EL CT
AA06BR200		25567		AAA4	00513	B	SCREW, CAP HEX HEAD	0005		EA	PAFZZ		DCY	0001.6656	1 06
AA06BR200	A	10855		AAA7	00517	B	SCREW, CAP, HEX HD	0001		EA	PAFZZ		DCY	0001.6656	3 06
A4544		41947		AAAX	00507	B	CAP, TUBE	0001		EA	PAFZZ		DCY	0001.6656	7 07
A4622		41947		AAAQ	00501BA	C	COUPLING, FEMALE	0002		EA	PAFZZ		DCY	0001.6656	7 06
A50407-481		41625		AABA	00520	B	SCREW, CAP, HEX HD	0002		EA	PAFZZ		DCY	0001.6656	7 06
A5051		41947		AAAV	00505	B	NUT, TUBE, COUPLING	0004		EA	PAFZZ		DCY	0001.6656	7 06
END7AA271		06534		AAA6	00515	B	VALVE	0001		EA	PAFZZ		DCY	0001.6756	7 12
END7AA348		10855		AAAW	00506	B	VALVE, SERVICE	0001		EA	PAFZZ		DCY	0001.6756	7 06
MS20066-229		96906		AAAO	00509	B	KEY, SQUARE	0001		EA	PBFZZ		DCY	0001.6767	1 06
MS27183-13		96906		AAA9	00519	B	WASHER, FLAT	0004		EA	PAFZZ		DCY	0001.6767	3 06
MS90728-60	A	96906		AAAL	00501AS	C	SCREW,CAP	0004		EA	XDFZZ		DCY	0001.0767	3 06
TH-WW3510		04643		AAAP	00501AZ	C	WASHER, LOCK	0001		EA	PAFZZ		DCY	0001.2230	3 06
05DA500143		66935		AAAN	00501AZ	C	GASKET, CYL HEAD	0002		EA	PAFZZ		DCY	0001.2230	7 06
05DA500153		10855		AAAK	00501AE	C	GASKET, VALVE PLATE	0002		EA	PAFZZ		DCY	0001.2323	7 09
142-0033		44940		AACA	00540	C	GASKET KIT	0001		EA	PAFZZ		DCY	0001.4434	3 06
3302		59730		AAAR	00501BB	C	BOX CONNECTOR	0001		EA	XBFZZ		DCY	0001.4545	3 06
442827		24617		AAAY	00508	B	NUT, SELF-LOCK HEX	0004		EA	PAFZZ		DCY	0001.4545	3 06
5D40-1182		66935		AAAS	00502	*	GASKET SCTN MANI	0001		EA	PAFZZ		DCY	0001.4545	7 06
5D43-139-A		10855		AAAA	005	A	COMPRESSOR, ASSY	0001		EA	PAFFF		DCY	0001.4545	7 18
5F20-1631		10855		AAA1	00510	B	WASHER, FLAT	0002		EA	PAFZZ		DCY	0001.4545	7 06
5F20-781		10855		AAA2	00511	B	INDICATOR.SIGHT	0001		EA	PAFZZ		DCY	0001.4545	3 06
6D23-1421		10855		AAA8	00518	*	GASKET	0001		EA	PAFZZ		DCY	0001.5545	7 06
6D23-522		10855		AAAJ	00501	B	VALVE PLATE ASSY	0002		EA	PAFZZ		DCY	0001.5545	1 07
6D40-112		10855		AAA3	00512	B	STRAINER, SUCTION	0001		EA	PAFZZ		DCY	0001.5545	7 06

Fig. A-64. LSA-151—Provisioning Parts List Index.

LSA-152   RCC D   CYCLE 0007

LOGISTIC SUPPORT ANALYSIS RECORD

87/01/07   PAGE   1

PART II PLISN ASSIGNMENT/REASSIGNMENT

START LCN 0   STOP LCN   PCCN AUTOPL   LCN STRUCTURE 122221   PTD SELECT

NEW RECORD DATA ON PARTS MASTER FILE

OLD RECORD DATA ON PARTS MASTER FILE

REFERENCE NUMBER	SCC	LCN	ALC	PLISN	IND CD	NHA PLISN	PRIOR ITEM PLISN	STAT CODE	SEQ METH	NHA PLISN IND CODE	PCCN	PLISN	IND CD	START PLISN	NHA PLISN	SAME AS PLISN	PRIOR ITEM PLISN	LCN IC
								P	A	X			A	0000	X		AAAE	
F10000RG-2		0		AAAE	A	AAAE	AAAA				AAAA01	AAAA	A					
F10000R-6		0	A	AAAF	A	AAAK	AAAB				AAAA01	AAAB	A					
8742SPTEQGRP		00S		AAAJ	B	AAAE						AAAJ	B					
74639		001		AAAK	B	AAAE	AAAJ				AAAA01	AAAK	C					
74817		00101		AAAL	C	AAAK	AAAK				AAAA01	AAAL	C					
74643		00101	A	AAAM	C	AAAK	AACZ				AAAA01	AACZ	C					
74639-1		00102		AAAN	C	AAAK	AAAL				AAAA01	AAAL	C					
74640-2		00102AA		AAAP	D	AAAN	AAAM				AAAA01	AAAM	D					
AD44BS		00104		AAAQ	C	AAAK	AAAP				AAAA01	AAAP	C					
MS51861-45		00105		AAAR	C	AAAK	AAAQ				AAAA01	AAAQ	C					
MS35489-123		00106	A	AAAS	C	AAAK	AAC0				AAAA01	AAC0	C					
53580-10-12		00108		AAAT	C	AAAK	AAAS				AAAA01	AAAS	C					
72992-1		00109		AAAU	C	AAAK	AAAT				AAAA01	AAAT	C					
72993-3		00110		AAAV	C	AAAK	AAAU				AAAA01	AAAU	C					
72993-1		00110	A	AAAW	C	AAAK	AAC1				AAAA01	AAC1	C					
74639-2		00111		AAAX	C	AAAK	AAAV				AAAA01	AAAV	C					
72943-1		00112		AAAY	C	AAAK	AAAW				AAAA01	AAAW	C					
72944		00113		AAAZ	C	AAAK	AAAX				AAAA01	AAAX	C					
53557-3		00114		AABA	C	AAAK	AAAY				AAAA01	AAAY	C					
74640-1		00115		AABB	C	AAAK	AAAZ				AAAA01	AAAZ	C					
72995-3		00117		AABC	C	AAAK	AAA1				AAAA01	AAA1	C					
74669-1		00118		AABD	C	AAAK	AAA2				AAAA01	AAA2	C					
74821-1		00119		AABE	C	AAAK	AAA3				AAAA01	AAA3	C					

Column headers (right section): PLISN TYPE, START PLISN GAP, MODEL PLISN RESV, SAME AS PLISN, MODEL PLISN AAAE, PRIOR ITEM PLISN, ASSIGN CONVERT INDENT, LCN IC, SIC

Fig. A-65. LSA-152—PLISN Assignment/Reassignment.

351

LSA-154   RCC A   CYCLE 0019

LOGISTIC SUPPORT ANALYSIS RECORD
PROVISIONING PARTS BREAKOUT SUMMARY   89/03/22   PAGE   1

EIAC	ITEM NAME	START LCN	ALC	STOP LCN	UDC	CTIC1	CTIC2	SRC CD	REFERENCE NUMBER	SCC
END	ENGINE	006		006						

REFERENCE NUMBER   SCC   FSCM   RNCC   RNVC   DAC   ITEM NAME
CCKA-MS/3834J   44940   3   2   1   ENGINE

TOT QTY
RECOMMENDED
005000

NSN
2B05-01-10B-9240

CTIC   FSCMS
CG   9694487350413709328O

UM PRICE   LOT QUANTITY
00001015.64   FROM   TO
                             000001   005000

CPC TUC PUC UM AMC AMSC
N   EA   2

LCN	ALC	UDC(S)	IND CD	PCCN	PLISN	SMR	QTY ASSY	QTY EI	NHA PLISN	NHA REF NO	SCC
006		DCY,FF,	B	AAAAO1	AABW	PAFZZ		0001			
006		DCY,FF,	A	TESTPL	AAAA	PAFZZ					

Fig. A-66. LSA-154—Provisioning Parts Breakout Summary.

LSA-155   RCC A   CYCLE 0019

LOGISTIC SUPPORT ANALYSIS RECORD
RECOMMENDED SPARE PARTS LIST FOR SPARES ACQUISITION INTEGRATED WITH PRODUCTION (SAIP)   89/03/22   PAGE   1

EIAC	ITEM NAME	START LCN	ALC	STOP LCN	UDC
END	REFRIGERATION UNIT	0			

REFERENCE NUMBER	SCC	ITEM NAME				TOTAL QUANTITY RECOMMENDED	PLT FSCM
A4622		COUPLING, FEMALE					06 41947

NO.	LCN	ALC	UM	UM PRICE	LOT QUANTITY FROM	TO	CPC	TUC
001	00501BA		EA	00000000.30	000001	001200	Y	C

REFERENCE NUMBER APPLICATIONS

MAINTENANCE TASK DISTRIBUTION
MRRI   ORR   NRTS   CAD   CBD
0001.6656 0.05

REFERENCE NUMBER	SCC	ITEM NAME				TOTAL QUANTITY RECOMMENDED	PLT FSCM
142-0035		SPRING					09 44940

NO.	LCN	ALC	UM	UM PRICE	LOT QUANTITY FROM	TO	CPC	TUC
001	00607AL		EA	00000001.54	000001	001500	Y	A

REFERENCE NUMBER APPLICATIONS

MAINTENANCE TASK DISTRIBUTION
MRRI   ORR   NRTS   CAD   CBD
0001.2323 0.02

REFERENCE NUMBER	SCC	ITEM NAME				TOTAL QUANTITY RECOMMENDED	PLT FSCM
142-0039		SHAFT, FLOAT					09 44940

NO.	LCN	ALC	UM	UM PRICE	LOT QUANTITY FROM	TO	CPC	TUC
001	00607AE		EA	00000002.10	000001	001500	Y	C

REFERENCE NUMBER APPLICATIONS

MAINTENANCE TASK DISTRIBUTION
MRRI   ORR   NRTS   CAD   CBD
0001.2323 0.05

REFERENCE NUMBER	SCC	ITEM NAME				TOTAL QUANTITY RECOMMENDED	PLT FSCM
142-0431		CARBURETOR ASSY				000007	18 44940
							18
							18

NO.	LCN	ALC	UM	UM PRICE	LOT QUANTITY FROM	TO	CPC	TUC
001	00607		EA	00000049.56	000001	000500	N	A
				00000046.00	000501	001000	Y	B
				00000039.95	001001	010000	N	C

REFERENCE NUMBER APPLICATIONS

MAINTENANCE TASK DISTRIBUTION
MRRI   ORR   NRTS   CAD   CBD
0001.3323 0.01   05

Fig. A-67. LSA-155—Recommended Spare Parts List for Spares Acquisition Integrated with Production.

B

Abbreviations and Acronyms

AAL	additional authorized list		CBIL	common bulk items list
ACO	administrative contracting officer		CCB	configuration control board
ADM	advanced development model		CDR	critical design review
ADP	automated data processing		CDRL	contract data requirements list
AFLC	Air Force Logistics Command		CECOM	communications electronics command
AFSC	Air Force specialty code		CFE	contractor-furnished equipment
ALC	Air Logistics Center		CM	configuration management
AMC	Army Material Command		COEI	components of end item
APO	acquisition program office		CON	concept
ATE	automatic test equipment		CPFF	cost plus fixed fee
			CPIF	cost plus incentive fee
BAFO	best and final offer		CPM	critical path method
BCS	baseline comparison system		CPU	computer processor unit
BII	basic issue item		CRISD	computer resources integrated support document
BIT	built-in test			
BITE	built-in test equipment		CRT	cathode-ray tube
BOA	basic ordering agreement		CSC	computer software component
BOM	bill of material		CSCI	computer software configuration item
			CSD	computer software documentation
CA	criticality analysis		CSI	contractor source inspection
CAD	computer-aided design			
CAE	computer-aided engineering		D	depot
CAGE	commercial and government entity		D&V	demonstration and validation
CALS	computer-aided logistics support		DCAS	Defense Contract Administration Service
CAM	computer-aided manufacturing			
CBD	*Commerce Business Daily*		DCN	design change notice

Appendix B   Abbreviations and Acronyms

DEMVAL	demonstration validation	GPTE	general purpose test equipment
DID	data item description	GSA	General Services Administration
DLA	Defense Logistics Agency	GSI	government source inspection
DLSC	Defense Logistics Service Center		
DM	data management	HWCI	hardware configuration item
DMWR	depot maintenance work requirements		
DSARC	Defense Systems Acquisition Review Council	I	intermediate
		ICC	item category code
		ICD	installation control drawing
EAC	estimate at completion	ICS	interface control specification
ECP	engineering change proposal	ID	interface device
ECR	engineering change request	IDR	initial design review
EDM	engineering development model	ILS	integrated logistics support
EIAC	end item acronym code	ILSMRT	ILS management review team
EOQ	economic order quantity	ILSMT	integrated logistics support management team
ESML	expendable supplies and materials list		
ESS	environmental stress screening	ILSP	integrated logistics support plan
ETC	estimate to complete	IPB	illustrated parts breakdown
		ISIL	interim support items list
FAR	federal acquisition regulations	ISP	integrated support plan
FCA	functional configuration audit	ISSPP	integrated system safety program plan
FFIP	firm fixed incentive price		
FFP	firm fixed price		
FMEA	failure modes and effects analysis	JTWG	joint technical working group
FMECA	failure modes, effects, and criticality analysis	LCC	life-cycle cost
FMS	foreign military sales	LLCSC	lower-level computer software component
FQR	formal qualification review		
FRACAS	failure reporting, analysis, and corrective action system	LLTIL	long lead-time items list
		LO	lubrication order
FRB	failure review board	LORA	level-of-repair-analysis
FSC	federal stock classification	LSA	logistics support analysis
FSCM	federal supply code for manufacturers	LSACN	logistics support analysis control number
FSD	full-scale development		
FSED	full-scale engineering development	LSAP	logistics support analysis plan
FTE	factory test equipment	LSAR	logistics support analysis record
G&A	general and administrative expenses	MAC	maintenance allocation chart
GFE	government-furnished equipment	MCRL	master cross reference list
GFP	government-furnished property	MHE	material handling equipment
GIDEP	government/industry data exchange program	MICOM	Missile Command
		MIL-HDBK	military handbook
GPETE	general purpose electronic test equipment	MIL-SPEC	military specification
		MIL-STD	military standard

MILSTAMP	military standard transportation and movement procedure
MILSTRIP	military standard requisition and issue procedure
MMH/MA	mean manhours per maintenance action
MMH/OH	mean manhours per operating hour
MOS	military occupational specialty
MPTA	manpower, personnel, and training analysis
MRSA	Material Readiness Support Activity
MTBF	mean time between failures
MTBM	mean time between maintenance
MTTR	mean time to repair
NATO	North Atlantic Treaty Organization
NAVAIR	Naval Air Systems Command
NAVSEA	Naval Sea Systems Command
NETT	new equipment training team
NHA	next higher assembly
NICP	national inventory control point
NIIN	national item inventory number
NRLA	network repair-level analysis
NSN	national stock number
NTE	not to exceed
O	organization
O&S	operation and support
ODC	other direct costs
OJT	on-the-job training
OMB	office of management and budget
OPER	operation
ORLA	optimum repair-level analysis
OST	order ship time
PCA	physical configuration audit
PCO	procurement contracting officer
PDM	preliminary development model
PDR	preliminary design review
PERT	program evaluation and review technique
PHS&T	packaging, handling, storage, and transportability

PLISN	provisioning list item sequence number
PLT	production lead time
PM	program manager
PMCS	preventive maintenance checks and services
PMO	program management office
PPDS	preservation and packaging data sheet
PPL	provisioning parts list
PPP	personnel performance profile
PPR	production readiness review
PPS	provisioning performance schedule
PPSL	program parts selection list
PRAT	production reliability acceptance test
PROD	production
PRS	provisioning requirements statement
PTD	provisioning technical documentation
QA	quality assurance
QC	quality control
QPEI	quantity per end item
QQPRI	qualitative and quantitative personnel requirements information
QVL	qualified vendor list
R&D	research and development
R&M	reliability and maintainability
RAM	reliability, availability, and maintainability
RCM	reliability-centered maintenance
RD/GT	reliability development/growth testing
RFI	request for information
RFP	request for proposal
RFQ	request for quotation
RIL	repairable items list
RLA	repair-level analysis
ROP	reorder point
RPSTL	repair parts and special tools list
RQT	reliability qualification test
SCD	source control drawing
SCD	specification control drawing
SDL	software development library
SDR	system design review

Appendix B Abbreviations and Acronyms

SDRL	subcontract data requirements list
SE	support equipment
SERD	support equipment recommendations data
SMR	source, maintenance, and recoverability
SOW	statement of work
SPETE	special-purpose electronic test equipment
SPS	software procurement specification
SPTD	supplementary provisioning technical documentation
SPTE	special-purpose test equipment
SRR	system requirements review
SSC	skill specialty code
SSP	system safety program
SSPP	system safety program plan
SSR	software specification review
SSWG	system safety working group
STE	special test equipment

T&M	time and material
TACOM	Tank Automotive Command
TDA	table of distribution and allowances
TDP	technical data package
TLCSC	top-level computer software component
TM	technical manual
TMDE	test, measurement, and diagnostic equipment
TO	technical order
TOE	table of organization and equipment
TP	test program
TPI	test program instruction
TPS	test program set
TRD	test requirements document
TRR	test readiness review
TTEL	tools and test equipment test
UUT	unit under test
WBS	work breakdown structure

C

References

The following are military and DoD publications.

MILITARY STANDARDS

MIL-STD 12	Abbreviations for Use on Drawings, Specifications, Standards, and in Technical Documents
MIL-STD 129	Marking for Shipment and Storage
MIL-STD 137	Material Handling Equipment
MIL-STD 280	Definitions of Item Levels, Item Exchangeability, Models, and Related Terms
MIL-STD 335	Technical Manuals: Repair Parts and Special Tools List
MIL-STD 470	Maintainability Program for Systems and Equipment
MIL-STD 471	Maintainability Verification/Demonstration/Evaluation
MIL-STD 482A	Configuration Status Accounting Data Elements and Related Features
MIL-STD 680A	Contractor Standardization Program Requirements
MIL-STD 756B	Reliability Modeling and Prediction
MIL-STD 781	Reliability Design Qualification and Production Acceptance Tests: Exponential Distribution
MIL-STD 785B	Reliability Program for Systems and Equipment Development and Production
MIL-STD 794	Procedures for Packaging of Parts and Equipment
MIL-STD 810D	Environmental Test Methods and Engineering Guidelines
MIL-STD 839	Selection and Use of Parts with Established Reliability Levels
MIL-STD 881A	Work Breakdown Structures for Defense Material Items
MIL-STD 882B	System Safety Program Requirements
MIL-STD 965A	Parts Control Program
MIL-STD 1309C	Definition of Terms for Test, Measurement, and Diagnostic Equipment
MIL-STD 1319A	Item Characteristics Affecting Transportability and Packaging and Handling Equipment Design
MIL-STD 1345B	Preparation of Test Requirements Document
MIL-STD 1364	Standard General Purpose Electronic Test Equipment
MIL-STD 1365	General Design Criteria for Handling Equipment Associated with Weapons and Weapons Systems
MIL-STD 1366	Definition of Transportation and Delivery Mode Dimensional Constraints

MIL-STD 1367	Packaging, Handling, Storage, and Transportability Program Requirements for Systems and Equipment
MIL-STD 1379C	Military Training Programs
MIL-STD 1387	Preparation and Submission of Data for Approval of Nonstandard General Purpose Electronic Test Equipment
MIL-STD 1388-1A	Logistics Support Analysis
MIL-STD 1388-2A	DoD Requirements for a Logistics Support Analysis Record
MIL-STD 1390	Level of Repair
MIL-STD 1472	Human Engineering Design Criteria for Military Systems, Equipment, and Facilities
MIL-STD 1510	Procedures for Use of Container Design Retrieval System
MIL-STD 1519	Preparation of Test Requirements Document
MIL-STD 1521B	Technical Reviews and Audits for Systems, Equipment, and Computer Software
MIL-STD 1552	Uniform Department of Defense Requirements for Provisioning Technical Documentation (superceded by MIL-STD 1388-2A)
MIL-STD 1556A	Government/Industry Data Exchange Program
MIL-STD 1561	Uniform Department of Defense Provisioning Procedures
MIL-STD 1567A	Work Measurement
MIL-STD 1629	Failure Modes, Effects, and Criticality Analysis
MIL-STD 1635	Reliability Growth Testing
MIL-STD 2068	Reliability Development Tests
MIL-STD 2073-1A	Procedures for Development and Application of Packaging Requirements
MIL-STD 2073-2	Packaging Requirement Codes
MIL-STD 2076	General Requirements for Unit Under Test Compatibility with Automatic Test Equipment
MIL-STD 2077	General Requirements for Test Program Sets
MIL-STD 2173	Reliability-Centered Maintenance Requirements for Naval Aircraft, Weapon Systems and Support Equipment

MILITARY HANDBOOKS

MIL-HDBK 217	Reliability Prediction of Electronic Equipment
MIL-HDBK 220B	Glossary of Training Device Terms
MIL-HDBK 259	Life-Cycle Cost in Navy Acquisitions
MIL-HDBK 338	Electronic Reliability Design Handbook
MIL-HDBK 472	Maintainability Prediction
MIL-HDBK 759A	Human Factors Engineering Design for Army Material

MIL-HDBK 63038-1   Technical Manual Writing Handbook
MIL-HDBK 63038-2   Technical Writing Style Guide

MILITARY SPECIFICATIONS

MIL-A-8421	General Specification for Air Transportability
MIL-D-26239A	Qualitative and Quantitative Personnel Requirements Information (QQPRI) Data
MIL-G-29011	Preparation of Guides for Operation and Maintenance of Training Aids
MIL-H-46855B	Human Engineering Requirements for Military Systems, Equipment and Facilities
MIL-M-38784B	Technical Manuals: General Style and Format Requirements
MIL-M-38807A	Technical Manuals: Preparation of Illustrated Parts Breakdown
MIL-M-63036A	Preparation of Operator's Technical Manual
MIL-M-63038B	Technical Manual: Organizational or Aviation Unit, Direct Support or Aviation Intermediate, and General Support Maintenance
MIL-M-63041C	Technical Manuals: Preparation of Depot Maintenance Work Requirements
MIL-M-81919A	Preparation of Support Equipment Technical Manuals
MIL-P-116	Methods of Preservation
MIL-P-9024G	Packaging, Handling, and Transportability in System/ Equipment Acquisition
MIL-T-23991E	General Specification for Military Training Devices
MIL-I-29053A	Training Requirements for Aviation Weapon Systems

DoD STANDARDS

DoD-STD 100C	Engineering Drawing Practices
DoD-STD 480A	Configuration Control - Engineering Changes, Deviations and Waivers
DoD-STD 1685	Comprehensibility Standards for Technical Manuals
DoD-STD 2167	Defense System Software Development

DoD HANDBOOKS

DoD HDBK 743	Anthropometry of U.S. Military Personnel

DoD DIRECTIVES

DoD-D-1000B	Drawings, Engineering and Associated Lists

D

MIL-STD 1388-2B

Author's Note—As the manuscript for this text nears publication, a revision to MIL-STD 1388-2 is in process that makes significant changes to the Logistic Support Analysis Record and the attendant data processing and reporting systems. This appendix uses the most current draft version of the impending revised standard as reference. Prior to implementing an LSAR per MIL-STD 1388-2B, you are advised to refer to the final released version of the standard.

The updating of MIL-STD 1388-2 from revision A to revision B makes two significant changes to the Logistics Support Analysis Record. The single most important change in converting the LSAR database system from fixed record-length batch processing to relational data processing. The other notable change is a reduction in the number of standard LSA summary reports. However, there is no change to the Logistics Support Analysis program tasks of MIL-STD 1388-1A. The changes are only in the recording and reporting of the results of the analysis tasks.

RELATIONAL DATA PROCESSING SYSTEM

Changing to a relational database system represents a very significant change to the entire process for generating and recording information in the LSAR database. First, and foremost, is the cultural change of elimination of the hardcopy forms for LSA data records. The data records of MIL-STD 1388-2A have been replaced with relational data tables. There will no longer be any data sheets for manual entry or printouts of this data for sheet-by-sheet review. Additionally, redundant data entry of like data elements will be eliminated. Because of this change to a relational data processing system, the contents of MIL-STD 1388-2B that address the data system have been changed drastically.

Relational Data Tables

The 15 LSA data records of MIL-STD 1388-2A are replaced by 119 LSA relational data tables in MIL-STD 1388-2B. This sounds like a major increase in the amount of data that is required for the LSA database. When you consider, however, that each data table addresses a specific portion of data, rather than a broad topic, the change is not as drastic as it would appear on the surface.

Figure D-1 lists the new LSA relational data tables. As shown, each data table has been assigned a two-character alphabetic identifier. To aid in cross-referencing the new data table to the previous LSA Data Records, the first character of the identifier is the same as the data record in which the data was previously found. For example, the first item shown on the list, data table EA, is data that was previously recorded on the LSA Data Record E. The only seemingly new items are the data tables that make the relational data processing system work. These tables are identified by an "X" in the first position and provide the link for relationships between data elements and the appropriate hardware configuration.

Figure D-2 illustrates LSAR Relational Data Table EA, Adapter Interconnection Device. Note that this data table addresses only the information necessary to describe the interconnection devise necessary to connect a UUT to an item of support equipment. There are five types of information contained in the data table explanation:

1. a data element dictionary number
2. a data element title
3. a six-character data element name acronym
4. formatting field information
5. identification of data elements that are mandatory for a valid data table.

A complete data element dictionary is provided in appendix E of MIL-STD 1388-2B.

Note that each data field of each data table has been assigned its own six-character acronym. The acronym is in two parts: the first four characters are an abbreviation of the data element name, and the last two characters identify the data table where the information is recorded. For example, the first data element on data table EA has the acronym AIDREFEA, which signifies *AID* (adapter interconnection device) *REF*erence (manufacturer's part number) recorded on data table EA. Also noteworthy is that DED 302 shown as the first data element line on data table EA refers to the description of a reference number generically, rather than the specific use of the term. Many of the elements on the data table have the same DED reference, which enables better understanding of the exact data requirement for the field.

MIL-STD-1388-2B
Appendix A
Appendix A - Section 1
Listing of LSAR Relational Tables

Table Code	Table Title
EA	Adaptor Interconnector Device
HA	Additional Item
JA	Air
JB	Aircraft
EB	Allocation Allowance Range
EC	Allocation Data
XA	Alternate Part Application Usage
HB	Application Reference Designator
JC	Contained
HC	Contractor Technical Information Code Commercial and Government Entity
HD	Design Change
EJ	Design Data
HE	End Item Ratio Basis of Issue
FA	Facility
FB	Facility Baseline
FC	Facility Usage
BA	Failure Mode
BB	Failure Mode Task
XB	Functional Physical Structure Mapping
JD	Helicopter
XC	Higher Assembly
JE	Highway
EK	Input Power Source
AA	Inter Operability Requirement
HF	Item
XD	Item Breakdown Structure
XE	Item to Item Structure Mapping
HG	Item Packaging Requirement
HH	Item Quantity Basis of Issue
HI	Item Serial Effectivity
HJ	Item Unit of Issue Price
HK	Item Unit of Measure Price
BC	Item Failure Mode Mission Phase
HL	Kit Repair Next Assembly
XF	Measurement Base
BD	Mission Phase Operational Mode
AB	Maintenance Level Requirement
HZ	Model Configuration Option One
FD	New or Modified Facility
GA	New or Modified Skill
XG	Next Assembly
JF	Non Self Propelled
AI	Operation/Maintenance Level Modeling Data
AC	Operations/Maintenance Level Requirements
FE	Operations/Maintenance Level Subtask Personnel Facility Requirement
AJ	Operations/Maintenance Level Shipping Requirement

Fig. D-1. LSAR relational data tables. (Continued to page 364).

Table Code	Table Title
FF	Operations/Maintenance Level Task Facility Requirement
EL	Operational Test Program
AD	Organizational Level Operations/Maintenance Requirement
XH	Part Application Usage
HM	Part Application Provisioned Item
JG	Rail
BE	Reliability, Availability and Maintainability Characteristic
BF	Reliability, Availability and Maintainability Criticality
BG	Reliability, Availability and Maintainability Indicator
BH	Reliability, Availability and Maintainability Indicator Characteristic
BI	Reliability, Availability and Maintainability Logistic Consideration
AF	Reliability, Availability and Maintainability Requirement
HN	Repair Part Tool Description
JH	Sea
JI	Sectionalized Item
JJ	Self Propelled
HO	Serial Number Effectivity Range
XI	Service
AG	Skill Operations/Maintenance Requirement
GB	Skill Specialty
HP	Support End Item Model Effectivity
EP	Support Equipment Authorization
ER	Support Equipment Integrated Logistic Support Requirement
ES	Support Equipment Integrated Logistic Support Equipment Category Code
EV	Support Equipment Using Service
HR	Support End Item Design Change Model Effectivity
XO	Support End Item Structure Model Effectivity
CA	Subtask
CB	Subtask Reference
CC	Subtask Requirement
EM	Supercedure Data
EN	Support Activity
XH	Support End Item
XK	Support End Item Model
EO	Support Equipment
EQ	Support Equipment Design Data
ET	Support Equipment Parameters
EU	Support Equipment Recommendation Data
EZ	Support Equipment Item Unit Under Test
EO	Support Equipment Item Unit Under Test Fault Isolated Replaceable Unit
E1	Support Equipment Item Unit Under Test Support Equipment
E2	Support Equipment Item Unit Under Test Support Equipment Adaptor Interconnection Device
E3	Support Equipment Item Unit Under Test Support Equipment Operational Test Program
EW	System Equipment
CH	Task Manual
CD	Task Remark
CE	Task Remark Reference
CF	Task Requirement
CG	Task Support Item
XL	Technical Manual
EX	Test Program Instruction
XQ	Text

Appendix D   MIL-STD 1388-2B

Table Code	Table Title
JK	Tracked
JL	Tracked Wheeled
DA	Training
EY	Training Equipment
JM	Transport by Fiscal Year
JN	Transport From
JO	Transportation Requirement
HQ	Unit of Issue
HY	Unit of Measure
ED	Unit Under Test
BJ	Usage Based Preventive Maintenance Task
EF	Unit Under Test Fault Isolated Replaceable Unit
EG	Unit Under Test Support Equipment
EH	Unit Under Test Support Equipment Adaptor Interconnection Device
EI	Unit Under Test Support Equipment Operational Test Program
AH	War/Peace Operations/Maintenance Requirement
XM	Weapon System End Item
XN	Weapon System End Item Model
JP	Wheeled
XP	Weapon System Support End Item Model Effectivity
BK	War/Peace Reliability Maintainability Indicator Characteristic

Data Selection

The change to relational data tables necessitates a revision of the DD Form 1949-1, LSAR Data Selection Sheet. The multipage form—the first three pages are shown in FIG. D-3,—now consists of two parts: delivery requirements, and data element selection.

Delivery requirements are segregated into requirements for delivery of the LSA database, provisioning data delivery in the form of LSA-036 reports, and packaging data delivery in the form of LSA-025 reports. This part of the form, with the exception of highlighting the LSA-025 report is basically the same as the previous version.

The data selection portion of the form correlates to the new relational data tables. As shown on the third page of FIG. D-3, the form consists of three not very distinctly segregated portions. First, the data table and data elements are listed on the lefthand side of the form. The second portion, the REQ (required) column is in the middle of the form and is used to identify data elements required for a specific LSA database. The third portion addresses provisioning and packaging data reporting requirements. Note that the column heading "036 CARD/BLOCK" cross-references data elements to the obsolete but still standard MIL-STD 1552 format for provisioning data. Only those data elements with annotations in this column are used to product provisioning data in the form of an LSA-036 summary report. Each column under the section entitled "PTD LISTS" refers to a specific provisioning list, i.e., long lead time items list (LL) or provisioning parts list (PP), that can be generated using the LSA-036 summary report.

MIL-STD-1388-2B
Appendix A

Appendix A - Section 2

LSAR Relational Tables

EA   *Adapter Interconnection Device*

This table contains pricing and item name information for items needed to allow interfacing of support equipment and the units under test.

302	AID_REFERENCE	AIDREFEA 32 X L	M
47	AID_CAGE	AIDCAGEA 5 X F	M
25	ADPTR_INTRCNCTR_DVC_AC_NNRC	AIDUCNEA 8 N R	
25	ADPTR_INTRCNCTR_DVC_AC_RC	AIDUCREA 8 N R	
164	ADPTR_INTRCNCTR_DVC_ITM_NM	AIDITNEA 19 X L	

HA   *Additional Item*

This table contains additional Reference Numbers and CAGEs and associated RNCC and RNVCs to a primary or ITEM Reference Number and CAGE.

304	ADTNL_ITM_RFRNC_NMBR_VRTN_CD	ADRNVCHA 1 N F -	
6	ADDITIONAL_REFERENCE	ADDREFHA 32 X L -	M
47	ADDITIONAL_CAGE	ADCAGEHA 5 X F -	M
303	ADTNL_ITM_RFRNC_NUMBR_CTGRY_CD	ADRNCCHA 1 X F -	
47	PRIMARY_CAGE	CAGECDHA 5 X F -	M
302	PRIMARY_REFERENCE	REFNUMHA 32 X L -	M

JA   *Air*

This table will identify the type of air (Aircraft, Helicopter) transportation that can be used to transport the system/ equipment under analysis.

409	TRANSPORTATION_REQUIREMENT_KEY	TRANMRJA 1 A F -	M
141	AIR_TYPE	HOATINJA 1 A F -	M
178	LSA_CONTROL_NUMBER	LCNCODJA 18 X L -	M
181	LSA_CONTROL_NUMBER_TYPE	LCNTYPJA 1 A F -	M
88	END_ITEM_ACRONYM	EIACODJA 10 X L -	M
97	EXT_OR_INT_LOAD_INDICATOR	EOILINJA 1 A F -	M
19	ALT_LSA_CONTROL_NUMBER_CODE	ALTLCNJA 1 X F -	M

Fig. D-2. Example of an LSAR relational data table.

Data Processing Systems

The change from a fixed record to a relational database means that the software used to process the LSAR data also must change. This change creates several concerns to potential users. First will be the expense of acquiring updates or total new data processing capabilities in order to meet the relational data processing standard.

LSAR DATA SELECTION SHEET

LSAR DATA DELIVERY:

    7-TRACK   ___   EVEN PARITY   ___

    9-TRACK   ___   ODD PARITY   ___

    BPI   _____   BLOCKING FACTOR   _____

ASTERISKS (*) UNDER REQUIRED (REQ) COLUMN ARE MANDATORY DATA IF ANY DATA ELEMENT WITHIN THE DATA TABLE IS ALSO SELECTED.

LSA-036 REPORT DELIVERY:

    7-TRACK   ___   EVEN PARITY   ___   BCD   ___

    9-TRACK   ___   ODD PARITY   ___   EBCDIC   ___

    800 BPI   ___   1600 BPI   ___   6250 BPI   ___

    NUMBER OF RECORDS PER BLOCK IS: _____

SEQUENCE: LCN <u>(L)</u>   REFERENCE NUMBER <u>(R)</u>

TYPE PROVISIONING LISTS (PTD LISTS):   REQUIRED
                                                    (L OR R)

    1.   LL (LONG LEAD TIME ITEMS LIST) IAW DI-V-7004A OR DI-ILSS-8GGGG, PARAGRAPH 10.2C.   ___

    2.   PP (PROVISIONING PARTS LIST) IAW DI-V-7002A OR DI-ILSS-8GGGG, PARAGRAPH 10.2A.   ___

    3.   SF (SHORT FORM PROVISIOINING PARTS LIST) IAW DI-V-7003A OR DI-ILSS-8GGGG, PARAGRAPH 10.2B.   ___

    4.   CB (COMMON AND BULK ITEM LIST) IAW DI-V-7008A OR DI-ILSS-8GGGG, PARAGRAPH 10.2G.   ___

    5.   RI (REPAIRABLE ITEMS LIST) IAW DI-V-7005A OR DI-ILSS-8GGGG, PARAGRAPH 10.2D.   ___

    6.   IS (INTERIM SUPPORT ITEMS LIST) IAW DI-V-7006A OR DI-ILSS-8GGGG, PARAGRAPH 10.2E.   ___

    7.   PC (POST CONFERENCE LIST) IAW DI-V-7011A OR DI-ILSS-8GGGG, PARAGRAPH 10.2H   ___

DD FORM 1949-1

Fig. D-3. Revised DD Form 1949-1.

LSAR DATA SELECTION SHEET

8. **TT** (TOOL AND TEST EQUIPMENT LIST) IAW DI-V-7007A OR   ___
DI-ILSS-8GGGG, PARAGRAPH 10.2F.

9. **SC** (SYSTEM CONFIGURATION PROVISIONING LIST IAW DI-V-7192   ___
OR DI-ILSS-8GGGG, PARAGRAPH 10.2I.

10. **AR** (AS REQUIRED BY THE REQUIRING AUTHORITY) AND SPECIFIED   ___
IN THE CONTRACT STATEMENT OF WORK.

DATA ELEMENTS WITH AN 036 CARD/BLOCK ANNOTATED MUST HAVE THE APPLICABLE
PTD LIST(S) SELECTED.

LSA-025 PACKING CATEGORIZATION:

1. **CO** (COMMON) IAW MIL-STD-2073-1B, PARAGRAPH 3.3.1.

2. **SE** (SELECTIVE) IAW MIL-STD-2073-1B, PARAGRAPH 3.3.2.

3. **SP** (SPECIAL) IAW MIL-STD-2073-1B, PARAGRAPH 3.3.3.

OTHER INSTRUCTIONS:

DD FORM 1949-1

Fig. D-3. (Continued).

LSAR DATA SELECTION SHEET

TABLE NAME (TABLE CODE)	R	036	----- PTD LISTS -----| PACK
	E	CARD/	L|P|S|C|R|I|P|T|S|A|A|C|S|S
DED NUMBER SHORT NAME	Q	BLOCK	L|P|F|B|I|S|C|T|C|R|R|O|E|P

ADAPTOR_INTERCONNECTOR_DEVICE (EA)			
25 ADPTR_INTRCNCTR_DVC_AC_NNRC			
25 ADPTR_INTRCNCTR_DVC_AC_RC			
164 ADPTR_INTRCNCTR_DVC_ITM_NM			
47 AID_CAGE			
302 AID_REFERENCE			
ADDITIONAL_ITEM (HA)			
47 ADDITIONAL_CAGE		A/05	
6 ADDITIONAL_REFERENCE		A/06	
303 ADTNL_ITM_RFRNC_NMBR_CTGRY_CD		A/07	
304 ADTNL_ITM_RFRNC_NMBR_VRTN_CD		A/08	
47 PRIMARY_CAGE			
302 PRIMARY_REFERENCE			
AIR (JA)			
141 AIR_TYPE			
19 ALT_LSA_CONTROL_NUMBER_CODE			
88 END_ITEM_ACRONYM			
97 EXT_OR_INT_LOAD_INDICATOR			
178 LSA_CONTROL_NUMBER			
181 LSA_CONTROL_NUMBER_TYPE			
409 TRANSPORTATION_REQUIREMENT_KEY			
AIRCRAFT (JB)			
413 AIRCRAFT_TYPE			
19 ALT_LSA_CONTROL_NUMBER			
88 END_ITEM_ACRONYM_CODE			
178 LSA_CONTROL_NUMBER			
181 LSA_CONTROL_NUMBER_TYPE			
409 TRANSPORTATION_REQUIREMENT_KEY			
ALLOCATION_ALLOWANCE_RANGE (EB)			
15 ALLOWABLE_RANGE			
16 ALLOWANCE_DOC_NUMBER			
47 SUPPORT_EQUIPMENT_CAGE			
302 SUPPORT_EQUIPMENT_REFERENCE			
ALLOCATION_DATA (EC)			
15 ALLOC_DESIGN_DESC			
15 ALLOC_EXT_RNG			
15 ALLOC_LAND_OR_VESSEL_CODE			
15 ALLOC_MAINT_LVL_FUNCT			
15 ALLOC_STATION_ID_CD			
15 ALLOWANCE_DOC_NUMBER			
47 SUPPORT_EQUIPMENT_CAGE			
302 SUPPORT_EQUIPMENT_REFERENCE			
ALTRNT_PRT_APLCTN_USG (XA)			
19 ALC			
47 ALTERNATE_COMPONENT_CAGE			

DD FORM 1949-1

Fig. D-3. (Continued).

MIL-STD 1388-2B promotes the use of commercially developed software packages for LSAR data processing. Although there are significant differences in fixed versus relational database systems, users should be aware that any change must be carefully appraised to ensure that the requirements of the new standard can be met, and that there is transportability of existing fixed record data to any new relational database system. The government will still make available generic software capable of building and manipulating an LSAR database, but there is much to be considered in looking for alternatives that provide more flexibility for specific applications or business situations.

LSA REPORTS

The number of standard LSA summary reports is reduced by MIL-STD 1388-2B to only twenty (see FIG. D-4). The reduction in the number of reports is designed to focus on information that is normally required by most developmental contracts, and to keep the number of possible reports to a manageable level.

To fill the void where unique program requirements can justify additional reports being prepared, the standard has allocated a block of report numbers to be used by each service in developing program-specific reports (FIG. D-5). This reinforces the need for government contractors to have a LSA data processing system that has the flexibility of producing ad hoc or tailored reports for specific applications.

Report Number	Report Title
LSA-004	Maintenance Allocation Chart
LSA-023	Maintenance Plan Summary
LSA-024	Maintenance Plan
LSA-025	Packing Requirements Data
LSA-030	Repair Parts and Special Tools List
LSA-032	Defense Logistics Services Center (DLSC) Submittals
LSA-034	Stockage List Type Four
LSA-036	Provisioning Requirements
LSA-040	Authorization List Items Summary
LSA-045	Stockage List Type Three
LSA-056	Failure Modes, Effects and Criticality Analysis (FMECA) Report
LSA-065	Manpower Requirements Criteria
LSA-070	Support Equipment Recommendation Data (SERD)
LSA-072	Test Measurement and Diagnostic Equipment (TMDE) Requirements Summary
LSA-074	Support Equipment Tool List
LSA-076	Calibration/Measurement Requirements Summary (CMRS)
LSA-077	Depot Maintenance Interservice Data Summary
LSA-085	Transportability Summary
LSA-151	Provisioning Parts List Index
LSA-155	Recommended Spare Parts List for Spares Acquisition Integrated with Production (SAIP)

Fig. D-4. MIL-STD 1388-2B LSA Summary Reports List.

Service/Organization	Assigned Report Numbers
U.S. Army	200 – 299
U.S. Air Force	300 – 399
U.S. Navy	400 – 499
U.S. Marine Corps	500 – 599
National Security Agency	600 – 699
Federal Aviation Administration	700 – 799

Fig. D-5. Project Unique LSAR Report Numbering System.

OTHER CONSIDERATIONS

Although the most apparent changes in the revision of MIL-STD 1388-2 are the change to relational data processing and the reduction in the number of summary reports, several other points must be given due consideration: tailoring of the LSAR under the new standard, manual preparation of the LSAR, management and review of the LSAR, and relationships to other databases.

LSAR Tailoring

Accurate tailoring of the LSAR becomes even more important with the new standard. In the past, users often tailored the LSAR database simply by selecting the LSA data records applicable to the program. This was a relatively easy task since there were only 15 from which to choose. Because this is no longer the case, the government agency that is tailoring the LSAR must be very selective and cognizant of the unique program requirements when the LSAR Data Selection Sheet is prepared. Additionally, the contractor must be very attuned to program requirements when recommending changes or modifications to the LSAR.

As a guide, tailoring should begin with identification of the minimum data needed to document analyses and make tradeoff decisions. Once this determination has been made, the appropriate data table should be selected that will record the information necessary to produce reports summarizing the results. There is really no other way to approach the tailoring process. Appendix D of MIL-STD 1388-2B provides guidance on how to approach the tailoring issue for LSAR.

Manual LSAR

The revised standard addresses manual preparation of the LSAR. In the past, many smaller programs used the manual LSAR as a way of reducing costs. Companies that did not have an automated capability used the manual process to fulfill LSAR requirements.

Although manual preparation is still possible with the new standard, it is not a very feasible or practical alternative. Since the fixed-length hardcopy LSAR forms have been made obsolete by the relational database system, trying to meet the LSAR requirements manually would be a monumental task even on a small piece of equipment. Any contractor considering such a course of action should be urged to look for assistance in automated preparation of the LSAR.

LSA Management and Reviews

One of the major cultural changes that must take place with the implementation of the relational data processing system is the change in mindset of being able to touch and count LSAR data records. The question that must be answered is how to manage and review LSAR data that resides inside a computer. In the past we simply printed out copies of all the data records and looked at them. Now that there are no more data records, how can we possibly manage or review the LSAR?

Managing the LSAR should not be, nor should it have ever been, the primary concern. We should be looking at managing the LSA process, not recording the data. Maybe we will now focus on what should have been our main concern all along, and that is doing the analysis correctly. Any attempt to manage an LSA program by focusing on the LSAR is a basic error in understanding the LSA process.

The review of LSAR data is a different kind of problem. In the past, again, to review the LSAR we looked at hardcopy data records. This activity all too often degenerated into a clerical or grammatical exercise in which specific entries on data records became the issue of reviews, rather than the process that produced the data. If hardcopy printouts of LSAR data are really needed, then the data processing system software being used should have an ad hoc report generator to produce only the specific information necessary for review. This brings up the real point of directing the historically required quarterly LSA reviews toward addressing the real issues of the LSA program, i.e., analysis techniques, tradeoff studies, design considerations, resource requirements, support considerations, etc., rather than looking at pages upon pages of computer printouts.

Database Relationships

The move to a relational data processing system for the LSAR provides the vehicle for easier sharing of data between databases and points toward integrating the LSAR into an overall comprehensive database for a system. This is of course supportive of the Computer-Aided Acquisition and Logistics Support (CALS) initiative.

Establishment of the LSAR database in a relational environment moves the entire logistics process into the mainstream of computerization of most companies using state-of-the-art computer technologies. With this move goes all the problems and pitfalls of integration and data sharing. However, a planned implementation of the relational data processing system that takes into consideration networking the LSAR with other internal and external computer systems creates the potential for timely data availability, data sharing, and long-term cost savings that cannot be overlooked.

Glossary

availability A measure of the degree to which an item is in an operable and commitable state at the start of a mission when the mission is called for at an unknown (random) time.

baseline comparison system (BCS) A current operational system, or a composite of current operational subsystems, which most closely represents the design, operational, and support characteristics of the new system under development.

comparative analysis An examination of two or more systems and their relationships to discover resemblances or differences.

computer resources support The facilities, hardware, software, and manpower needed to operate and support embedded computer systems. One of the principal elements of ILS.

constraints Restrictions or key boundary conditions that impact overall capability, priority, and resources in system acquisition.

contract data requirements list (CDRL), DD Form 1423 A form used as a sole list of data and information, which the contractor will be obligated to deliver under the contract, with the exception of that data specifically required by standard Defense Acquisition Regulation (DAR) clauses.

corrective maintenance All actions performed as a result of failure to restore an item to a specified condition. Corrective maintenance can include any or all of the following steps: Localization, Isolation, Disassembly, Interchange, Reassembly, Alignment, and Checkout.

data item description (DID), DD Form 1664 A form used to define and describe the data required to be furnished by the contractor. Completed forms are provided to contractors in support of and, for identification of, each data item listed on the CDRL.

design parameters Qualitative, quantitative, physical, and functional value characteristics that are inputs to the design process, for use in design tradeoffs, risk analyses, and development of a system that is responsive to system requirements.

end item A final combination of end products, component parts, and/or materials that is ready for its intended use; e.g., ship, tank, mobile machine shop, aircraft.

facilities The permanent or semipermanent real property assets required to support the material system, including conducting studies to define types of facilities or facility improvements, locations, space needs, environmental requirements, and equipment. One of the principal elements of ILS.

failure modes, effects, and criticality analysis (FMECA) An analysis to identify potential design weaknesses through systematic, documented consideration of the following: all likely ways in which a component or equipment can fail; causes for each mode; and the effects of each failure (which may be different for each mission phase).

goals Values, or a range of values, apportioned to the various design, operational, and support elements of a system, which are established to optimize the system requirements.

government-furnished material (GFM) Material provided by the Government to a contractor or comparable Government production facility to be incorporated in, attached to, used with or in support of an end item to be delivered to the Government or ordering activity, or which may be consumed or expended in the performance of a contract. It includes, but is not limited to, raw and processed materials, parts, components, assemblies, tools and supplies. Material categorized as Government Furnished Equipment (GFE) and Government Furnished Aeronautical Equipment (GFAE) are included.

integrated logistics support (ILS) A disciplined approach to the activities necessary to (1) cause support considerations to be integrated into system and equipment design, (2) develop support requirements that are consistently related to design and to each other, (3) acquire the required support; and (4) provide the required support during the operational phase at minimum cost.

logistics support analysis (LSA) The selective application of scientific and engineering efforts undertaken during the acquisition process, as part of the system engineering and design process, to assist in complying with supportability and other ILS objectives.

logistics support analysis documentation All data resulting from performance of LSA tanks conducted under this standard pertaining to an acquisition program.

logistics support analysis record (LSAR) That portion of LSA documentation consisting of detailed data pertaining to the identification of logistics support resource requirements of a system/equipment. See MIL-STD-1388-2A for LSAR data element definitions.

maintainability The measure of the ability of an item to be retained in or restored to specified condition when maintenance is performed by personnel having specified skill levels, using prescribed procedures and resources, at each prescribed level of maintenance and repair.

maintenance levels The basic levels of maintenance into which all maintenance activity is divided. The scope of maintenance performed within each level must be commensurate with the personnel, equipment, technical data, and facilities provided.

maintenance planning The process conducted to evolve and establish maintenance concepts and requirements for a material system. One of the principal elements of ILS.

manpower The total demand, expressed in terms of the number of individuals, associated with a system. Manpower is indexed by manpower requirements, which consist of quantified lists of jobs, slots, or billets that are characterized by the descriptions of the required number of individuals who fill the job, slots, or billets.

manpower and personnel The identification and acquisition of military and civilian personnel with the skills and the grade required to operate and support a material system at peacetime and wartime rates. One of the principal elements of ILS.

objectives Qualitative or quantitative values, or range of values, apportioned to the various design, operational, and support elements of a system, which represent the desirable levels of performance. Objectives are subject to tradeoffs to optimize system requirements.

operating and support (O&S) costs The cost of operation, maintenance, and follow-on logistics support of the end item and its associated support system. This term and "ownership cost" are synonymous.

operational concept A statement about intended employment of forces that provides guidance for posturing and supporting combat forces. Standards are specified for deployment, organization, basing, and support from which detailed resource requirements and implementing programs can be derived.

operational scenario An outline projecting a course of action under representative operational conditions for an operational system.

operational suitability The degree to which a system can be satisfactorily placed in field use, with consideration being given availability, compatibility, transportability, interoperability, reliability, wartime usage rates, maintainability, safety human factors, manpower supportability, logistics supportability, and training requirements.

optimization models Models which accurately describe a given system and which can be used, through sensitivity analysis, to determine the best operation of the system being modeled.

packaging, handling, storage, and transportation The resources, processes, procedures, design considerations, and methods to ensure that all system, equipment, and support items are preserved, packaged, handled, and transported properly including: environmental considerations and equipment preservation requirements for short- and long-term storage, and transportability. One of the principal elements of ILS.

personnel The supply of individuals, identified by specialty or classification, skill, skill level, and rate or rank, required to satisfy the manpower demand associated with a system. This supply includes both those individuals who support the system directly (i.e., operate and maintain the system) and those individuals who support the system indirectly by performing those functions necessary to produce and maintain the personnel required to support the system directly. Indirect support functions include recruitment, training, retention, and development.

preventive maintenance All actions performed in an attempt to retain an item in specified condition by providing systematic inspection, detection, and prevention of incipient failures.

provisioning The process of determining and acquiring the range and quantity (depth) of spares and repair parts and support and test equipment required to operate and maintain an end item of material for an initial period of service.

readiness drivers Those system characteristics that have the largest effect on a system's readiness values. These may be design (hardware or software), support, or operational characteristics.

reliability (1) The duration or probability of failure-free performance under stated conditions. (2) The probability that an item can perform its intended function for a specified interval under stated conditions.

reliability-centered maintenance A systematic approach for identifying preventive maintenance tasks for an equipment end item in accordance with a specified set of procedures and for establishing intervals between maintenance tasks.

repair parts Those support items that are an integral part of the end item or system that are coded as nonrepairable.

requiring authority That activity (government, contractor, or subcontractor) which levies LSA task or subtask performance requirements on another activity (performing activity) through a contract or other document of agreement.

scheduled maintenance Preventive maintenance performed at prescribed points in the item's life.

sensitivity analysis An analysis concerned with determining the amount by which model parameter estimates can be in error before the generated decision alternative will no longer be superior to others.

site survey An examination of potential locations and supporting technical facilities for capability to base a system.

source, maintenance, and recoverability (SMR) codes Uniform codes assigned to all support items early in the acquisition cycle to convey maintenance and supply instructions to the various logistics support levels and using commands. They are assigned based on the logistics support planned for the end item and its components. The uniform code format is composed of three, 2-character parts: Source Codes, Maintenance Codes, and Recoverability Codes, in that order.

spares Those support items that are an integral part of the end item or system that are coded as repairable.

standardization The process by which member nations achieve the closest practicable cooperation among forces; the most efficient use of research, development, and production resources; and agree to adopt on the broadest possible basis the use of (1) common or compatible operational, administrative, and logistics procedures; (2) common or compatible technical procedures and criteria; (3) common, compatible, or interchangeable supplies, components, weapons, or equipment; and (4) common or compatible tactical doctrine with corresponding organizational compatibility.

supply support All management actions, procedures, and techniques required to determine requirements for, acquire, catalog, receive, store, transfer, issue, and dispose of secondary items. This includes provisioning for initial support as well as replenishment supply support. One of the principal elements of ILS.

supportability The degree to which system design characteristics and planned logistics resources, including manpower, meet system peacetime operational and wartime utilization requirements.

supportability assessment An evaluation of how well the composite of support considerations necessary to achieve the effective and economical support of a system for its life cycle meets stated quantitative and qualitative requirements. This includes integrated logistics support and logistics support resource-related O&S cost considerations.

supportability factors Qualitative and quantitative indicators of supportability.

supportability-related design factors Those supportability factors that include only the effects of an item's design. Examples include inherent reliability and maintainability values, testability values, transportability characteristics, etc.

support concept A complete system-level description of a support system, consisting of an integrated set of ILS element concepts, which meets the functional support requirements and is in harmony with the design and operational concepts.

support equipment All equipment (mobile or fixed) required to support the operation and maintenance of a material system. This includes associated multiuse end items, ground handling and maintenance equipment, tools, metrology and calibration equipment, communications resources, test equipment and automatic test equipment, with diagnostic software for both on- and off-equipment maintenance. It includes the acquisition of logistics support for the support and test equipment itself. One of the principal elements of ILS.

support plan A detailed description of a support system covering each element of ILS and having consistency among the elements of ILS. Support plans cover lower hardware indenture levels and provide a more detailed coverage of maintenance level functions than support concepts.

support resources The material and personnel elements required to operate and maintain a system to meet readiness and sustainability requirements. New support resources are those that require development. Critical support resources are those that are not new but require special management attention due to schedule requirements, cost implications, known scarcities, or foreign markets.

support system A composite of all the resources that must be acquired for operating and maintaining a system or equipment throughout its life cycle.

system engineering process A logical sequence of activities and decisions transforming an operational need into a description of system performance parameters and a preferred system configuration.

system/equipment The item under analysis, be it a complete system or any portion thereof being procured.

system readiness A measure or measures of the ability of a system to undertake and sustain a specified set of missions at planned peacetime and wartime utilization rates. System readiness measures take explicit account of the effects of system design (reliability and maintainability), the characteristics and performance of the support system, and the quantity and location of support resources. Examples of typical readiness measures are sortie rate, mission capable rate, operational availability, and asset ready rate.

tailoring The process by which the individual requirements (sections, paragraphs, or sentences) of the selected specifications and standards are evaluated to determine the extent to which each requirement is most suitable for a specific materiel acquisition and the modification of these requirements, where necessary, to ensure that each tailored document invoked states only the minimum needs of the Government.

technical data Recorded information regardless of form or character (e.g., manuals, drawings) of a scientific or technical nature. Computer programs and related software are not technical data; documentation of computer programs and related software are. Also excluded are financial data or other information related to contract administration. One of the principal elements of ILS.

testability A design characteristic that allows the status (operable, inoperable, or degraded) of an item and the location of any faults within the item to be confidently determined in a timely fashion.

thresholds Values, or a range of values, apportioned to the various design, operational, and support elements of a system that impose a quantitative or qualitative minimum essential level of performance. Thresholds are usually associated with a goal.

tradeoff The determination of the optimum balance among system characteristics (cost, schedule, performance, and supportability).

training The structured process by which individuals are provided with the skills necessary for successful performance in their job, slot, billet, or speciality.

training and training devices The processes, procedures, techniques, and equipment used to train active and reserve personnel to operate and support a material system. This includes individual and crew training, new equipment training, and logistics support for the training devices themselves. One of the principal elements of ILS.

transportability The inherent capability of material to be moved with available and projected transportation assets to meet schedules established in mobility plans, and the impact of system equipment and support items on the strategic mobility of operating military forces.

unscheduled maintenance Corrective maintenance required by item conditions.

Index

Index